D0064661

THE SOCIETY OF THE SIGMA XI
DEVOTED TO THE
ENCOURAGEMENT OF RESEARCH IN SCIENCE

Sigma Xi
National Lectureships
1947 and 1948
and the
Silliman Lectures, 1947,
Presented at the Centennial
of the Sheffield Scientific School,
Yale University, October 1947

———

SCIENCE IN PROGRESS

SIXTH SERIES

☆ ☆ ☆ ☆ ☆ ☆

Science in Progress

BY

H. D. SMYTH	L. ZECHMEISTER
JOHN A. WHEELER	W. M. STANLEY
ERNEST O. LAWRENCE	RENÉ J. DUBOS
GLENN T. SEABORG	G. W. BEADLE
LINUS PAULING	A. H. STURTEVANT

CHARLES E. KELLOGG

———

Edited by

GEORGE A. BAITSELL

SIXTH SERIES

☆ ☆ ☆ ☆ ☆ ☆

New Haven

YALE UNIVERSITY PRESS

LONDON · GEOFFREY CUMBERLEGE · OXFORD UNIVERSITY PRESS

1949

PREFACE 43662

Now more than ever, great importance attaches to the wide dissemination of authoritative accounts of active programs of research. It is therefore with a feeling of service rendered that a new volume of *Science in Progress* is presented, the sixth in a sequence of volumes which makes available current research papers of foremost significance. These books, published at intervals of two years, contain contributions from leading scientists who are actively engaged in various fields of research, and provide a permanent record of important scientific studies in progress.

The readers of this book may be impressed once again by the fact that modern science has virtually swept away the boundaries between the traditional compartments of knowledge. Creative thinking flourishes in the no man's land between what were once separate systems of ideas; both facts and methods are freely transferred across frontiers of rapidly diminishing significance. In an age of heightening interdependence between fields of scientific investigation and also between science and statesmanship, the sphere of the individual scientist is becoming increasingly the province of every other scientist, indeed, of every intelligent person.

Of the eleven papers in the present volume, seven are based upon manuscripts prepared originally for presentation in the Sigma Xi National Lectureships during 1947 and 1948. The remaining four papers, Chapters III, V, VII, and IX, are based upon Silliman Lectures presented at Yale University in October, 1947, on the occasion of the Centennial of the Sheffield Scientific School.

The contributors are briefly identified in the following paragraphs.

H. D. Smyth, B.A., M.A., Ph.D. (Princeton); Ph.D. (Cambridge). Professor of Physics and Chairman of the Department of Physics at Princeton University. Dr. Smyth has been at Princeton since 1923. During the recent war years he served as a consultant for the National Research Council, the Office of Scientific Research and Development, and the Manhattan Project. In 1945 he published *Atomic Energy for Military Purposes*—the War Department's official report on atomic bombs. In the introductory chapter of the present volume Dr. Smyth traces the history of atomic physics from its inception, toward the close of the nineteenth century, with the discovery of the X ray, radioactivity, and the electron, to its world-shaking conclusion based on the first nuclear chain reaction in December, 1942.

John A. Wheeler, Ph.D. (Johns Hopkins). Professor of Physics at Princeton University. While still in his twenties Dr. Wheeler, in collaboration with Niels Bohr, developed the theory of the mechanism of nuclear fission (1939). He was one of the original staff of the Metallurgical Laboratory at Chicago, where the first divergent nuclear chain reaction was achieved— the climax of nucleonic physics. The new physics, subnucleonic science, is the subject of Dr. Wheeler's authoritative discussion.

Ernest O. Lawrence, B.A. (South Dakota); M.A. (Minnesota); Ph.D. (Yale); Sc.D. (South Dakota, Yale, Stevens, Princeton, Harvard, Chicago, Rutgers); LL.D. (Michigan, Pennsylvania). Professor of Physics at the University of California, Berkeley, and Director of the Radiation Laboratory. National Academy of Sciences. A leader in research in nuclear physics, Dr. Lawrence has received many distinguished awards, including the Nobel prize in physics in 1939. His development of the cyclotron, described in a National Sigma Xi lecture in 1937, was published as Chapter I of the first series of *Science in Progress*. In this volume Dr. Lawrence gives an account of recent research in the Radiation Laboratory at Berkeley, where his new 184-inch synchro-cyclotron is in operation.

Glenn T. Seaborg, B.A. (California at Los Angeles); Ph.D. (California). Professor of Chemistry at the University of California, Berkeley. National Academy of Sciences. In 1940 Dr. Seaborg was co-discoverer of element 94 (plutonium), and the following year of isotope Pu^{239}, the explosive ingredient for the atomic bomb. In 1944 he and his colleagues, working at the Metallurgical Laboratory at Chicago, discovered elements 95 and 96. The present contribution describes the discovery, within a single decade, of the eight new artificial elements; the first four of these complete the periodic system of 92 elements, and the remaining four, all discovered since early 1940, constitute the transuranium elements.

Linus Pauling, B.S. (Oregon); Ph.D. (California Institute of Technology); Sc.D. (Oregon, Chicago). Professor of Chemistry at the California Institute of Technology, Chairman of the Division of Chemistry and Chemical Engineering, and Director of the Gates and Crellin Laboratories of Chemistry. National Academy of Sciences. Dr. Pauling has received international recognition for his research on molecular structure and activity. In this paper he surveys the progress of chemical science through the past century, and discusses new concepts with important implications for the medical biologist in chemotherapeutics and immunochemistry.

L. Zechmeister. Professor of Organic Chemistry at the California Institute of Technology. Hungarian Academy of Science. Born in Hungary and educated in Switzerland, Dr. Zechmeister received a diploma in chemistry and a degree in engineering from the Polytechnic Institute at Zurich. Before coming to California he taught chemistry in Berlin and Copenhagen and was professor of chemistry and director of the chemistry laboratory in a Hungarian medical school. In 1935 he received the Pasteur medal, and in 1937 the great prize of the Hungarian Academy of Science. He is co-author of a book on chromatography, a field in which he occupies a position of leadership.

W. M. Stanley, B.S. (Earlham); M.S., Ph.D. (Illinois); Sc.D. (Earlham, Harvard, Yale). National Academy of Sciences. Dr. Stanley has been associated with the Rockefeller Institute since 1931. A brilliant biochemist in the field of virus research, he is the recipient of an imposing array of awards, culminating in the Nobel prize in chemistry in 1946. An earlier paper by Dr. Stanley was published in Series I of *Science in Progress.*

René Dubos, B.S. (Institut National Agronomique, Paris); Ph.D. (Rutgers); Sc.D. (Rochester). National Academy of Sciences. After fifteen years with the Rockefeller Institute for Medical Research, Dr Dubos came to the Harvard Medical School in 1942 as George Fabyan Professor of Comparative Pathology and Professor of Tropical Medicine. In 1947 he returned to the Rockefeller Institute, where he is at present engaged in bacteriological research.

G. W. Beadle, B.S., M.S. (Nebraska); Ph.D. (Cornell). Professor and Chairman of the Department of Biology at the California Institute of Technology. National Academy of Sciences. Dr. Beadle is an outstanding investigator in the modern science of genetics. In the present paper he shows how current research in genetics is associated with some of the most fundamental and elusive problems in the entire field of biology. An earlier article by Dr. Beadle appeared in Series V of *Science in Progress.*

A. H. Sturtevant, B.A., Ph.D. (Columbia). Professor of Genetics at the California Institute of Technology. National Academy of Sciences. Dr. Sturtevant, an internationally known geneticist, was one of the distinguished research team that studied inheritance in *Drosophila,* the fruit fly, at Columbia and California under the direction of that great figure in genetics, the late Dr. T. H. Morgan. His present paper is concerned with one of the fundamental questions in biological science.

Charles E. Kellogg, B.S., Ph.D. (Michigan). Chief of the Division of Soil Survey and Head Soil Scientist in the United States Department of Agriculture. Following work in Michigan, Wisconsin, and North Dakota, Dr. Kellogg entered the federal service in 1935 and in 1942 became head soil scientist. The present paper reflects his interest in the relation of soils to the societies which they support, and emphasizes the enormous potentialities awaiting realization with the application of modern soil science.

To the distinguished authors of these papers, to Professor E. W. Sinnott, Director of the Sheffield Scientific School and Chairman of the Silliman Lecture Committee, to the *American Scientist,* to the Yale University Press, and to Sigma Xi groups all over the country—in short, to all who by their generous cooperation have made possible the publication of *Science in Progress,* Series VI—the editor extends sincere thanks.

Acknowledgments are also due to Miss Yvette Gittleson and

to Mrs. Harriet Coverdale Marsh for careful editorial work, preparation of index, and proof reading.

GEORGE A. BAITSELL
Executive Secretary
The Society of the Sigma Xi

Yale University
New Haven, Connecticut
  January, 1949

CONTENTS

ILLUSTRATIONS

Science in Progress

I

FROM X RAYS TO NUCLEAR FISSION

By H. D. Smyth

Princeton University

Since the end of the second World War, science and scientists have been more in the public eye than ever before. It has become recognized that some of the most important national and international questions arise from scientific and technological developments. In fact, sometimes it is difficult to discern the dividing line between science and politics; at least we find physicists talking about world government, statesmen discussing nuclear fission, and everyone sure that we are on the threshold of an "atomic age." At such a time scientists in general and physicists in particular should study their methods and should examine the power and limitations of science. This article on 50 years of atomic physics is offered as a contribution along these lines. In it I shall not catalogue the great discoveries of the past half century, but I shall discuss some of those that seem to me most significant or most typical. I shall start with a description of the state of physics in 1895 and I must end, inevitably, with the chain reaction in 1942.

In the 300 years since Galileo, a large body of knowledge had been built up and a method firmly established. Much was known of mechanics, electricity and magnetism, heat, sound, and light; these divisions of the subject had become traditional—indeed they persist in most modern textbooks.

The successes of the electromagnetic theory of light, of the kinetic theory of gases, and of the application of the fundamental laws of mechanics had been very great. Many physicists felt that the major discoveries in the field had been made. In fact, there is an often-quoted statement [1] attributed to Professor Michelson that runs as follows:

"While it is never safe to affirm that the future of physical science has no marvels in store, even more astonishing than those of the past, it seems probable that most of the grand underlying principles have been firmly established and that further advances are to be sought chiefly in the rigorous application of these principles to all the phenomena which come under our notice."

The importance of a statement like this can easily be over-emphasized. In a way it was correct if it was applied to physics in the strictly classical sense. Perhaps atomic physics as now known would have seemed to Michelson more chemistry than physics. Certainly, if we are thinking of the origins of atomic physics we must consider not just the state of physics in 1895, but the state of the physical sciences. The atomicity of matter had been firmly established by the chemists; it was possible to estimate the sizes and velocities of atoms and molecules, however roughly. The laws of electrolysis had suggested rather clearly that electrical charge was made up of atoms or particles of identical size. Yet most of physics was not concerned with these ideas. In fact, many a college textbook of physics in use today does not mention atoms or electrons before the last two or three chapters. Except for the kinetic theory of gases, physics was all in terms of continuous media and continuous exchange of energy. No discontinuities appeared in the theoretical picture of electricity and magnetism nor in heat flow nor in light nor sound. In spite of the success of the electromagnetic theory of light, the classical divisions of the subject mentioned above were still almost water-tight compartments. The unifying principle that did exist, however, was the point of view that sought to explain everything in terms of the laws of mechanics and of mechanical models. Unaffected by the success of the electromagnetic theory, the ether was generally accepted as a necessary medium for the transfer of light vibrations. There was even a theory of atomic structure which attempted to explain the existence of atoms and the forces between them in terms of vortex rings in the ether.

One might properly have expected that further knowledge

about atoms and molecules and any discoveries about their structure—if they were in fact not indivisible—would come from chemistry rather than physics. Physics was supposed to be concerned with energy and its transformations, chemistry with matter. But it so happened that the study of electricity was a province of physics. For some 30 or 40 years physicists had studied the electrical discharges in gases at low pressure and they had also worked in the field of electrolysis, which the chemists had not yet taken over. It was out of the study of electrolysis that the suggestion of the atomicity of electricity had come, and it was out of the study of discharge in gases that many of the great discoveries of the modern period were to come, directly or indirectly.

THREE GREAT DISCOVERIES

The first of these great discoveries and, in many respects, the most sudden and startling was the discovery of X rays by Roentgen in 1895. The second was the discovery of radioactivity by Becquerel in 1896; and the third, which was not nearly so clear-cut, was the discovery of the electron. I should like to examine these three discoveries as illustrations of the scientific method and the ways in which it is used to increase our knowledge.

In the fall of 1895 Roentgen [2] was studying the passage of cathode rays through thin aluminum windows. This was one more experiment in the innumerable series on the discharge of electricity through gases which has been going on now for nearly a hundred years, has given us the fluorescent lamp and other devices, but has still not told us what happens in an electrical discharge in gases. On November 8, 1895, in the laboratory at Wuerzburg, it happened that a fluorescent screen was lying near the discharge tube, and Roentgen noticed that it became luminous when the discharge tube was running, even though the tube was covered with black paper. Roentgen had the imagination and the curiosity to look into the matter further, and within a week he had discovered many of the principal properties of X rays. Nevertheless he kept his discovery to himself for nearly two months, during which he devised and carried out a whole series of experiments. He first announced his discovery in a paper [3, 4, 5] submitted to the Physical Medical Society of Wuerzburg on December 28, 1895. This paper has deservedly become a scientific classic, both because of the importance of the discovery it announces and the clarity and modesty of its presentation. It describes the stepwise establishment of the properties of X rays by a sequence of experiments logically following each other. It is a beautiful example of logical analysis of new data continually used to guide new experiments. Furthermore, the observed facts and suggested interpretations are clearly distinguished. At the end, Roentgen suggests that X rays may be longitudinal vibrations in the ether, but he does not press the point and has provided enough information about the experiments to enable the reader to judge the validity of the interpretation for himself. I wish I could escape the feeling that if Roentgen were publishing today his paper would be entitled "Demonstration of Longitudinal Waves in the Ether," would begin by a mathematical treatment of the expected properties of these waves based on unstated assumptions, and would conclude by a report of experimental results which did not condescend to say what was actually done but gave graphs showing the comparison between theory and experiment.

The discovery of radioactivity by Becquerel [6] was somewhat similar to that of X rays. In the tubes used by Roentgen the X rays came largely from the glass walls of the tube when cathode rays impinged on them. This phenomenon was accompanied by the fluorescence of the glass. Becquerel, who was a specialist in the phenomena of fluorescence and phosphorescence, had the idea that there might be a definite relation between the fluorescence of the glass and the emission of X rays and that he might find that phosphorescence was always accompanied by X rays. Certain salts of uranium are phosphorescent, that is, they continue to glow in the dark for some time after they have been exposed to sunlight. Becquerel proved that a layer of uranium salt which had been exposed to sunlight could produce an effect on a photographic plate which had been wrapped in black paper so that no ordinary light got to it. This was fine evidence of the correctness of his hypothesis. Fortunately, he was a

careful worker, and a lucky one. He prepared a combination
of photographic plate, black paper, and uranium salt for con-
firming his experiments, but the sun went under a cloud after a
short exposure so that he laid the combination away in a drawer,
expecting to use it later. Fortunately, he decided to develop it
without further exposure and found to his surprise that the
blackening of the plate was very striking. In other words, the
exposure of the uranium to sunlight in his previous experiments
had nothing to do with the blackening of the photographic plate.

Notice that both the discovery of X rays and of radioactivity
were "accidental." In Roentgen's work there was no initial hypothesis, merely extremely shrewd observation followed by
analysis and a logical series of successive experiments. There was
a tentative final interpretation as there should have been. That
this ultimately proved to be wrong was not so important as that
it was sensible in terms of the evidence and that it suggested
further experiments. In Becquerel's work there was a sensible
working hypothesis, which appeared at first to be right but later
turned out to be wrong.

The discovery of the electron [7] was quite a different matter.
In fact, one could probably say the discovery of the electron took
nearly 50 years, from the discovery of Faraday's laws of electrolysis to the exact measurement of the electronic charge by
Millikan. Nevertheless, it is true that the experiments by J. J.
Thomson [7] and his students in the last five years of the nineteenth century did establish definitely the existence of small
particles carrying identical negative electrical charges and having
identical masses, about 1/2,000 of the mass of a hydrogen atom,
and further established that these particles or electrons could be
obtained from all kinds of matter. This then was the first definite
evidence that there is at least one constituent common to every
known chemical element, and suggested strongly that atoms have
structure.

In terms of method, these experiments on electrons correspond more nearly than either of the other two to the conven-
tionally accepted scientific procedure. From many sources the
idea had grown up that electricity might be atomic. Cathode
rays had been discovered many years earlier and studied by many

investigators. Two different hypotheses had been advanced as to their nature: (1) that they were corpuscular; (2) that they were waves. The deflection of cathode rays by magnetic fields had been observed and in some cases measured. Thus a whole series of investigations had determined many of the properties of cathode rays more or less quantitatively, even before J. J. Thomson and his pupils did definitive experiments in measuring the ratio of mass to charge and preliminary experiments in measuring the charge alone. Evidently this was a much more cooperative and complicated process than the discovery of X rays happened to be. It is not nearly so well suited to Sunday-supplement science, but is the only kind of discovery in which most scientists today, however able, can expect to participate. Men like Roentgen are not only very able but also very lucky.

THE NUCLEAR ATOM

As a result of the three major discoveries which we have been discussing, and many auxiliary experiments, physics at the beginning of the century was engaged on a totally new set of problems concerned with atomic structure. Not that the old problems were settled; the ether was still with us, and there still remained the need of the kind of accurate measurements to which Michelson referred in the statement quoted. In the course of the next 15 years atomic physics developed along two separate lines; in modern terms we would call one nuclear physics and the other the electronic structure of the atom. Actually the study of nuclear structure was very largely a straight experimental study of the properties of radioactive substances and their radiations. To one who takes pleasure in simple and ingenious experiments which produce really significant results, a study of this period is most rewarding. Mathematical theory was almost nonexistent, but good logical analysis of experimental results and imaginative planning of new experiments were constantly in evidence. To cite only one example, consider the experiment of Rutherford and Royds [8] on the production of helium by alpha particles from radium emanation.

This work was done in 1908 and the results published in 1909.

By that time enough evidence of one sort and another had been accumulated to indicate that the alpha particles emitted by radioactive substances are in fact atoms of helium carrying two positive charges, or as we would now say, the alpha particles are helium nuclei. Nevertheless, this conclusion depended on an involved chain of deduction from the results of various experiments. In order to clinch the matter, Rutherford and Royds carried out an experiment which is described in Rutherford's Nobel lecture [9] as follows:

"A cylinder of glass was made with walls so thin that alpha particles could shoot right through them, and yet the walls remained quite gas tight. Radium emanation was introduced into this cylinder and the alpha rays were collected in an outside tube, and compressed in another fine tube through which a spark was passed. After a time the spectrum of helium appeared, proving that the alpha particles were, or became helium!"

Notice that this experiment differs quite fundamentally from the other three we have described. It is a very direct and very elegant experimental proof of a conclusion that had already been drawn and generally accepted. Its value lay not in the novelty of the results, which were not at all surprising, but in the economy of logic required to draw a significant conclusion from experimental results. I believe that the most satisfactory experiments are the ones where the complexity comes in designing or performing the experiment, not in the interpretation of the result. The kind of experiment where a year is spent in setting up the apparatus, in getting every irrelevant variable eliminated, but only a day is spent in obtaining results of immediate significance, seems to me far nearer the scientific ideal than an experiment which takes reams of data over a period of many months, data which then require elaborate statistical analysis before any conclusions can be drawn.

To return to the general development in the field of nuclear physics, the significant results that had been obtained by 1912 from the studies of radioactivity were the establishment of the nature of the three radiations, the nature of the law of disintegration, and the so-called displacement laws. According to these laws, a radioactive atom has a certain probability of spontaneously emitting either an alpha particle or an electron. Either of these changes produces a new atom which is chemically different from the parent. The emission of an alpha particle corresponds to a displacement of two places to the left in the periodic table, that is, the daughter atom is chemically analogous to an element two places to the left of the parent element in the periodic table. In the emission of an electron, the daughter atom is displaced one column to the right in the periodic table. Thus it was established not only that atoms were divisible but that one chemical element could be made from another. Furthermore, the high velocities of some alpha and beta particles showed that very great energies might be released in such transformations.

Curiously enough the indirect contribution of radioactive materials to the knowledge of atomic structure was at least comparable in importance to the direct contribution. The alpha particles were probes for the study of atomic structure vastly superior to anything that could then be produced in the laboratory, and it was the study of alpha particle scattering that led Rutherford [10, 11] in 1911 to suggest the modern picture of a nuclear atom, just as the study of the scattering of cathode rays had led Lenard to suggest a similar structure in 1903 [12]. More specific knowledge of the nature of the charge on the nucleus and its relation to chemical properties was established by the work of Moseley on the X-ray spectra of various elements. This experiment or series of experiments is so well known that there is no need to describe it in detail.

Nor is it necessary to review the many experiments on the properties of electrons, on positive rays and gaseous discharge in general, which took place in the first 15 years of this century. In relation to the general development of atomic physics, they were hardly comparable in importance with the radioactivity experiments. In 1900 we were almost sure that all atoms had electrons in them and that there must be some positive charge to compensate them. By 1914 we knew that all atoms had electrons in them and that an equal positive charge was concentrated on a very small but very massive nucleus, that the amount of the positive charge and consequently the number of external electrons increased step by step from hydrogen up through the heavier elements; but we knew practically nothing about the arangement of the electrons or the laws governing their behavior.

OTHER DEVELOPMENTS BEFORE 1913

I might mention, however, one interesting series of experiments which illustrates still a different kind of occurrence in the development of science, namely, the Zeeman effect [13]. It was first found experimentally by Zeeman in 1896. In the so-called normal Zeeman effect an ordinary spectral line is split up into three when observed transversely to a magnetic field, the middle line being polarized parallel to the field and the outside lines at right angles to the field, but when a spectral line is observed longitudinally, that is, with the magnetic field parallel to the light path, it splits into two components, each of which is circularly polarized. This effect was beautifully explained by Lorentz in terms of an electron oscillating in a magnetic field, that is to say, in purely "classical" terms. This was before the quantum theory had ever been heard of. Unfortunately for the classical theory, further study of the Zeeman effect showed that in fact there was often a so-called anomalous effect in which a spectral line split into many components and this effect was never explained until the quantum theory had been well worked out. Here then we have an example of a satisfactory explanation of an incomplete observation by a theory that later proved inadequate, yet there is no doubt that both Zeeman's discovery and Lorentz' early explanation were of immense importance in stimulating both experimental and theoretical research in the field of atomic physics.

I have deliberately avoided discussing the developments in theoretical physics that occurred in the first decade of the century, not because they were unimportant, but because they did not have any very immediate influence on the contemporary experimental work here described. I would merely recall two major items: first, the development of the quantum theory, and second, the suggestion of the equivalence of mass and energy by Einstein [14] in his famous paper on relativity.

Classical theory was able to make predictions about the radiation given off by hot bodies. These predictions were based solely on the existence of some sort of electromagnetic oscillators in solids and did not specifically say anything about atomic structure or even about the atomicity of matter. The predictions turned out to be at variance with experiments, in fact, at variance with common sense since they led to an infinite rate of radiation of energy. In an attempt to avoid this difficulty, Planck [15] in 1900 introduced the hypothesis that the emission and absorption of radiant energy by matter does not take place continuously but in finite quanta of energy, each quantum containing hv ergs of energy where h is a universal constant and v is the frequency of the radiation. This hypothesis of Planck not only led to a reasonable theory of the emission of continuous radiation by matter but, as modified by Einstein, succeeded in explaining photoelectric phenomena which were completely contradictory to classical ideas. According to Einstein, electromagnetic radiation itself had a kind of atomicity, that is to say, when light was emitted it was emitted in packets of energy, each of which flew through space like a corpuscle traveling with the speed of light. These quanta of light, or photons as we now call them, when striking a metallic surface, released electrons photoelectrically and these electrons had kinetic energies determined by the frequency of the radiation rather than its average intensity.

Still another set of data must be cited which were woven into the fabric of atomic theory in the next period to be discussed. For many years it had been known that different substances gave out different spectra. The use of the diffraction grating had made the measurements of the frequencies characteristic of the different elements among the most accurate measurements ever made. For certain substances such as hydrogen and the alkali metals, the number of observed lines in the spectra was small and the lines appeared to be related in definite patterns. For other elements such as iron, thousands of spectral lines were found and the complexity of their relations defied analysis. Though the precision of measurement and apparent simplicity of some spectra had made it possible to establish very accurate empirical relations between the frequencies of some spectral lines, for example, to arrange them in series like the Balmer series for hydrogen, these relations proved to be of a totally novel kind, utterly different from the harmonics familiar in music and expected in terms of classical theory. Fortunately, earnest spectroscopists had continued to make measurements and to arrange their data as well as they could in definite empirical patterns. This is one of the many cases in physics where the empirical relations were still so complicated as to be very difficult to grasp. Only later, when the interpretation had been made by Bohr and his successors, did the whole scheme fall into an intelligible pattern, a pattern in fact that can be extended to include great amounts of material that would never have been correlated by purely empirical methods. For this reason no attempt will be made here really to describe a spectral series from an empirical point of view [16].

ENERGY LEVELS, SPECTRA, AND ELECTRON IMPACT

I now come to a period in physics extending roughly from 1913 to 1930, during which theory and experiment went along hand in hand in a remarkable way. In 1913 Niels Bohr published his work on the structure of the hydrogen atom, thereby laying the foundation for our present-day picture of the arrangement of the electrons around the nucleus. It is hardly necessary to recall the fundamental principles of this theory, which is now taught in every elementary course in physics and chemistry, but I should like to go back to the position of a student beginning graduate work in physics at the end of the first World War. Remember that there were still educational institutions in this country and probably abroad where the very existence of atoms was viewed with skepticism. Although these were rare, certainly the idea of a nuclear atom composed of positive and negative charges was still vague except in research centers. Yet here was Bohr [17] proposing that electrons revolved in certain specified orbits around a positively charged nucleus but that they gave off no radiation except when they changed from one permitted orbit to another. This meant that a given kind of atom, say hydrogen, could absorb energy only in definite quanta, and would then reëmit energy in definite quanta of radiation, thereby producing a line spectrum. Thus according to Bohr's picture normal neutral hydrogen has one electron moving in the innermost permitted orbit. In terms of energy content of the atom as a whole this condition represents the lowest energy state of the hydrogen atom. If this one electron is completely ejected from the atom we have a hydrogen ion, and in returning the electron may pause in any one of the permitted orbits, that is, the atom may exist momentarily in any one of the permitted energy states. A less drastic disturbance than complete ejection of the electron will leave the atom in some energy state higher than normal, i.e., in a so-called excited state but still neutral. In changing from a state of energy E_1, to a one of lower energy E_2, a quantum of energy is given off as electromagnetic radiation of definite frequency determined by the equation $h\nu = E_1 - E_2$, where ν is the frequency and h is Planck's constant.

Since this theory was designed to explain the spectrum of hydrogen, it is not surprising that it did so. Attempts to extend it to more complex atoms ran into difficulties so far as details of electron orbits were concerned, but the concepts of permitted orbits and corresponding energy states did explain in a general way the whole set of empirical relations that had been observed in spectra. What had been called spectral terms now could be identified with energy states, and the fact that the wave numbers of spectral lines corresponded to differences between spectral terms immediately made sense.

Furthermore, a simple prediction could be made that many kinds of energy transfer to and from atoms could occur only in quanta. Specifically, electrons could not transfer energy to an atom except in quanta. This idea led to a whole series of experiments on the collisions of electrons in gases and vapors. Experiments of this kind were initiated by Franck and Hertz [18] in 1914 following the general pattern of earlier experiments by Lenard.

According to our theory, if an electron has less than a certain amount of energy, corresponding to a transition from normal to the lowest excited energy state of the target atom, it collides elastically with the atoms without any transfer of energy (since the electrons are so light compared to the atoms, an elastic collision transfers a negligible amount of energy). If, however, an electron has slightly more than the minimum exciting energy, it can transfer most of its energy to the target atom, leaving the atom in an excited state and the electron with little or no kinetic energy. Such effects can be detected in several ways. It was shown that the electrons do in fact suffer no loss of energy at low speeds but do lose this whole quantum of energy once they are above the threshold. It was shown that at a still higher energy, corresponding to complete removal of the orbital electron, positive ions are produced. But perhaps the most interesting experiment of all that was done in this period was one which demonstrated that atoms bombarded with electrons of just over the minimum exciting energy radiated one and only one spectral line instead of a whole series. Thus, from a combination of theoretical suggestions of Bohr, experimental work of Franck and Hertz and many others on electron collisions and on spectra, the idea of discrete energy levels in atoms was firmly established.

Attempts to extend Bohr's ideas of the motions of electrons around nuclei soon ran into difficulty. More and more quantum numbers were introduced and modifications of Bohr's original principles made. Finally, in 1925 and 1926, the work of Schroedinger [19] and Heisenberg [20] gave a new basis of quantum mechanics for the theory of electronic structure and of spectra. I wish I could discuss the philosophical implications of Heisenberg's and Schroedinger's ideas. Perhaps I can say just this much: that their work, and even more the later work of Dirac, represents an almost complete departure from the idea of a mechanical model of an atom. In that sense Bohr's theory is intermediate between the old vortex ring ether model mentioned earlier, and the point of view of Schroedinger and Heisenberg. Bohr introduced radical new laws but was still working with a model. Heisenberg, particularly, attempted to work only from observations, emphasizing the danger of extending to sub-microscopic atomic phenomena the ideas of length, motion, and position which are familiar to us from ordinary experience.

There remained many problems to be solved about the details of spectra and the behavior of electrons in chemical reactions; nevertheless it is fair to say that by 1926 the principles govern-ing the electronic structure of atoms and their chemical behavior had been laid down, and by 1930 the detailed application of these principles to the known elements was well advanced. Throughout this period, there had been a remarkable interplay between theory and experimental results, one example of which has been discussed in some detail.

UNFASHIONABLE PHYSICS, 1913–1930

Returning to the subject of radioactivity and nuclear physics, I feel that the period from 1912 to 1930 was relatively unex-citing. There were, however, a number of discoveries which fore-shadowed the brilliant developments that have occurred in the past 15 years.

By 1913 a study of the radioactive elements had made it clear (Russell, Soddy, and Fajans [21]) that many places in the periodic table were multiply occupied. Apparently it was possible to have atoms of identical chemical properties but different radioactive properties. Such atoms were called isotopes. The existence of such isotopes in ordinary elements was first demonstrated by J. J. Thomson [22] in 1913 and was investigated thoroughly by Aston [23] in 1919 and subsequent years. The result of these studies showed that all atomic species have masses that are very nearly integral multiples of the mass of hydrogen. In the many cases where the atomic weights chemically determined are not integral, it was found that the elements are mixtures of two or more iso-topes of different masses so that the atomic weight is merely an average depending on the proportions of different isotopes and their masses.

Without describing the mass spectrograph that Aston con-structed nor elaborating on his results, it may be interesting to note that he is a rare example of a physicist whose work was of sufficient importance to earn him a Nobel Prize and yet was so narrow in scope that after his student days he worked with only three instruments, each a modification and improvement of the former one. Aston showed that the masses of most nuclei were nearly whole numbers but that they certainly were not exactly whole numbers. He not only proved this but was able to measure the amount by which the masses of nuclei differed from whole numbers.

The other work that was of first importance in the nuclear field in this period was Rutherford's discovery [24] that he could break up the nuclei of atoms artificially by striking them with alpha particles. In 1919 Rutherford announced that he had succeeded in changing a few atoms of nitrogen into atoms of oxygen by bombarding them with alpha particles and that in the course of this change a hydrogen nucleus or proton was ejected.

Perhaps this is an appropriate point to discuss the very great importance of unfashionable physics. I do not know whether in the period from 1900 to 1914 the physicists of the world in general and this country in particular were as given to fads as they now seem to be, but the work in spectroscopy in that period was certainly not flashy or spectacular and I suspect it was somewhat difficult to interest graduate students in doing theses in that field. The techniques had already been well developed and the theory was almost nonexistent so that the work must have consisted largely in meticulously accurate measurements of the lines emitted by various sources. There was some doubt as to what lines came from what elements and there was some interest attached to the study of the Zeeman effect, the Stark effect, the Doppler effect, and so forth, but the major interest in this accumulated material did not come until the theory began to develop. However, the development of the theory would have been very much retarded had there not been this large body of dependable empirical data available. It was, to be sure, incomplete and had to be vastly extended in the period from 1915 to 1930 when spectroscopy was fashionable.

On the other hand, nuclear physics, or—speaking more strictly—radioactivity, fashionable in the earlier period, went rather out of style from 1915 to 1930. Similarly the study of isotopes was carried on almost exclusively by one man, Aston, although Dempster and one or two others did make significant contributions. Yet, as we have seen, it was Rutherford's work on the disintegration of nitrogen by alpha particles that experimentally foreshadowed the whole field of modern nuclear physics, while Aston's work on isotopes provided data of great value to the modern idea of transmutation of elements with the release of energy.

THE STATE OF PHYSICS IN 1930

Perhaps we should look at the state of physics in 1930 and compare it with that in 1895. More than two thirds of the 50-year period I have chosen to consider had passed. There had of course been vast developments in the fields of technological and applied physics. Many of these, such as the thermionic effect, had gone almost directly from the laboratory to industrial use, and their industrial development had then been reflected in vastly strengthened laboratory techniques. For example, in so fundamental a problem as the measurement of small currents, the electrometer and the high sensitivity galvanometer had largely been replaced by amplifier systems of greater sensitivity and reliability.

Similarly high vacuum techniques developed in the laboratory had been carried over into the lamp and radio tube industry for further development. Thermionic and gas-filled rectifiers, added to the industrial development of transformers and high voltage technique, had also provided new tools for fundamental science.

Perhaps most important of all, the major problems in external atomic structure had been solved, so that young and imaginative physicists were looking for new fields to conquer. It had been a period of radical developments in our knowledge of physics and in our point of view. Both theory and experiment had established the nuclear atom on a firm basis and had specified the numbers of electrons in various atoms, their arrangement, and the laws that govern their behavior. The introduction of the theory of relativity and of the quantum theory had brought to an end the idea that the universe could be explained in terms of mechanical models. Little was known of nuclear structure, but there was at least good reason to suppose that nuclei did have structure and that all nuclei were made up from only a few kinds of particles.

Rutherford's experiment on the disintegration of nitrogen by alpha particles was well known, and a number of other similar experiments had been performed. Einstein's equation $E = mc^2$ was familiar and had been used to explain Aston's results and the great energies involved in radioactive processes. The idea of converting mass into energy had been discussed, but as a practical possibility it seemed remote. No one would have ventured a prediction like that of Michelson quoted at the beginning of this paper, but few would have guessed that the discoveries of the next decade would have been as brilliant as those of Roentgen, Becquerel, Thomson, and the Curies. Yet in the one year, 1932, the neutron [25], the positron, and the deuteron were all discovered, and the first nuclear disintegration by artificially accelerated particles was achieved; even the discovery of artificial radioactivity in 1934 really belongs to this same group. In 1939 uranium fission was first observed, and in 1942 the first nuclear chain reaction using uranium fission went into operation. A very fruitful decade!

THE NEUTRON

It should be interesting to compare the work of this last decade in our 50-year period with that of the first. We discussed the manner in which X rays, radioactivity, and the electron were discovered as typical of the ways in which science progresses. For the sake of comparison we shall describe three major discoveries in this most recent period, namely, the neutron, uranium fission, and the chain reaction.

It is difficult to say when the idea of a neutral particle of about the mass of a proton was first suggested. It is the kind of thing that was probably talked about in groups of physicists almost as soon as the proton itself had been discovered; but the history of the actual experimental discovery of the neutron really began in 1930 when Bothe and Becker in Germany found that if the very energetic natural alpha particles from polonium fell on certain of the light elements, specifically beryllium, boron, or lithium, an unusually penetrating radiation was produced. At first this radiation was thought to be gamma radiation although it was more penetrating than any gamma rays known, and the details of experimental results were very difficult to interpret on this basis. The next important contribution was reported in 1932 by Irène Curie and F. Joliot in Paris. They showed that if this unknown radiation fell on paraffin or any other hydrogen-containing compound it ejected protons of very high energy. This was not in itself inconsistent with the assumed gamma-ray nature of the new radiation, but detailed quantitative analysis of the data became increasingly difficult to reconcile with such a hypothesis. Finally (later in 1932), J. Chadwick in England showed that the gamma-ray hypothesis was untenable. He suggested that in fact the new radiation consisted of uncharged particles of approximately the mass of the proton, and he performed a series of experiments verifying his suggestion. Thus the existence of neutrons was established.

Even in this very brief account of the discovery of the neutron, we see several points that are characteristic of the scientific method: first, the observation of an unusually penetrating radiation, i.e., of a new effect; second, the attempt to explain the effect in terms of what was already known, i.e., as gamma rays; third, further experiments correlating this unknown radiation with another observation, the ejection of protons of high energy; fourth, the gradual accumulation of quantitative data which disprove the previous explanation; fifth, a new hypothesis and experiments to test this hypothesis which in effect confirm it. I should say that this is a perfectly typical course of events in scientific discovery, exactly similar to those which led to discoveries in the seventeenth century or in the last decade of the nineteenth century. It was also typical in being based on a free interchange of information and on the assumption that that information was reliable. I should also like to point out that the contributions came from individuals or very small groups working independently because these problems interested them. There was no organization or direction.

URANIUM FISSION [26]

One of the most striking characteristics of atomic and nuclear physics is the use of bombarding particles as instruments of investigation. We produce X rays by bombarding targets with electrons, we study atomic structure by bombarding atoms with alpha particles and observing the scattered alpha particles, and so on. To a good physicist a new particle is potentially a new projectile, so it was natural that neutrons were seized upon for this purpose. Furthermore, they had the great advantage of being uncharged so that they would not be repelled by the nuclear charges of atoms as are the alpha particle, the proton, and the electron. This advantage appeared particularly favorable for the study of heavy atoms where the nuclear charge is greatest. Consequently, by 1934 Fermi, in Rome, had begun to study the results of bombarding uranium with neutrons. It was anticipated that effects would be observed similar to those of natural or artificial radioactivity, that is, that the neutron might be absorbed with the emission of an alpha particle, a proton, or an electron, and the consequent formation of a new element. But these elements would differ from uranium in mass and nuclear charge by only a small number of units. Such appeared to be the explanation of the initial results of Fermi and his group. As more data accumulated, this interpretation proved more and more difficult. The initial hypothesis was inadequate. It was not clearly wrong, as in Becquerel's discovery of radioactivity; it was more like Lorentz' theory of the Zeeman effect, or Roentgen's suggestion that X rays were longitudinal waves in the ether.

By 1939 it was clear that we did not understand what happened when neutrons struck uranium nuclei. Note the relatively long preliminary period of confusion in contrast to the rapid clarification after the discovery of the neutron or of X rays. The techniques are difficult, involving precise chemical separations in short times on a microscopic scale. Only the perfection and careful repetition of these methods by Hahn and Strassman [27] gave the clue. In Berlin in 1939 they convinced themselves that at least one of the new elements formed from uranium by neutron bombardment was not a close neighbor in the periodic table, not a heavy element of nuclear charge one or two units greater or less than uranium; on the contrary, it was barium, whose nucleus has not much more than half the mass or charge of uranium.

On hearing this news, Meitner and Frisch [28] in Copenhagen guessed that the bombarding neutrons were splitting the uranium nucleus into two parts each about half the size of the original nucleus. They also realized that an immense amount of energy would be released in the process. News of the discovery and its interpretation spread rapidly through the scientific world and within a few months the energy released by the "fission" process had been observed in many laboratories. Much as with X rays, there were many laboratories equipped to observe the process once they knew what to look for. Curiously enough, although the two discoveries were approached very differently, their immediate world-wide verification [29], the recognition of their importance, and their rapid utilization were very similar.

In many respects the discovery of uranium fission marks the end of an era in scientific research. It was truly international, it was made by small groups working on a small scale, for the most part in university laboratories, and it was made in the atmosphere of freedom and frankness that had meant so much to science. It remains to be seen how fully we can return to such conditions.

THE CHAIN REACTION

The chain reaction, the next and last discovery to be mentioned, was made under circumstances superficially very different—in secret, in a war laboratory, heavily financed by the United States Government. Even now, a complete quantitative description of the chain reaction has not been published. The beauty of Roentgen's paper or of those on fission was that anyone who read them could repeat the experiment. This is perhaps the most fundamental principle of science; its methods of operation are so objective and its means of communication so precise that its results are reproducible. Each man can build on the other's work so that knowledge is advanced by a vast cooperative movement.

But we cannot work in this way when atomic bombs may be the reproducible result in a world that is politically unable to control them. Hence, we have had to violate our fundamental principles and keep silent about numbers and dimensions. Yet I think enough has been published [30] about the first chain reaction to indicate the way in which it was approached. Under other conditions, all the necessary scientific constants might have been measured first and the theory so well worked out that the experiment would have been analogous to that of Rutherford and Royds, a confirmation of an anticipated result, though on an engineering scale. In fact, the first nuclear reactor was approached very much in the scientific tradition, conceived, prepared, and carried out by a professor with the help of his students and colleagues working on a university campus. Furthermore, up to the time that Fermi and his group first made the nuclear chain reaction go, the uranium project was essentially scientific in aims and methods. December 2, 1942, represents the end of the epoch of atomic physics that began in 1895. Whether the effort of scientists in this period will ultimately benefit mankind or destroy it remains to be seen. The power of the scientific method has been amply demonstrated.

CONCLUSION

The thoughtful scientist reviewing his present situation is deeply concerned. He can take pride in the achievements of the past 50 years. They show what human beings can do when they work with disciplined minds and objective methods in a spirit of coöperation and freedom. Yet mankind has failed to understand the lesson of method. Apparently the method is inadequate for social and political problems, or its use conflicts too violently with long-cherished prejudices and shortsighted ideas of self-interest. The world ignores the free interchange of thought, the precision of method and communication, the disciplined imagination which science has proved so potent, and instead seizes on the power released by science, and with an eager impulse toward suicide turns it to purposes of destruction. Some scientists themselves, suddenly awakened to the world in which they live, make political pronouncements in a spirit of emotionalism and panic that would never be tolerated in their own field.

What can the scientist do? Each must act according to his judgment, as he would in his own field, listening to all sides, attempting to evaluate and criticize such evidence as is presented, opposing authoritarian dogma as he would in science. He must be humble, recognizing the limitations of his own knowledge and that of others. He must be restrained and infinitely patient. He must think imaginatively but not emotionally. He must be willing to alter his ideas to meet changing conditions. All these processes are part of his training and have proved themselves as powerful tools. They should be easier for the scientist than for many of his fellows. Perhaps he can help those whose concern with immediate human problems has prevented them from developing an objective attitude. To render such help he must learn from those familiar with the fields of politics and human affairs, of which he knows so little. He must remember that he has no monopoly on brains but is merely the lucky custodian of a method well designed to meet the kind of problems that have heretofore confronted him. It remains to be seen whether this method can be applied successfully to the larger field of human relations.

For References see p. 291.

ELEMENTARY PARTICLE PHYSICS [1]

By John A. Wheeler

Princeton University

ACHIEVEMENT of the first divergent nuclear chain reaction [2] on the second of December, 1942, was a dramatic demonstration that the science of the rearrangement of nuclear particles had reached maturity, and a signal to those of pioneering bent to turn their attention to the internal transformations of these particles.

The relation of Einstein between mass and energy is an ever-present notice that the most energetic nuclear transformation so far known, the fission of a heavy nucleus, releases only one part in a thousand of the energy which is locked up in its mass, and a declaration that not uranium alone, but all forms of matter whatsoever, gram for gram, have the same intrinsic energy. The discovery of how to release this energy on a reasonable scale might completely alter our economy and the basis of our military security. It would certainly give wonderful new insight into the nature of matter and energy. On both accounts the attention of experimental and theoretical physicists is now concentrating on all branches of elementary particle physics cosmic-ray phenomena, mechanisms of the production of stellar and cosmogonic energy, theories of elementary interactions, and particle transformation physics—where a single development may lead to a great advance.

Five particles and four modes of energy transmission are the subject matter of the new science. One of the particles, the electron, responsible for the outer planetary structure of atoms, is the basis of all chemistry. The electron occurs normally in nature with a negative charge and is sometimes more specifically denoted as a *negaton* [3], to distinguish it from the positively charged variety of electron, the *positon*.

The positon is equal in mass to the negaton. The two particles are so closely related that they can be created or undergo annihilation in partnership. The annihilation process occurs so readily that the positons, brought to rest in solid matter, quickly disappear by combination with atomic electrons.

The importance which the electron has for the structure of the atom is equalled by the significance of the third and fourth particles, the *proton* and *neutron,* for the constitution of the nucleus. Both entities have masses roughly 1,840 times greater than that of the electron and have been given the common name of nucleon. In accord with this name, nucleonic physics is understood to be the science of those changes—radioactivity, nuclear disintegration, and fission—in which there occurs a rearrangement but no change in the total number of nucleons present. This science, which is the basis of the atomic bomb and the chain reacting pile, is in respect to heats of reaction and rates of reaction now nearly as fully developed as chemistry itself [4]. In contrast, elementary particle physics or subnucleonic science may be said to be concerned with the transformations in which the elementary particles change their character or are created or destroyed.

Most interesting additions to the world of subnucleonic physics are the *mesons.* The most common variety of meson (*meso,* Greek for intermediate; and ending, *on,* for noun) has a mass approximately 210 times that of the electron [5], about ⅑ that of a nucleon, and, like the positon, was found by Anderson in the course of sea-level studies of the cosmic radiation [6]. They occur with either sign of electric charge. These particles of intermediate mass are found to disintegrate spontaneously with a characteristic life of approximately 2.15 microseconds [7]. In addition to these mesons, there were found in 1947 in the course of high-altitude cosmic-ray studies [8] heavier mesons, with a mass of approximately 300 times that of the electron and with both signs of electric charge. Both kinds of mesons were produced artificially for the first time in 1948, by nuclear bombardment in the Berkeley cyclotron [9]. Finally, striking new evidence was found in October, 1948, for still another particle of roughly thousandfold the electronic mass, which appears to disintegrate into three mesons of lesser mass (see photograph p. 294) [9a].

To describe the forces which act between the elementary particles has so far required four types of interaction. Of these the oldest and most familiar is the gravitational attraction between every pair of masses. The second type of force, equally well verified by experience, is the electromagnetic interaction between elementary electric charges. Third is an interaction between nucleons which has been postulated to account for the stability of atomic nuclei. The properties of this specific nuclear force have been deduced in some detail from the properties of the known nuclei [10]. However, there exists no comprehensive theory of this interaction which can be claimed to be nearly so well founded as the theories of gravitation and electromagnetism. We cannot even exclude the possibility that our purely empirical description of the specific nuclear forces will find an interpretation in terms of a more fundamental type of interaction between elementary particles. The fourth and last mechanism which we recognize as a means for transferring energy and momentum from one system of elementary particles to another is a field of interaction to the quanta of which has been given the name of neutrinos [11]. The neutrino field transmits energy with the speed of light, as do the gravitational field and the electromagnetic field, and its quanta possess an intrinsic angular momentum equal to that of the electron. Otherwise the properties of this fourth mode of interaction are imperfectly understood.

To uncover the relations between the elementary particles and the basic interactions, physicists must first make energetic particles available for workaday experimentation; second, observe the changes which occur when matter is bombarded by such radiations, and determine the stability of systems formed by the union of elementary particles; third, reduce to the order of a consistent theory our knowledge of the genetic interrelations of the elementary particles and of the interactions between them.

ENERGY REQUIREMENTS

Let us first consider the question of what energies are required to produce ultranucleonic transformations and how these energies can be obtained. There appear to be two fairly distinct mileposts on the way to higher energies: one level of the order of 200–400 Mev (million electron volts) required for the creation of mesons, and another of the order of 5–10 Bev (thousand million electron volts) necessary for the production of mesons in high yield.

Helium nuclei with energies up to 380 Mev are produced by the Berkeley cyclotron and are already known to be able to produce both light (210 mass) and heavy (300 mass) mesons. Soon there will be available accelerators which will provide electromagnetic radiation with quantum energies up to about 300 Mev. It is not yet known whether these photons will create mesons in significant quantity [12].

Energies of a higher order, 5–10 Bev, will probably be necessary to get mesons produced with high efficiency, according both to theoretical calculations [13] and to recent cosmic-ray experimental evidence [14]. It may also be necessary to go to such energy if we are to observe the most striking type of ultranucleonic transformation now known, the sudden production in a single act of many mesons. Schein and collaborators, through balloon observations near the top of the atmosphere [15], discovered the existence of this phenomenon and the fact that it is brought about by single cosmic-ray particles, presumably protons.

From these considerations we conclude that there is an appreciable probability that we shall have to have particles in the billion electron volt range of energies in order to be able to observe the full variety of elementary particle transformations.

One method for reaching this second milepost of energies is to construct artificial accelerators of a capacity which is much in excess of anything now available. Many principles of acceleration are known of which a few have been proved in practice, others are under active discussion, and some are to receive large-scale tests in the next few years [16]. There is no doubt that it is technologically possible to reach billion volt levels.

To construct devices of this power will be extremely expensive in money and, most of all, in drain on the country's scientific man power. Wise division of the burden between universities, industry, and the government will do much to advance elementary particle physics. Fortunately, the National Laboratories [17] supported by the Atomic Energy Commission are taking a leading part in this work. However done, it is reasonable to believe that an accelerator of protons for the multibillion electron volt range must and will be built.

COSMIC RADIATION AS A
SOURCE OF PARTICLES

A second source of very energetic particles is the cosmic radiation itself [18]. This natural source and the artificial sources which we have discussed both have their own characteristic advantages. Neither can take the place of the other. One supplies high intensity, reproducible energy, well-defined timing. The other not only provides a wealth of phenomena, which so far have been explored only in part, but also offers for experimentation particles with energies ranging all the way from the billion electron volt level up to energies at least as great as 10^{17} electron volts [19], a figure not likely soon to be duplicated in the laboratory. When we consider the wonderful advances made by Rutherford and his collaborators in nuclear physics with sources separated out of the minerals of the earth, and then note that for subnucleonic research also this globe is supplied with particles of the necessary energy, we marvel at the richness of nature.

The cosmic radiation is becoming a workaday source for elementary particle research. Rockets are regularly carrying more than a thousand pounds of equipment per flight to altitudes exceeding 60 miles for periods of a few minutes, long enough to get reliable statistical information on the most frequent types of events [20]. Balloons support lighter equipment for many hours at altitudes of 100,000 feet, where little more than 1 per cent of the atmospheric mass remains overhead [21].

The General Mills Aeronautical Research Laboratory, at the request of the Office of Naval Research, has developed constant volume balloons capable of reaching such altitudes with a load of 60 pounds [22]. Some facilities are available at mountain elevations in Colorado for work with heavy equipment such as magnets and cloud chambers [23]. Efforts are being made to establish there a full-time high-altitude elementary particle research laboratory. Other high-altitude laboratories are available abroad [24]. Work in sea-level laboratories is convenient and has yielded great dividends. For absorption measurements on the most energetic particles, mines and lakes have proved their worth. The Army Air Force, in collaboration with the Office of Naval Research and other agencies, has given valuable assistance in transporting experimental equipment weighing several tons on prolonged flights to altitudes between 30,000 and 40,000 feet [25]. Improved techniques have been developed to detect ionizing particles [26].

These successful efforts to make the most of the cosmic radiation must go forward.

Our survey of the means which we must develop to get swift particles for ultranucleonic research has ended with our viewing the cosmic radiation in the light of a research tool. However, the nature and source of this radiation are also matters of interest in their own right.

It is believed that the cosmic-ray phenomena observed on the earth's atmosphere are due principally to the bombardment of matter with protons of sufficiently great energy; however, the presence of other particles in the radiation incident on the earth has been shown by very recent observations. Cosmic-ray tracks have been found at 100,000 feet altitude which have an amazingly high [27] ionization. The Minnesota and Rochester groups responsible for this discovery show that these effects can be due only to nuclei of atoms heavier than hydrogen coming in from outside the earth. The abundance of these heavy nuclei is very slight compared to the frequency of the normal singly charged particles and is not out of line with the abundances of the elements in the stars [28].

It has been suggested on speculative grounds that a fraction of the radiation striking the earth may contain negative protons [29]; however, there is to date no reliable experimental foundation for such a proposal, and there appear to be no convincing arguments that such particles are present in the cosmic radiation. It is believed that no mesons enter the earth from outside because of the very short natural lifetime of these particles. Directional intensity measurements within the atmosphere show that more of these particles of intermediate mass come from the western sky than from the east [30]. This observation, together with the polarity of the earth's magnetic field, indicates that the primaries responsible for meson production are mostly positively charged, if not altogether so. The transformations produced by these positively charged primary particles are quite different from those initiated by positons. Moreover, recent experiments show that electrons cannot constitute more than 1 per cent of the cosmic-ray particles coming in from the outside of the earth [31]. With both positons and mesons from outside thus excluded as sources of the mesons in the atmosphere, we have no convincing reason to believe the cosmic radiation contains anything more than atomic nuclei, with hydrogen constituting the same overwhelming proportion of this radiation that it constitutes among the chemical elements in interstellar space.

Passing from the problem of the nature of the cosmic rays to the question of where they get their energy, we have to recognize that much remains to be done before we can exclude the existence of a straightforward mechanism of acceleration of charged particles in interstellar space, by electric fields developed through some combination of well-known phenomena in physics and astrophysics.

Prime movers which have been suggested in this connection are: (1) electromagnetic disturbances from sunspots [32]; (2) electromagnetic disturbances generated by the revolution of magnetized double stars [33]; (3) electromagnetic forces produced by such amazing variations in stellar magnetic fields as those recently observed for HD 125,248 which changes its polar field from + 7,800 gauss to — 6,500 gauss and back again every nine days [34]; (4) interstellar electric fields generated by the action of radiation pressure on dust particles [35]; (5) stellar electric fields generated at the time of ejection of matter from a star by differential separation of ions and electrons, much in the manner of a terrestrial thunderstorm [36]; (6) magneto-hydrodynamic disturbances generated by the motion of ion clouds relative to one another in the space between the stars of the Milky Way [36a]. All six proposed mechanisms have their difficulties; not one of them has been developed to the point where it gives a satisfactory explanation of the source of the cosmic radiation, with its characteristic energy distribution [37], nucleonic character, remarkable intensity, and amazing uniformity in direction [38]. However, it seems quite possible that an explanation may eventually emerge along such lines or from related ideas. Considerations relevant to almost any theory may be briefly reviewed: (1) The energy estimated to be present in the galaxy in the form of cosmic radiation requires for its maintenance only a small fraction of the energy output of the stars in this system [39]. (2) The galaxy may possess a very weak general magnetic field of its own [40]. Even a field as low as 10^{-7} gauss, acting throughout the galaxy, will oblige any charged particle with energy less than 10^{15} ev to circulate within the galaxy until it is ultimately absorbed. If such a field exists, the trapped particle will describe a motion of quasi-ergodic character. Particles arriving at the solar system will come from all directions in space with equal probability. (3) Particles circulating through the galaxy under the influence of a general galactic magnetic field and undergoing occasional interactions with particles of interstellar matter and radiation [41] will be expected ultimately to acquire a distribution in energy which follows some simple law. In particular, collisions of high-energy electrons with atoms will rob this constituent of the circulating radiation preferentially of its energy, for the high energy quanta produced in such collisions will escape from the galaxy without any hindrance from the galactic magnetic field. (4) The striking cutoff of the cosmic-ray spectrum below about 2 Bev is qualitatively consistent with the view that the cosmic radiation comes to the earth from outside the solar system [42]. Thus particles with energy less than the cutoff limit will be deviated away from the earth by the magnetic field of the sun—provided that the sun has a magnetic field as great as that indicated by older spectroscopic measurements [43]. Recent indications that the magnetic field of the sun may vary [44], open up the possibility of interesting balloon experiments to seek for corresponding changes in the cutoff energy in the cosmic-ray spectrum. Such changes must in any case be expected from the per cent variation in earth-sun distance throughout the year.

In view of rapid developments taking place in knowledge of stellar fields [45] and interstellar matter, it would be a bold person who would say that the origin of the cosmic radiation is not to be found within the framework of recognized astrophysical concepts.

TRANSFORMATIONS PRODUCED BY COSMIC RADIATION

Through exploitation of the natural cosmic radiation and the development of artificial accelerators of new power, physics is now well on the way toward getting fast particles for elementary corpuscle research. Its second great task is to observe the transformations initiated when these particles strike matter. Obviously, the nature of the transformations produced in a given energy range will be the same whether the particles acquire their energy naturally or artificially. The natural radiation was investigated first and has been studied far more extensively [24]. Consequently the richness and variety of subnucleonic changes are most easily seen when one makes a quick survey of the present status of cosmic-ray physics [46].

Fortunately the earth's atmosphere is thick enough so that the primary particles which enter from outside have ample opportunity to generate secondary particles and these to generate tertiary ones, etc. to a reasonably complete extent before the ground is reached. The investigation of the events happening underground, at sea level, on mountain tops, and at balloon and rocket elevations has thus made it possible to sort out a number of individual steps in a rather complicated sequence of changes.

At sea level approximately one particle crosses a horizontal square centimeter in every minute. Approximately ¾ of these particles are mesons and ¼ are electrons. The mesons are highly penetrating, whereas the electrons are stopped by a few inches of lead. The strong absorption of electrons makes it difficult to believe that these particles could have penetrated through the whole atmosphere in the form of electrons. Direct and indirect experimental evidence shows that most of the sea-level electrons have to be understood as particles generated by the mesons, partly by knocking on orbital electrons of the nitrogen and oxygen nuclei of the air, partly by radioactive disintegration of some of the mesons themselves into electrons [47]. An appreciable fraction of the sea-level mesons are believed to possess energies as high as 10^{12} ev, for this type of radiation has been observed in mines at a depth of the order of one mile [48].

The intensity of the meson component of the cosmic radiation increases by a factor of roughly two for mountain elevations up to 12,000 feet (3,500 m.), and to approximately six times its ground-level value at an elevation such that only 10 per cent of the atmospheric mass remains overhead. Naturally the meson intensity must drop to zero at short distances above the earth, because of the very short natural lifetime of mesons.

Good figures are not yet available on the number of heavy mesons in various levels in the atmosphere. So far, these particles have been detected in substantial numbers only at mountain elevations. This circumstance and more direct evidence indicate that the heavy mesons have a lifetime substantially shorter than that of the light mesons [49]. Additionally, the rapid decrease in number of heavies with elevation may indicate a high probability of interaction between this particle and a nucleus of oxygen or nitrogen in the air.

A positively charged heavy meson brought to rest in a photographic emulsion is observed to decay into the usual 200-mass meson with a characteristic energy of about 3.8 Mev [50]. A straightforward application of the laws of conservation of charge, energy, and momentum to this process shows that there must come out at the same time and in the opposite direction a light neutral particle with a characteristic mass at most only a few times that of an electron, according to present tentative determinations [51]. The other properties of this neutral meson are unknown. It may be a neutrino.

The electrons, which number only ¼ of the cosmic-ray particles at sea level and are there mainly by-products of mesons, increase with altitude considerably faster than the meson component, reaching at 14,000-foot mountain elevations roughly 6 times their sea-level intensity. The electron flux reaches a maximum of 40 times the ground-level value when roughly only ⅕ of the air mass remains overhead [52].

Above the altitude of the peak intensity the strength of the soft component decreases rapidly, indicating that the electrons, like the mesons, are secondary to the primary radiation. Accompanying the electrons are gamma rays or quanta of electromagnetic energy of comparable number and energy. The electronic and electromagnetic divisions of the cosmic radiation are found to have so close a physical connection with each other, and to be comparatively so easily absorbed, that together they have received the name of "soft component."

Recent analysis of the absolute intensity of this electron component suggests that the producing agency is absorbed in the atmosphere at the same rate as the nucleonic component of the cosmic radiation [53].

Direct counter- and cloud-chamber evidence has also been found for processes in which large numbers of electrons are generated in solid matter [54]. The nature of the act of production is now one of the most important questions in elementary particle physics. One proposal is that the electrons result from the breakup of very energetic neutral mesons, themselves created in the encounter [55]. Alternatively, a process of direct production of electrons from the nucleus itself is consistent with existing observations.

After the mesons and the electrons, the last major group of particles found in the earth's upper atmosphere consists of nucleons—fast neutrons and protons produced by nuclear explosions. These explosions have been observed as the so-called "stars" found on photographic plates exposed to the cosmic radiation, and also as multipronged events in cloud-chamber pictures and as bursts of intense ionization in ionization chambers [56].

Nucleons not only emerge from these stars, but also, in many cases, produce the stars in the first place. The experimental correlation between the neutrons and the stars is close. As far up as measurements have been extended in the lower $\frac{2}{3}$ of the atmosphere, the intensity of neutrons, protons, and nuclear explosions, rises at a rate roughly comparable with that of the electronic component and very different from that of the mesons. The intensity increase is approximately exponential. The magnitude of the absorption coefficient for all three radiations is consistent with the idea that one is dealing with the collision between a proton and a nucleus of nitrogen or oxygen, whose target area is comparable to its geometrical cross section.

Observations on the abundance of slow neutrons in the atmosphere show a rapid rise [57] paralleling that of the nuclear explosions until the slow neutron component reaches a maximum at an elevation where only $\frac{1}{5}$ or $\frac{1}{10}$ of the atmosphere is still overhead [58]. Theory predicts that the slow neutron intensity should fall off above this point as a result of diffusion of these particles out of the top of the atmosphere [59].

The quantitative relations between slow neutrons, fast neutrons, and the stars are now under active investigation. Some interesting effects have already come to light, connected with the remarkable capacity of hydrogen to convert fast neutrons into slow neutrons. Thus the number of slow neutrons close to the ground has been found to be almost twice as great as that 1,000 feet or so above the soil [60]. Likewise the slow neutron intensity as measured in an airplane shows abnormalities in the neighborhood of clouds [61]. So far, no detailed analysis of these effects has been given.

Apparent from this brief review are four fields of transformation physics which are now, and will be in the future, major centers of attention for work with cosmic rays and artificial accelerators: (1) the physics of the soft radiation,—positive and negative electrons, and gamma rays; (2) nuclear explosions and the physics of nucleons; (3) meson decay—or more generally, the physics of the neutrinos produced by the decay of these particles and of atomic nuclei; (4) the creation and absorption of mesons.

ELECTRON PHYSICS

Of these four fields the one best studied, both theoretically and experimentally, is the physics of the transformations of positive and negative electrons and electromagnetic radiations—processes in which atomic nuclei act at most as catalyzers. The laws governing (a) the creation of pairs of negatons and positons by radiation, and (b) the deceleration of pair particles with the production of more radiation, have now almost passed from matters to be checked experimentally on their own account to the position of well-proved tools in the investigation of the cosmic radiation as a whole [62]. It was a great triumph of the theory of electron pairs to explain in terms of the two mechanisms just mentioned the cascade multiplication and strong absorption in lead of the soft component of the radiation found in the earth's atmosphere [63]. Recent experiments have given a more detailed picture of the extensive cascade showers of electrons than was previously available [64]. Results are now available on the frequency of showers containing from 3 to 7,000 electrons per square meter, corresponding approximately to primary energies up to 10^{17} ev. The extension in space of such air showers has also been studied and found to accord with theory for counter separations more than half a mile [65]. Other detailed predictions of the theory have been checked by experiment. It has been found that a slow positon is annihilated by an electron at the expected rate [66]. Also the two quanta of radiation given out in this process have been found to have their planes of polarization oriented at right angles to each other [67].

Some branches of positon physics are yet to be explored. These particles, like protons, must have a characteristic chemistry of their own; they are capable of forming not only short-lived polyelectronic entities of the types

$$e^+e^-, \ e^+(e^-)_2, \ \text{and} \ (e^+)_2(e^-)_2,$$

but also molecular structures comparable to the system e^+Cl^- [68]. The latter heavy structures should be the more susceptible to experimental investigation. So far, only preliminary estimates have been made of the stability of such molecules. Does any such system exist with two or more stable energy levels between which optical transitions may be observed? What is the activation energy and probability for reactions of the type

$$e^+e^- + Cl_2 \rightarrow e^+Cl^- + Cl?$$

Only in the light of such considerations will one be able to give a complete life history for a positon which is being moderated in energy, through the stage where it picks up an electron from an atom, then is further slowed down until this light molecular type of entity combines with a heavier molecular system to bind the positon in a relatively stationary configuration.

Not yet solved from the experimental point of view is the task of finding a detector of slow positons as characteristic in its response and as convenient to use as the usual detectors of slow neutrons. Such a device would be a valuable tool in the study of the soft component of the cosmic radiation. Nor has one yet observed the backward scattering of high energy gamma rays by atomic nuclei. The gamma ray produces in the field of force of the atomic nucleus a negaton-positon pair which may subsequently annihilate and regenerate a gamma ray which now, however, goes off in a new direction [69]. This mechanism of scattering is of course different from true nuclear scattering of the gamma radiation. A measurement of its intensity would be an important datum for the theory of electron pairs. Also still to be tested experimentally are the predictions of theory about the polarization of energetic gamma rays scattered by electrons.

In addition to interactions which involve solely electrons and electromagnetic forces are those where the forces between electrons and other types of particles came into evidence. The first experiments designed to detect a specific interaction between neutrons and electrons over and above that due to the magnetic moment of the neutron showed no effect [70]; but more recent observations suggest that this interaction, while small, may be finite [71]. In these experiments one observes the scattering of neutrons due to atomic electrons. Information about the interaction between one particle and another comparable to that which one obtains from scattering experiments can be secured by studying the stationary energy levels of a system in which the two particles in question circulate about each other in continuous interaction. Thus both the usual spectroscopic technique and the newer magnetic resonance apparatus have made it possible to secure good evidence on the hyperfine structure of the energy levels of hydrogen and deuterium [72]. The comparison of the energy level splitting in the two cases indicates that the deuteron does not behave like a point particle in its interaction with the electron; instead the electric attraction of the proton brings the electron into closer interaction with this component of the proton-neuron system. Consideration of this effect brings the relative hyperfine structure of deuterium and hydrogen into substantial agreement, but leaves the absolute value in both cases slightly out of accord with predictions of earlier theory.

The remaining discrepancy received a reasonable interpretation in terms of the newly discovered anomalous magnetic moment of the electron. This anomaly was found at almost the same time by experiments on the splitting of spectral lines in magnetic resonance experiments [73] and in theoretical investigations of the finer consequences of the interaction of an electron with the surrounding electromagnetic and pair fields [74]. These investigations provide a remarkable extension of the range of validity of existing electron theory. They provide also an explanation of the newly discovered and otherwise not-to-be-understood shift in the energy levels of those states of a hydrogen atom where the electron spends an appreciable fraction of its time in the immediate neighborhood of the nucleus [75].

The recent remarkable advances just mentioned, together with the number of problems which are still open, indicate that the physics of electrons is in an active state of development.

NUCLEAR EXPLOSIONS

The second and likewise active field of transformation physics is the science of nuclear explosions. Independent means to observe these events are provided by ionization chambers, cloud chambers, and photographic emulsions. Of interest are both the agency responsible for the explosion and the nature of the disruption itself.

It is not clear that the major star-producing radiation is the same at the top of the atmosphere as it is at lower altitudes and at sea level. Ionization-chamber measurements show that the explosion rate increases steadily at balloon elevations and reaches a peak value above the atmosphere at rocket altitudes [76]. This result can be understood only if the explosions at such altitudes are produced mainly by the primary particles. The absorption coefficient of the star-producing radiation in air is consistent with the hypothesis that this radiation consists of nucleons, both at the highest altitudes and from mountain elevations on down. Though these nucleons are probably protons in the upper parts of the atmosphere, a neutronic character is indicated for the star-producing radiation at mountain elevations. Cloud-chamber photographs of stars taken there show that few of these events are caused by electromagnetic radiation or by electrically charged particles [77]. This conclusion is in contrast to the view advanced earlier [78] that stars are produced by the interaction of the high-energy electromagnetic radiation of the soft component with atomic nuclei. That view appeared reasonable because both gamma radiation and star intensity appear to vary in the same way with altitude. Even now we cannot exclude the possibility that this photonic mechanism may be responsible for a small fraction of the star intensity.

That light mesons are not responsible for a significant fraction of the star production follows from the entirely different altitude dependence of the two kinds of radiation. Moreover, underground observations show that the star rate falls off to a negligible level there [79], while the meson intensity decreases relatively slowly.

Important problems remaining for investigation are: (1) Investigation of the absorption of the star-producing radiation as a function of the atomic number of the absorber. Preliminary experiments have been made in which the ionization chamber is surrounded by appropriate absorbers, but much remains to be done before this subject is in order. (2) Investigation as to how the nature of the stars themselves depends upon the atomic number of the disintegrated nucleus. What is the frequency of stars in which one, two, three, etc. charged particles are given out? How frequent are neutrons compared to charged particles in the outgoing radiation? How often do explosions occur in which the nucleus is totally dissociated into individual nucleons? Several different and naturally complementary techniques are available for such studies: (a) cloud chambers and photographic emulsion studies at balloon altitudes; (b) photo-disintegration of nuclei with the 100-Mev electromagnetic radiation from the Schenectady betatron [80]; (c) bombardment with 380 Mev alpha particles from the Berkeley cyclotron [81]; and (d) direct action of the natural cosmic radiation itself upon a solution of the substance under investigation in a very large water tank—for one now has available for investigation of the radioactive residues of star formation the beautiful techniques developed during the war for the continuous extraction of very small amounts of radioactive substances from very large volumes of solution [82]. (3) Correlation of the number and energy of the particles ejected in explosions with the energy of star-producing radiation. (4) Extension of star-intensity measurements to very high altitudes to determine whether any neutrons are present in the primary radiation. (5) What are the proper concepts to use in discussing the penetration of nucleus through nuclear matter? For what energy is it appropriate to speak of a characteristic range for a nucleon and for what energies is the concept of cross section more suitable [83]? What can one say about the subsequent behavior of a nucleus which has been traversed by a high-energy nucleon: will there emerge only one or two high-energy secondary nucleons, or will there usually follow disruption of the nucleus as a whole? (6) Stars produced by electromagnetic radiation, infrequent as they appear to be in the atmosphere, give what information about the interaction of photons with nuclei? Does the cross section for interception of a quantum by a nucleus increase with the cube of the gamma-ray energy in the range above 10 Mev, as indicated by tentative theoretical considerations [84]; or does the cross section assume a substantial value only for frequencies near the characteristic frequency associated with the vibration of the neutrons of the nucleus against the protons [85]; and how does the cross section for photon production of stars fall off for still higher gamma-ray energies? It appears necessary to investigate thoroughly the physics of nuclear explosions in order to see at what energies meson production begins and sub-nucleonic transformations come into competition with purely nucleonic changes.

NEUTRINO PHYSICS

A third and much more difficult problem of transformation physics is to extend the range of our experience about the changes in which neutrinos take part. We already possess a wealth of experimental information about the process of emission of neutrinos, mostly from the radioactive decay of atomic nuclei [86], but also partly from the disintegration of mesons [87]. However, other processes in which neutrinos take part, whether of absorption or of scattering, are so far altogether unobserved. These processes and further details of the emission phenomenon require investigation.

Still unknown is the extent of the correlation in angle between the electron and the neutrino which come off together in the so-called beta decay of an atomic nucleus. However, ingenious experiments have already been performed to detect the recoil of the nucleus in the act of neutrino emission [88]. Increase in the precision of such observations via new experimental techniques will surely yield a determination of the angular correlation in question. Then it may become possible [89] to discriminate between a number of quite distinct, half-empirical, half-theoretical descriptions which have been proposed for the beta decay process. None of these descriptions appears to give a completely satisfactory account of existing evidence on beta decay. Presumably the discrepancies are due partly to inadequacies in our theoretical picture of the nucleonic rearrangements which accompany beta decay, and partly to insufficiently accurate determinations of the nuclear lifetimes and electronic energies themselves. These points are under active investigation. Particularly noteworthy are preliminary determinations of the lifetime of the free neutron against beta decay into a proton, electron, and neutrino [90]. A precise determination of this lifetime can be expected to fix the fundamental constant in the theory of beta decay independently of those questions of nucleonic rearrangement which occur in the case of other nuclei.

There is to date no direct evidence that the neutral particle

which is given out in decay of 200-mass mesons is the same particle with which one has to do in the case of beta decay. It nevertheless appears reasonable to believe that a neutrino comes off
in the decay of the light meson: (1) the lifetime of this meson
is in the range of orders of magnitude which one would predict
from nuclear beta decay theory for a process of such high-energy
release; (2) the energy taken by the decay electron is only a fraction of the 100-Mev rest energy of the meson, and no evidence
for emission of any other charged particles is found. Recent observations indicate that no high-energy electromagnetic radiation is given off in the normal meson decay process [91].

As of the present time, it appears impossible to exclude any
one of three possible interpretations of the decay process:
(1) The meson breaks up into a 50-Mev electron and a 50-Mev
neutrino going with equal momentum in opposite directions.
(2) The meson breaks up into two neutrinos and one electron,
the energy of which varies with the direction of emission of the
neutrinos and ranges from zero Mev to 50 Mev, with a most
probable energy of about 40 Mev. (3) The meson breaks up
into an electron, a neutrino, and the same neutral meson of mass
∼ 80, whose existence is manifested in the decay of heavy
mesons. In case (3) the electrons have a continuous spectrum
qualitatively comparable to that expected in case (2).

Several observers have made measurements on the energy of
the decay electrons but it is not certain whether the spectrum is
discrete or continuous [92]. Indirect evidence about the energy of
the electrons released in the lower atmosphere by decay of down-
coming mesons [93] suggests that the meson gives out less than
half its energy to the decay electron, an argument against decay
into only a pair of particles.

There is no direct evidence for beta decay of the heavy (300
mass) meson as an occasional alternative to the dissociation of
this particle into a 200-mass meson and a neutral entity. The
photographic emulsion evidence argues for a frequency of such
beta decays which is at most a fraction of the rate of normal disintegration. The lifetime against such disintegration has been

found to be about 10^{-8} seconds [94]. Consequently, if beta decay of the heavy meson occurs at all, the effective lifetime for this process must be several times 10^{-8} seconds or more.

From available data on the rate of neutrino emission it is possible with the aid of the principle of microscopic reversibility to predict the probability of certain processes of absorption of neutrinos by atomic nuclei, accompanied by simultaneous emission or absorption of an electron. The effective cross section presented by a nucleus for such processes is expected to be exceedingly small [95]. One should not have found evidence for absorption in any experiment so far performed. Moreover, if measurements had given for such cross section values large enough to be conveniently observable, then there would be a direct violation of the principle of microscopic reversibility, which allows a straightforward calculation of the absorption probability from measured values of radioactive decay constants. The very fact that the cross section for the process inverse to radioactive decay is subject to calculation tells us that we have to look for transformations of another character if knowledge of the interaction of neutrinos with matter is substantially to be extended.

This conclusion by no means diminishes the interest in a direct observation of the act of absorption. It is easily shown [96] that the large flux of neutrinos from one of the existing chain reacting piles, when allowed to fall on several thousand pounds of suitably chosen material, will produce an amount of induced radioactivity which will be on the border line of measurement when concentrated by well-established techniques [97]. As a procedure for measuring neutrino intensity is developed along this line or in some other way, it will be a matter of the greatest interest to determine the flux of these particles reaching the earth from the sun and thereby to investigate the absorption of these particles in the material of that star [98]. In the absence of such absorption, the intensity from this distant source will be as strong as the flux not very many feet away from a chain-reacting unit. Thus measurement of the absorbing power of the sun calls for a detecting device of a sensitivity not very different from that required to detect neutrinos in the first place.

It is an open issue whether the neutrinos given out in company with a negaton when a neutron transforms to a proton is the same as the particle given out in company with a positon when a nuclear proton transforms to a neutron. In order not to prejudge this issue it has been customary to give the name "antineutrino" to the particle given out in the latter process. Of the order of 5 per cent of the power of a nuclear chain-reacting pile is given out in the form of neutrinos, while the roughly comparable fraction of the energy set free in the sun by nuclear reactions comes out in the form of antineutrinos. According as the two kinds of radiation are identical or distinct, one will expect to use the same or different detectors to observe them.

It has to be expected that the absorption of an antineutrino will bring about the same reaction which normally accompanies the emission of a neutrino. Thus a nucleus which is unstable against emission of an electron and a neutrino will have its normal beta decay speeded up by a bombardment with antineutrinos. This circumstance offers an interesting possibility to tell whether antineutrinos are identical with neutrinos.

If the two entities are the same, then neutrino bombardment should also speed up the electron-neutrino emission processes. Consider therefore a nucleus in which two successive beta transformations may in principle occur. If neutrinos and antineutrinos are identical, then the neutrino from the first transition may be absorbed in the second transition with the net result that we have the emission of two electrons and no neutrinos at all. In this case the sum of the energies of the two emitted electrons will always add up to the same value in the decay of different specimens of the same nucleus. If neutrino and antineutrino are different, however, then the process just described will be impossible and the double beta decay can only come about with the emission of four particles—two electrons and two neutrinos. In either case, the double beta emission process can take place under circumstances where two successive single decay processes are forbidden by reason of unfavorable energy of the intermediate nucleus. The two alternative assumptions about neutrinos and antineutrinos lead, not only to marked differences in the expected division of energy between the decay electron in double beta transitions, but also to great differences in the expected lifetime of the original nucleus. Recent tentative experimental results speak in favor of the hypothesis that neutrinos and antineutrinos are not distinct [99].

MESON PHYSICS

The fourth and last major field of experimental transformation physics, and the field apparently much the richest in promise, is investigation of the creation, the properties, and the destruction of mesons. The preponderance of light mesons in the natural cosmic radiation at sea level makes them well suited to experimental investigation in existing laboratories. The recent wonderful discovery that light and heavy mesons are produced by nuclear bombardment opens the door to a still wider variety of observations and tests on both kinds of particles.

The mechanism of meson production presents many problems: (1) Why are both light and heavy mesons produced at the same time and in comparable number in the Berkeley bombardments? It is already known that heavy mesons are absorbed with great readiness by atomic nuclei [100]. Accordingly the principle of microscopic reversibility makes it reasonable that these particles should also be produced with significant yield in nuclear bombardment. But by the same token, one should find only in small yield the 200-mass mesons, which undergo only slowly any specific interaction with atomic nuclei. Is it possible that the light mesons are not produced directly in the 184-inch cyclotron experiments but instead arise by decay of the heavier mesons? This fundamental issue is under intense investigation. (2) What is the threshold for meson production and how does the yield depend on the energy of the bombarding nuclei? The cyclotron experiments with the helium nucleus as incident particle show that the yield diminishes rapidly below 380 Mev. No information is available above this level except at the Bev energies of the cosmic rays. Recent observations at magnetic latitudes from the equator to 50° North and from sea level up to 30,000 feet, allow tentative conclusions about the total number of mesons released in the atmosphere by primaries above any given energy. The results suggest that most of the meson production is due to primaries with energy greater than 10 Bev, though the average energy of the primaries is less than 10 Bev [101]. Protons with energy substantially below 10 Bev seem, however, to produce large numbers of nuclear disruptions, as evidenced by the large latitude effect recently found for neutron intensity in the atmosphere [102]. Apparently the meson yield diminishes in some not yet very well-known way relative to the yield of nuclear explosions until at cyclotron energies the yield of mesons is (from Berkeley observations) an exceedingly small fraction of the total. (3) Is the high multiplicity of the meson creation process observed in the upper atmosphere a property which is already associated with the collision between two nucleons, or is it due to the multiplicity of target nucleons in a typical oxygen or nitrogen nucleus [103]? (4) What circumstance of the production process contributes most to the 20 per cent excess of positive over negative mesons observed at sea level [104]? (5) What is the probability for an energetic quantum of radiation to produce mesons on encounter with a nucleus [105]? (6) When mesons arise in the collision of two nucleons, does one of the nucleons ever undergo destruction?

Cloud-chamber, counter, and ionization-chamber observations have been made on the production of showers of electrons and penetrating particles and nucleons and nuclear encounters [106]. So far relatively few generalizations have been established on the mechanism of such processes, partly because of lack of knowledge of the energy of the incident particle, partly because of ambiguities (except in favorable cases) about the identification of the ejected particles. Yet it can hardly be doubted that among these pictures one has representatives of the fundamental act of the cosmic radiation. It is the unique multiplicity of this act, rather than anything about the intensity of the primary radiation or the height of the layer of meson production, which is responsible for many of the difficulties encountered in studying this basic phenomenon of elementary particle physics.

These problems about the mechanism of production of mesons

lead to equally interesting questions about the properties of these particles: (1) Is the practical absence of heavy mesons at sea level as compared to their relative abundance at balloon altitudes a consequence of a rapid decay of these particles in flight [107], or is it due to a large probability of interaction between the heavy mesons in the oxygen and nitrogen nuclei of the air? (2) What happens to the neutral mesons released by the decay of the 300-mass mesons? (3) Can one confirm the increasing evidence for a particle of mass two to three times greater than the mass of the heavy meson; and if so, what are the genetic relationships between this particle and the already known mesons [108]? (4) Is the scattering and radiative deceleration of 200-mass mesons by atomic nuclei in satisfactory accord with the idea that electromagnetic forces alone determine the course of collision [109]? (5) Do the energy levels for the negative 200-mass mesons in the extended electrostatic fields of the nucleus, and the electromagnetic and electronic radiations ejected from the atom in transitions between these levels, confirm the idea that the nucleus interacts with light mesons almost entirely by way of electric forces [110]? (6) Does the mechanism of the capture of slow negative 200-mass and 300-mass mesons into Bohr orbits around atomic nuclei accord satisfactorily with the predictions of theory [111]?

Finally we have the question, what happens to those negative mesons which react with atomic nuclei? (1) Is the disappearance of a 300-mass meson at a nucleus associated with the emission from the nucleus of any other light particle; or is it true—as it is now tentatively supposed—that the sole consequence of the reaction is the conversion of a proton to a neutron? To establish that all the rest energy of the annihilated meson reappears as excitation energy of the final nucleus would not only argue against the emission of some unknown particle in the capture process, but also speak convincingly for a zero (or integral) spin for the heavy meson. (2) Does the capture of heavy mesons by deuterium release two neutrons with a characteristic energy of about 75 Mev each; or is one neutron left with essentially the same kinetic energy which it had in the deuteron, with the other neutron recoiling after emission of a gamma ray with energy of the order of 140 Mev? (3) What fraction of negative heavy mesons arrive in the lowest Bohr orbit about an atomic nucleus before undergoing nuclear capture; and what is the lifetime of the meson in the lowest Bohr orbit? (4) What is the mechanism of reaction of light mesons with atomic nuclei? The simple law predicted for the dependence of reaction probability upon atomic number is to a considerable extent independent of the precise details of the reaction and even of its general nature [112]. These predictions have received a reasonable confirmation through recent remarkable measurements of the lifetime and capture probability of negative 200-mass mesons [113]. However, a closer examination shows that certain minor variations from nucleus to nucleus are to be expected as compared with the original simple law, variations which have yet to be developed systematically on the theoretical side and brought into evidence on the experimental side. (5) Does the negative meson give its charge to the nucleus and depart as a neutral meson, perhaps the same neutral meson (or neutrino) which is emitted from decay of heavy mesons? (6) Is the excitation of the final nucleus in accord with the idea that a neutral meson takes away a substantial part of the mass energy brought in by the incident 200-mass meson?

This list of questions concludes our review of some of the outstanding experimental problems in elementary particle physics —problems concerned with negatons and positons, nuclear explosions, neutrino physics, and most of all, with the meson. With cosmic rays and new accelerators providing high-energy particles and photons for workaday experimentation, great discoveries must be expected in these fields.

THE PLACE OF THEORY

The last great task of fundamental physics is to reduce to order our newly gained experience. For the most effective progress, if the history of physics is any guide, this theoretical work must proceed hand in hand with experiment. Only by the analysis and interpretation of observations as they are made, and by the examination of the larger implications of the results, is one in a satisfactory position to pose new experimental and theoretical questions of the greatest significance. That two research projects involving the same expenditure of time and man power often give results whose importance differs by a factor of over a hundred is sometimes a matter of accident. But more often it is a matter of greater awareness in one project of what are the most significant questions susceptible at the moment to successful attack. This continual assessment of results of investigations and of choice of further problems in the light of the outstanding unsolved questions is essential in elementary particle physics. No branch of science can derive greater advantages from review articles, survey lectures, the library, and the seminar.

The task of reducing our experience to order includes not only this close collaboration of theory with experiment, but also the creative function to assimilate the fruits of such collaboration into a unified view of matter.

The theories by the creation of which science accomplishes this function of unification are always idealizations, valid within a certain domain of experience, and inapplicable outside. A large part of our physical experience is now summarized in a few great and well-founded theories: the theory of relativity [114], the theory of gravitation of Mach and Einstein [115], electromagnetism [116], the quantum theory typified by Bohr's contrasting principles of complementarity and of correspondence [117], and the theory of negaton-positon pairs [118]. Taken within their proper fields of application, these theories offer a solid basis of our further theoretical progress. The work for the future appears to be the union of the several points of view of these theories and the assimilation into all of them of certain limitations of our usual concepts which are imposed by the existence in nature of elementary particles. It seems reasonable to suppose that our further advance will depend less upon the invention of new laws of force and types of interaction than upon renewed analysis of the fundamental problems of measurement and observability of fields, electrons, and elementary particles, in general along the lines of the classical paper of Bohr and Rosenfeld [119] on the measurability of the electromagnetic field quantities.

It may give an impression of the task of elementary particle physics in the realm of theory to review briefly some of the problems of the theory of mesons, of the electron-pair theory, of electromagnetism, and the theory of gravitation.

MESON THEORY

The first topic, the theory of mesons, may be said to be at present in a state of free experimentation with ideas and great uncertainty as to principle, both because of the incompleteness of our present experimental picture, and because of difficulty in tying the proposed hypotheses to already existing theories. As a guide in these attempts, the assumption has been adopted [120] that mesons should play in the interaction between nucleons a rôle analogous to that of quanta of electromagnetic radiation in the interaction between charged particles. Some appreciable success has been achieved along these lines in giving a half-theoretical, half-empirical account of the most important features of the nuclear forces [121]. Along the same lines it has recently been possible to correlate the magnetic moment of the proton and the neutron, though without determining the absolute value of either of them [122]. For a time, it also appeared that meson theory provided a simple account of beta decay. The idea was that the nucleus gave out the electron and neutrino, not directly, but by first producing an intermediate meson, which then decayed [123]. The recent discovery that several varieties of mesons exist, and that the decay properties of the ordinary meson may not be as originally expected, leaves the successes of all such attempts in a state of great uncertainty. It is true that there now exist several varieties of meson field theory, and that these theories contain a number of adjustable constants, so that it is still possible to account along these lines for a large range of experimental results. It is an unsatisfactory sign, however, that the developments in this branch of meson theory have had to lag behind rather than precede the experimental advances.

The difficulties common to all present meson theories force us to question the common hypothesis on which they are based: that the force between mesons is entirely distinct in character and origin from electromagnetic forces, and that mesons constitute the quanta of this new force field. However suggestive this idea, originally put forward by Yukawa, it is not impossible that it is at the same time altogether misleading. The hypothesis would certainly have been both suggestive and misleading if it had been put forward with respect to the forces between atoms.

Imagine ourselves in a situation where quantum theory has been developed, but we know nothing about the internal structure of hydrogen atoms. We postulate that these systems are elementary particles, just as we make this assumption about nucleons. We carry out an elaborate series of experiments to determine the law of force between these "particles." We find an inverse seventh-power attraction at large distances, a repulsion at small distances. We conclude from the strength of the force that it can have nothing to do with gravitation, and from its dependence on distance that it is of nonelectromagnetic origin. Consequently, we postulate the existence of a fundamental new field of force, the "hydron" field. Quantum theory, in connection with the known range of action of this force, then tells us that the quanta of the new field possess a characteristic mass of their own, of the order of 10^{-27} grams. The subsequent discovery of the electron is then taken as confirmation of the hydron theory, just as the discovery of the particle of intermediate mass was considered as proof of meson theory.

The hydron theory is, of course, infantile in view of our knowledge of the actual structure of the hydrogen atom, and the question is always before us whether existing meson theories may not be equally misleading. We must certainly test such theories against experiment, and if they fail, we can remark with Bohr that one makes progress only by making all possible mistakes!

In this connection, it must be recognized that the present situation calls for a certain daring in considering and testing new ideas. Certain questions naturally arise from the analogy just drawn between atomic and nuclear physics. Is it possible that mesons, protons, and neutrons are all built up, in a sense which cannot yet be defined, from electrons and neutrinos? Is it possible that the order-of-magnitude agreement between nuclear dimensions and the so-called classical electron radius is no accident? It is clear that these questions cannot be answered now. They require an examination of the implications of electromagnetic and pair theories in the domain of very small distances. Such an examination, however it may turn out, is evidently one of the inescapable obligations of present-day theoretical physics.

PAIR THEORY AND ELECTROMAGNETIC THEORY

The theory of electron pairs has already shown itself comparable in unity, comprehensiveness, and richness of application to the classical theories of gravitation and electromagnetism. Its contribution to the understanding of the soft component of the cosmic radiation has already been mentioned. It has made well-verified predictions about other collision processes. Such investigations make use, not only of pair theory to predict how an electron moves under given electromagnetic forces, but also of electromagnetic theory to predict how the electromagnetic forces depend upon the motions of the electrons. In the treatment of the physical processes just mentioned, it is normally necessary and appropriate to treat the interaction of electron with the electromagnetic field as a small perturbation, and to develop the consequences of this perturbation in a power series in terms which are respectively proportional to the strength of the perturbing force, proportional to the square of this perturbation, to its third power, etc.

The more complicated the problem treated, the more difficult these computations have proved to be when carried out with the existing mathematical formalism.

The result of the calculation—either the displacement of an energy level, or the value of a collision cross section—comes out as a series of terms some of which are sometimes infinite and have to be dropped as having no physical significance. Unfortunately, the division of the total result into a finite and an infinite part has sometimes been difficult to make in an unambiguous way in the only form of the theory which was available until recently. This circumstance is due to the fact that the formalism, while in principle consistent with the requirements of relativity theory, was in notation and mode of description essentially nonrelativistic. Fortunately, Tomonaga and associated workers and Schwinger have very recently independently developed an alternative way of writing the equations of pair theory and electromagnetic theory [124]. This treatment is fully relativistic from the start and at the same time preserves the content of the already existing theory—including, unfortunately, the division of result into finite and infinite parts. However, it is now much simpler to make this division in an unambiguous way.

Along these lines, it has been possible easily to rederive previously established results of the theory and also to obtain two important new consequences of the theory in beautiful and satisfactory agreement with the result of recent experiments: the anomalous magnetic moment of the electron, and the shift in the energy level of those states of the hydrogen atom in which the electron part of the time comes close to the nucleus. The applications of the theory to other problems of actual physical interest are now being investigated actively with the aid of the theory.

So far, application of pair theory and electromagnetic theory has been limited to problems where the interaction between the electron and the field can be treated as a weak perturbation. Relatively little has yet been done in the case of strong interactions—on problems such as the state of the pair field in the neighborhood of an atomic nucleus, the influence of this field on the force between two massive, charged particles [125], and the interaction of the particles of the pair field with one another.

The tasks presented by these questions are not so much concerned with working out the mathematical implications of the present formalism as with extending the formalism itself, mathematically and conceptually. It appears likely that a new idea must be introduced into the theory to eliminate the characteristic infinities which so often emerge.

One conceivable means to arrive at a new idea is to express existing theory in equivalent language but from an alternative point of view. The fact that electromagnetism and pair physics are so closely entwined in existing theory is not an accident. One can in fact adopt the view that the electromagnetic field is not an independent entity of its own, but is a mathematical construct to describe the actually direct interaction between the elementary electrically charged particles. This standpoint of "action at a distance" permits one to look at problems of radiation and the so-called degrees of freedom of the electromagnetic field in a new and interesting light [126]. Naturally the ultimate complete equivalence of this approach to the usual field theoretical treatment makes it clear that nothing new can result so long as this equivalence is strictly maintained. What may come out by changes or reinterpretations of the existing theory of action at a distance is uncertain.

GRAVITATIONAL THEORY

The last theory to be mentioned, gravitation, is in a state quite comparable to that of electromagnetism, for the usual mode of description in both theories assumes a continuous distribution of mass and charge and the possibility of an unlimited number of test particles, in contrast to the atomistic distribution implied by the existence of elementary particles. Also, like electromagnetism, gravitation theory deals with equations of motion and field equation. Thus the general theory of relativity—which constitutes our theory of gravitation—gives an equation for the motion of matter in terms of the space-time metric in the region occupied by the matter, and another equation for the space-time metric in terms of the positions and velocities of the particles of matter. Just as in electrodynamics, however, the field is singular at the location of a point particle, and the equation of motion therefore becomes in principle inapplicable. To avoid this fundamental difficulty later work has abandoned the equation of motion as a separate condition and has obtained the motion from the field equations themselves. Not all the consequences of this altered point of view have yet been explored. In particular, the reaction of gravitational radiation upon an accelerated mass is a question which continues to attract interest [127]. And it is not clear that the altered point of view resolves the apparent paradox that the present gravitational field equations apply to the idealized problem of two point masses in otherwise empty space [128], a situation where it is in principle impossible to discuss changes in the distance between the two particles.

Just as recognition of the atomicity of matter suggests in the electromagnetic theory a replacement or modification in the use of the field concept equivalent to the introduction of the concept of action at a distance, so it would appear that in the gravitational theory we should be able in principle to dispense with the concepts of space and time and take as the basis of our description of nature the elementary concepts of world line and light cone. By a further development of this line of reasoning we may hope to get a more comprehensive view than we now possess of what types of interaction might reasonably be expected to occur in a classical description of nature.

From this survey of some of the problems of theory, it is apparent that many lines of progress are open. Elementary particle physics will accomplish its task to reduce our experience to order, just as it will get sources of energetic particles and use these sources to study the transformations of the elementary particles.

For References see p. 292.

III

HIGH ENERGY PHYSICS

By Ernest O. Lawrence

University of California

DEVELOPMENTS in atomic physics have been and are continuing to be so rapid and so fundamental in character as to constitute truly a revolution in our understanding of the properties of matter. Perhaps I can best indicate some major problems and convey a glimpse into the future by an account of certain current investigations in the Radiation Laboratory in Berkeley.

The total energy of a heavy atom like lead or uranium is about 200 billion electron volts; hence, studies of energy transformations over a vast range are essential for a deeper understanding of atomic phenomena. In ordinary nuclear reactions involving only a few nuclear particles, such as the radioactive transformations or the transmutation of one element into its neighbor, the energy changes are only a few million electron volts. To be sure, in cosmic-ray investigations fragmentary evidence of transformations of very much higher values have been obtained, but the discovery of atomic fission marked the real beginning of high-energy physics in the laboratory.

Long before the discovery of fission the vast extent of nuclear energies was of course appreciated, and likewise the importance of producing ever higher energy particles in the laboratory. Accordingly, almost ten years ago plans were laid to build a giant cyclotron—one as large as practicable both financially and otherwise—with the hope that such a great instrument would produce particles of the next higher energy range, hundreds rather than tens of millions of electron volts.

THE 184-INCH SYNCHRO-CYCLOTRON

The actual construction of the great cyclotron, with magnet pole pieces 184 inches in diameter and weighing more than 4,000 tons, was well started when the war necessarily interrupted the work. However, as is well known, the 184-inch cyclotron magnet was finished and served a useful purpose in the war effort in providing a splendid laboratory facility for the development of the calutron, that is, the electromagnetic process for the separation of the uranium isotopes.

Now, from the standpoint of the purely scientific objective of getting on with the job of exploring farther into the realm of the atom, the war interruption might have been a serious loss, a delay of some five years. Actually, this delay turned out to be a blessing in disguise for the wide experience gained in the war effort by the scientists and engineers concerned, as well as many new technological developments, contributed greatly to the rapid and successful carrying out of the undertaking. Moreover, my colleague Dr. Edwin McMillan [1] and independently V. Veksler [2] in Russia meanwhile elucidated the principle of phase stability in the multiple acceleration of particles, embodied in the synchrotron. They pointed out so clearly and so convincingly the way to higher energies that when the 184-inch program was resumed, immediately after the war, the great instrument was redesigned, following their ideas, as a synchro-cyclotron, thereby more than doubling the power of the great accelerator. In the long view, therefore, and indeed in the light of new discoveries already made with these high-energy particles, one may say that the delay of the war years will soon be made up, if it has not been already, by the more rapid progress in the accumulation of knowledge of atomic phenomena afforded by the availability of these higher energy particles in the laboratory.

The 184-inch synchro-cyclotron was turned on for the first time on November 1, 1946, and since that time has been producing deuterons of energies up to 200 million electron volts (Mev) and alpha particles up to 400 Mev. Since nowadays cyclotrons are in such wide use and, indeed, since so many synchrocyclotrons are planned or are under construction in various laboratories in this country and abroad, it is hardly necessary for me to undertake a general description of these machines here. But perhaps it is of interest to show some pictures of the 184-

inch installation which is now in operation in Berkeley (Figs. 1, 2, 3, 4).

There follows a brief account of some recent investigations that have been carried out with this most powerful of atom

FIG. 1. The synchro-cyclotron under construction. The magnet pole faces, 184 inches in diameter, can be seen within the cyclotron chamber behind Professor R. L. Thornton. The large dee is seen ready to be moved into position.

smashers—for, indeed, as we shall see, particles of hundreds of millions of electron volts do a very thorough job of breaking up even the heaviest of the elements!

A BEAM OF HIGH-ENERGY NEUTRONS

When the 184-inch instrument was first turned on, a sharply defined beam of penetrating radiation was observed from the probe target in the cyclotron chamber. This extraordinarily interesting phenomenon, of course, was immediately the subject of some preliminary exploratory experiments. First of all, measurements of the penetrating power of the radiation were made

FIG. 2. General view of the new 184-inch synchro-cyclotron, now in operation at the Radiation Laboratory at Berkeley. The cyclotron vacuum chamber is in the center, and the radio frequency oscillator is on the right.

by interposing various thicknesses of different materials in the path of the beam and observing the resulting reduction in intensity of the radiation as indicated by an ionization chamber. The early results obtained in this way by Moyer, Hildebrand, Knable, Parmley and York [3] are shown in Figure 5. It is seen that the radiation was found to be extraordinarily penetrating.

Apart from the scientific interest, the great penetrating power of these rays raised an immediate and urgent practical laboratory health problem—the provision of adequate radiation protection; for it was quite obvious that if the cyclotron were to be operated at full power for extended periods of time, radiation

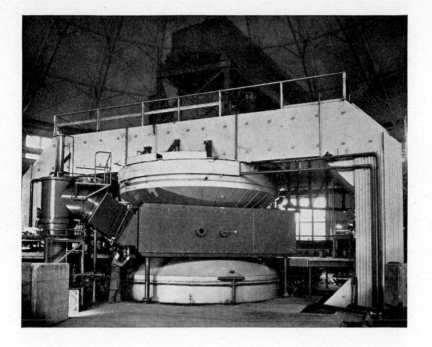

FIG. 3. A view of the 184-inch synchro-cyclotron showing the large oil diffusion pumps on the left. The beam of high-energy neutrons emerges from the chamber at maximum intensity precisely at the center of the vertical white line inscribed on the steel plate.

shielding would have to be of massive proportions. Indeed, on the basis of these and many later measurements, it was determined that a concrete wall ten feet thick surrounding the cyclotron would be required for present levels of operation,* and this is shown in Figures 6 and 7.

* It will doubtless be necessary to provide additional shielding when the synchro-cyclotron is modified to produce 350-Mev protons and larger currents of deuterons.

These early observations also showed that the beam was made up largely of neutrons, because lead was not nearly so effective per unit mass as water or concrete in absorbing the radiation. Furthermore, reasonably good estimates of the energy of the neutrons could be made from the absorption coefficients, and on this basis it was concluded that their average kinetic energy was

FIG. 4. The control desk of the synchro-cyclotron.

of the order of 100 Mev. That the neutrons were of such high energy was also established during those first few days of operation of the cyclotron by Wilson Powell [4], who placed a cloud chamber in the beam and observed (Fig. 8) great numbers of high-energy recoil protons, many up to 100 Mev and a few in the neighborhood of 200 Mev.

There could be no doubt as to the general character of the penetrating radiation. Here was a truly remarkable beam of high-energy neutrons. Before settling down to careful quantitative investigations, all concerned could not resist the urge to attempt numerous quick and easy qualitative experiments in order to observe some of the properties of the radiation. For example, various substances were placed in the beam, and a glimpse of some of the resulting nuclear reactions was obtained by the ob-

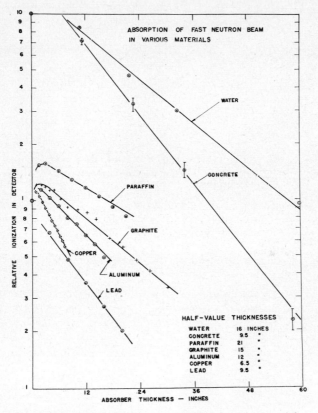

FIG. 5. Absorption of fast neutron beam in various materials.

servation of the induced radioactivities. In this way, Perlman, Goeckermann, Templeton and Howland [5] discovered that these high-energy neutrons produced fission in a number of heavy elements including lead and bismuth. Another interesting and immediately useful observation was the production of radioactive carbon in graphite disks placed in the beam. This reaction, C^{12} (n, 2n) C^{11}, has a threshold of about 20 Mev and, there-

FIG. 6. General view of radiation shield surrounding cyclotron. The concrete side walls are ten feet thick.

FIG. 7. Entrance to cyclotron through concrete shield.

fore, serves as a convenient detector of high-energy neutrons.*

By placing small disks of graphite across the beam and measuring the induced activity, Helmholz, McMillan and Sewell [6] were able easily to map out the shape of the beam with consid-

FIG. 8. Early cloud-chamber photograph showing a high-energy proton track. The dark arrow marks the track of a proton which had an energy of 190 Mev ± 15 per cent and which was traveling in the direction of the beam. All the tracks shown are initiated by the neutron beam from a 190-Mev deuteron beam from the 184-inch cyclotron. Gas in the chamber was oxygen, and the five-prong "star" is the result of a neutron collision with an oxygen nucleus. A magnetic field of 9,000 gauss was used.

erable precision. They established that the neutron rays were largely confined to an angular spread of about ten degrees in the direction of the 200-Mev deuterons striking the cyclotron target. This interesting result was not unexpected, as will be seen in the following.

* Recent experiments indicate that well above the threshold value, the induced radioactivity is insensitive to the energy of the neutrons and therefore proportional to the flux.

SPLITTING OF THE DEUTERON

A deuteron consists of a neutron and a proton held together with a binding energy of about 2 Mev, which is quite negligible in comparison to the kinetic energy of the deuterons striking the cyclotron target. Thus, in effect, the collision of a 200-Mev deuteron with an atomic nucleus would be much the same as

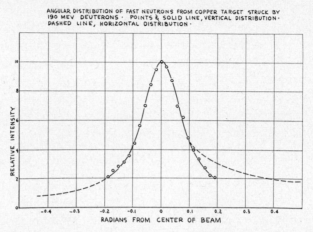

FIG. 9. The experimental observations by Helmholz, McMillan, Peterson, and Sewell of the shape of the beam of high-energy neutrons from the cyclotron target. The circles represent experimental data on relative neutron flux as indicated by activity in carbon disks placed across the beam. The solid line represents the expected distribution according to the theory of Serber.

the simultaneous collision of a 100-Mev neutron and a 100-Mev proton. In other words, the particles are held together so loosely in the deuteron that in a nuclear collision they are "on their own," so to speak.

With these considerations in mind, it is easy to see that sometimes in a collision the proton might just scrape a nucleus while the neutron would miss it altogether, thence (in view of the loose binding), proceeding on its way in a straight line with the velocity it had at the instant of the collision. According to Professor R. Serber [7], this is without doubt the process responsible for the observed beam of high-energy neutrons.

Serber has worked out in detail the expected angular distribution of the neutron beam produced in this way. He pointed out that the neutron and proton in the deuteron in effect are not at rest relative to their center of gravity but have essentially a vibrational energy of some 2 Mev. In quantum mechanical terms one would say that the particles have "an intrinsic uncertainty in momentum," while in old-fashioned mechanical terms one would describe the deuteron as made of two heavy balls (neutron and proton) oscillating back and forth and held together by an elastic spring. Therefore, according to Serber, the expected distribution of velocities of the neutrons released on collision of the deuterons in the target would be given simply by adding their intrinsic velocity distribution to the velocity of the deuteron as a whole at the instant of collision. Calculations in this way gave the theoretical curve of Figure 9, which is seen to be in excellent agreement with the experimental observations.

A BEAM OF HIGH-ENERGY PROTONS

Now, on the other hand, if in a nuclear collision the neutron of the deuteron just hits the nucleus, the proton will proceed with the velocity it had at the instant of the impact, and so a beam of protons would also be expected from the cyclotron target. Such charged particles, of course, would not proceed out from the target in a straight line like the neutrons, for they would be bent in the cyclotron magnetic field in circles half the diameter of the circles of the target deuterons. Thus, it was expected that protons would be observed bent to the central region of the cyclotron with energies in the range of 100 Mev, and, needless to say, they were immediately observed.

The distribution in velocities of these protons, which according to Serber's ideas would be the same as for the neutrons, have recently been investigated by Chupp, Gardner and Taylor [8]. They placed both photographic plates and disks of graphite with suitable shielding and diaphragms in the central region of the cyclotron, as shown in Figure 10. Counts of proton tracks in the plates, and observations of the activity induced in the pieces of graphite by the reaction, C^{12} (p, pn) C^{11}, agreed with Serber's theoretical distribution, as shown in Figure 11.

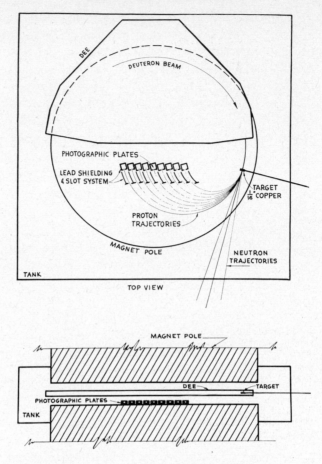

LOCATION OF PHOTOGRAPHIC PLATES FOR STUDY OF PROTONS FROM THE TARGET

FIG. 10. Diagram of arrangement for the study of the distribution of the protons from the cyclotron target resulting from the splitting of the deuterons. The neutrons proceed in straight lines with average velocities in the direction of the deuterons at the target. The protons emerge from the target in the same initial directions as the neutrons, but because of their electric charge are bent in the magnetic field in circles as shown. In some of the observations the photographic plates were replaced by carbon disks, and thereby the protons were detected by induced radioactivity.

NEUTRON PROTON SCATTERING—CHARGE EXCHANGE AND ORDINARY FORCES

Attention may now be turned to the fundamental problem of the interaction of neutrons and protons—a fundamental problem

indeed, for an understanding of this simplest of nuclear interactions must surely precede any general theory of nuclear matter.

Our present knowledge of nuclear forces is based very largely
on the results of scattering experiments in the region of a few
million electron volts.* However, some years ago Heisenberg
proposed the idea of charge exchange in the interaction of protons

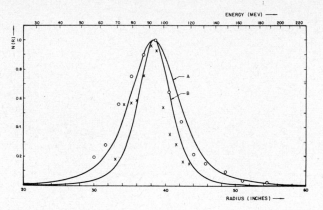

FIG. 11. Distribution of protons from the target.
   Circles. Numbers of protons measured by carbon activation method.
   Crosses. Numbers of protons measured by photographic plates.
   Curve A. Theoretical distribution for slit system used with carbon activation
                method (protons accepted over a wide horizontal angular distribu-
                tion).
   Curve B. Theoretical distribution for slit system used with photographic
                plates (protons accepted in forward direction only).

and neutrons, to explain the constancy of the binding energy of
particles in light and heavy nuclei. The low-energy scattering
experiments gave no evidence one way or the other on the reality
of such a charge exchange phenomenon; nevertheless, for some
time now it has appeared probable that there may be two types of
forces between the nuclear particles—(a) ordinary forces and
(b) exchange forces.

The former are not unlike the forces in billiard ball collisions
or in Rutherford scattering, and in a sense are understandable

---

* Professor Gregory Breit, for example, was the first to work out in detail the
expected neutron proton scattering on the assumption of a finite range of the forces,
and also the analysis of neutron proton scattering data in the range of a few million
electron volts.

in terms of older ideas. But the exchange force is essentially a new concept. This force arises from a charge exchange phenomenon. To put the matter in concrete terms, the charge ex-

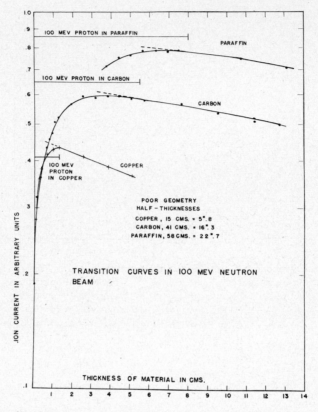

FIG. 12. The variation with wall thickness of the ionization in a small air ionization chamber produced by a beam of 100-Mev neutrons. These results show that many protons ejected by the neutrons penetrated more than two inches of paraffin and therefore are of energy comparable to the neutrons. These early observations constitute the first direct experimental evidence for the charge exchange hypothesis in theories of interaction of protons and neutrons.

change hypothesis means that when a neutron and proton collide, even just barely "touch" each other, the proton's charge oscillates back and forth between the particles, so that when the particles move apart after the collision there is a likelihood that the neutron will have acquired the charge, therefore turning into a proton, whereas the proton will have become a neutron.

The first truly convincing experimental evidence for the reality of this charge exchange between particles was given by

FIG. 13. The experimental arrangement for the study of the interaction of high-energy neutrons with protons. The neutron beam emerges from the concrete wall surrounding the cyclotron through a copper-lined hole two inches in diameter, seen in the upper left of the photograph. The neutron beam strikes first a thin block of paraffin ejecting protons at a convenient angle which are detected by two proportional counters in a coincidence circuit, serving thereby as a measure of the relative beam intensity. Herbert York is shown placing further on in the beam a thin sheet of carbon from which the angular distribution of protons ejected by the neutrons is recorded in quadruple coincidence by four proportional counters in line. These are seen at the right, set for an angle of some 30° to the primary neutron beam. An absorbing plate seen between the third and fourth counters determines a lower limit to the energy of the observed recoil protons. By comparing the particles from carbon and paraffin, the recoil protons from hydrogen are determined.

the observation of Moyer and co-workers on transition effects in the walls of the ionization chambers used in the early measurements of the beam of high-energy neutrons. They observed, as did Loevinger later (Fig. 12), that the 100-Mev neutrons produced an abundance of correspondingly high-energy recoil protons, quite in accord with the idea of the neutrons just touching protons in hydrogenous material and exchanging charge, thereby turning into high-energy protons.

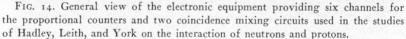

FIG. 14. General view of the electronic equipment providing six channels for the proportional counters and two coincidence mixing circuits used in the studies of Hadley, Leith, and York on the interaction of neutrons and protons.

This important matter has continued to be vigorously investigated. In order to gain more quantitative information, J. Hadley, C. E. Leith, and H. York have recently observed the secondary protons from carbon and paraffin. They used proportional counters in quadruple coincidence as a proton detector, and by suitable absorbers between the counters were able to select the higher energy particles. Their experimental arrangement is shown in Figures 13 and 14. They found, as indicated in Figure 15, that the most probable direction of a high-energy proton ejected from hydrogenous material by a 100-Mev neutron is in the forward direction, which is in accord with the charge exchange idea.

These observations leave little doubt about the reality of the exchange process, but they do not rule out the possibility of part of the interactions of these high-energy neutrons and protons being of the ordinary billiard-ball type. In random collisions of billiard balls (as every billiard player knows!) the chance of a

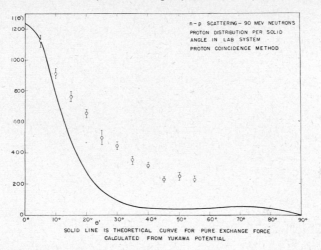

FIG. 15. The observations of Leith, Hadley, and York of the angular distribution of the recoil protons in hydrogen traversed by a beam of high-energy neutrons. The most probable direction of the secondary protons is in the direction of neutrons indicating charge exchange.

dead center knock on wherein the recoiling ball takes the whole energy of the cue ball is the same as one in which the cue ball just nicks the struck ball, the former proceeding on with little loss of energy and the latter moving sideways with relatively little energy. And so, the ordinary forces in neutron-proton collisions would give rise to large numbers of recoil protons of low velocity moving almost at right angles to the neutron beam.

To look into this question, Wilson Powell and Walter Hartsough have been using the cloud chamber, which is best suited for the observation of low-energy recoil particles. Their experimental arrangement is shown in Figure 16, and examples of their cloud-chamber pictures are shown in Figures 17 and 18.

Their collected observations of the recoil protons in the hydrogen-filled chamber are shown in Figure 19. They find, in confirmation of the observations of Hadley, Leith, and York, that

FIG. 16. General view of Dr. Wilson Powell's experimental arrangement for the cloud-chamber study of the collisions of high-energy neutrons with nuclei. The sharply defined neutron beam emerges from the two-inch channel in the concrete shield surrounding the cyclotron (seen at the left).

This beam is further defined by a tube of paraffin seen in the center of the photograph. The channel through the paraffin is only ⅝ inches in diameter, and the resulting narrow beam passes through the cloud chamber at the right. By the use of a thin window in the wall of the cloud chamber the relative number of observed particles originating in the gas of the chamber is considerably increased. The cloud chamber is 16 inches in diameter and is surrounded by Helmholz coils which produce suitably pulsed magnetic fields of 13,400 gauss. From the observed curvature of the tracks in this high field, as well as their range and their specific ionization, the type and energy of the particles are determined.

there is a preponderance of high-energy protons in the forward direction, but in addition there are more low-energy particles recoiling at large angles to the beam than would be expected on the basis of the charge exchange hypothesis.

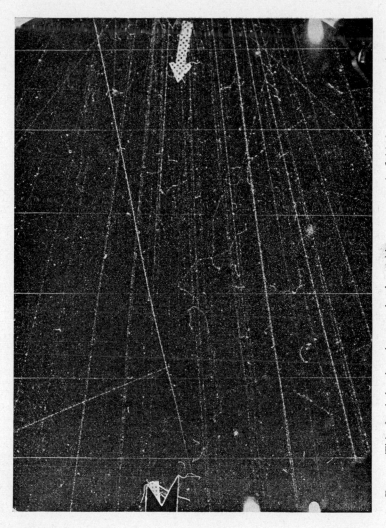

FIG. 17. This cloud-chamber photograph taken without a magnetic field shows a spray of protons out of paraffin initiated by a beam of high-energy neutrons. The paraffin was placed just outside the chamber. Gas in the chamber was a half atmosphere of hydrogen. The track which starts in the middle of the picture and goes off to the left is a proton knocked out of the gas by a neutron.

FIG. 18. The "stars" in this cloud-chamber photograph (seen in a row through the center) are disintegrations of carbon and oxygen nuclei when bombarded by a well-collimated neutron beam which had an energy spread peaking at 90 Mev. The gas in the chamber was a half atmosphere of hydrogen plus water and alcohol vapors. Curvature of the tracks was produced by a field of 13,000 gauss, which is enough to bend a low-energy proton through more than 180°. The long, very curved track out of the "star" nearest the arrow was made by a 1.8-Mev proton, which stops in the chamber. The reactions demonstrated by these "stars" (proceeding from the arrow to the bottom of the picture) most probably are: *Star 1*. Carbon 12 + neutron → 2 helium 4 + 2 hydrogen 1 + 3 neutrons. *Star 2*. Oxygen 16 + neutron → 3 helium 4 + 2 hydrogen 1 + 3 neutrons. *Star 3*. Oxygen 16 + neutron → 4 helium 4 + 1 neutron. The incident neutron had an energy of 114 Mev and dissipated 40 Mev in the collision. *Star 4* (*bottom of picture*). Carbon 12 + neutron → 2 helium 4 + 2 hydrogen 1 + 3 neutrons.

Also visible are 3 protons knocked out of the hydrogen gas by neutrons.

Thus, we are led to the conclusion that both ordinary and exchange forces are necessary to describe the interaction of neutrons and protons. The experimental data in this field should soon provide much food for thought for our theoretical confrères!

STARS

One might infer from the foregoing that thus far the experimental observations into these higher energy levels of nuclear

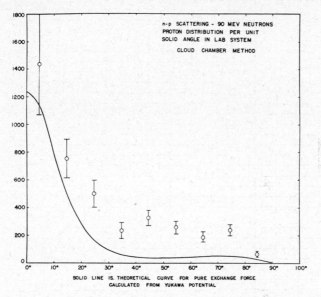

FIG. 19. Angular distribution of recoil protons in hydrogen-filled chamber.

phenomena have been simple, orderly, and understandable. Actually, of course, this is by no means the case, as many new phenomena have been observed which are not understood and await further investigation. To illustrate, there are the star disintegrations which have occasionally been observed in the cosmic rays and which now are a common feature of the cloud-chamber pictures in our laboratory. Thus, in Figure 18, one of the stars was apparently produced by a 115-Mev neutron hitting an oxygen nucleus, splitting it into four alpha particles, and glancing off with 75-Mev energy. Are energy and momentum really con-

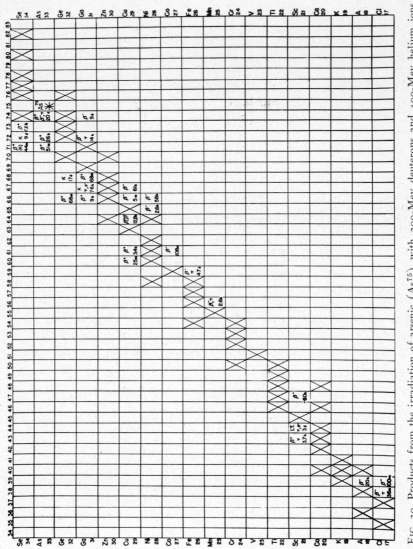

FIG. 20. Products from the irradiation of arsenic (As⁷⁵) with 200-Mev deuterons and 400-Mev helium ions. Spaces marked by X show positions of stable isotopes.

served in such individual nuclear collisions? Some day perhaps we shall know the answer.

NEW RADIOACTIVE ISOTOPES

Now to return to the early exploratory experiments. Professors Seaborg * and Perlman [9] and their associates in chemistry were naturally curious as to the radioactive isotopes that would be produced by the high-energy particles, and they therefore

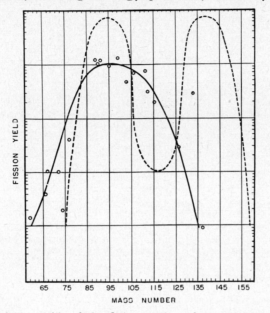

FIG. 21. Relative yields of the fission products from 200-Mev deuterons on bismuth. (The dotted curve represents the fission product distribution for the fission of U^{235} with slow neutrons. The positions of the two curves on the ordinate scale are arbitrary.)

made quick "spot checks" of the activities produced in various bombarded targets. They were confronted with a delightfully bewildering complex of radioactivities, for it appeared that practically every chemical extraction showed several decay periods. With their extensive background and experience in the field, they were able to proceed rapidly in the identification of a large number of activities. They soon found many new radioactive isotopes, and in addition they were able to establish certain interesting general features of the nuclear reactions concerned.

* Cf. Chapter IV.

Perhaps an idea of the wide variety of nuclear reactions may be gained by considering some of their data on arsenic shown in Figure 20. It may be seen that as many as 20 or more nuclear particles are knocked out from arsenic nucleus, and almost every conceivable combination of fragments is the result.

It appears that more than 100 new radioactive isotopes will

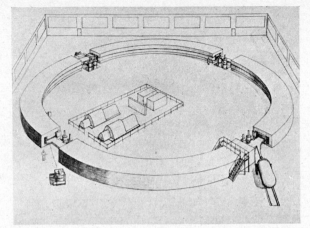

FIG. 22. The Bevatron. Artist's sketch of the preliminary design for a high-energy multi-billion volt proton accelerator. The protons would be injected from a Van de Graaff generator and accelerated by a frequency modulated oscillator to 10-billion volt energy. An increasing magnetic field would hold the ions at a constant radius as their energy increases. The magnet is estimated to weigh 13,000 tons. (Prepared by the University of California Radiation Laboratory.)

eventually be identified; and, apart from their intrinsic scientific interest, no doubt they will soon find usefulness as tracers in other fields.

FISSION OF MANY HEAVY ELEMENTS

It was natural also at an early date to bombard the heavy elements and determine whether imparting these higher energies to the nuclei would result in fission. Again, the observations were interesting to the point of bewilderment, as bombarding elements such as uranium, bismuth, and lead produced not only what were evidently fission products but also a great many other radio-isotopes over almost the whole periodic table. In consequence, studies along this line are only well started. However, one interesting feature of the fission process at these high energies, in the elements ranging from tantalum to uranium, has already emerged. It is the quite different distribution of fission products shown in Figure 21. Again, we must look to the future and to our theoretical colleagues for the meaning of these interesting observations.

HIGHER ENERGY PARTICLES

Thus, we see that the production in the laboratory of accelerated particles in the 100-Mev range has opened up a rich domain for investigation. Perhaps we should now be content to devote all of our attention to the experimental attack on the problems in this field. But the very richness of the atomic phenomena already apparent in the 100-Mev level surely beckons us on to greener pastures—the domain of billions of electron volts!

It is, therefore, understandable that as soon as the synchrocyclotron was well launched on its operating career, W. M. Brobeck, who was chiefly responsible for the engineering design of the great machine, should have given some thought to the next step up the energy scale. It did not take him long to reach the conclusion that it was well within the realm of practical feasibility to construct a great proton accelerator for the 10-billion electron volt level. Already he has completed preliminary engineering designs for such an instrument (Fig. 22) [10].

For References see p. 306.

THE EIGHT NEW SYNTHETIC ELEMENTS

By Glenn T. Seaborg

University of California, Berkeley, California

The history of the discovery of the chemical elements is a fascinating story which begins during prehistoric times and extends through the ages to the present. These building blocks of nature, which now total 96 in number, have been patiently sought out, one by one, in careful researches carried out by investigators in many lands. In the great majority of the cases recorded history has passed on to us the names of the discoverers and the circumstances under which the discoveries were made.

Researches within the last ten years have filled all of the remaining gaps among the elements, thus for the first time completing with certainty the list of positively identified elements between hydrogen and uranium, and, further, they have extended the list beyond these limits. Including these elements beyond uranium, eight new chemical elements have been definitely identified within the last decade, and for most of these, in fact probably all, this has also constituted the first true identification and hence the discovery of the element.

The present discussion is concerned with these eight elements and the circumstances surrounding their discovery. Four of them fill the last gaps in the periodic system of the elements—gaps which were previously shrouded with uncertainty. The other four elements are outside the confines of the classical periodic system, that is, they are all heavier than the previously known heaviest element, uranium. These new elements are therefore known as the "transuranium" elements, and they have a particular importance in relation to the recent successful release of nuclear energy.

THE DISCOVERY OF THE ELEMENTS:
HISTORICAL BACKGROUND

By way of background it is desirable at the beginning to review briefly the history of the discovery of the elements, beginning with the earliest information which is known on this subject. A number of the elements were known during biblical times, although of course the present concept of the chemical elements was not recognized. Thus the metals gold, silver, copper, iron, lead, tin, mercury, and also possibly zinc, as well as the nonmetals sulfur and carbon, were all known and written about some 2,000 years ago. In fact, it is a matter of record that a number of these were known as long as 5,000 years ago and some probably were recognized and used in prehistoric times. Nothing is known about the discoverers, reference to these substances appearing only in a general way throughout the early writings of mankind.

The next elements to make their appearance within the scope of man's knowledge are mentioned in the writings of the alchemists, those mystical searchers for a method to transform base metals into gold, who in their wandering study of substances with crude apparatus were the forerunners of the modern chemist. These investigators succeeded in identifying the substances arsenic, antimony, and bismuth during the period from the twelfth through the sixteenth century, and since the rather strange records of this period give only fragmentary information concerning a number of the individuals involved, it is again not possible to assign a particular discovery to any individual. Glimmerings of recognition of one or two other substances, now recognized as elements, also are evident during this period or possibly even earlier; the mention in early writings of "white gold," now identified as platinum, is an example.

The first man to be credited with the discovery of an element was a German merchant named Hennig Brandt, who first brought to light the element phosphorus in 1669. This marks the beginning of the period when the detailed recording of the circumstances surrounding the discovery of elements began to take place, and for all of the remaining elements many facts as to discoverer, place of discovery, and circumstances surrounding it are known.

The eighteenth century saw the beginning of the development of our present concept of the chemical element, although the understanding was still somewhat vague. During this century the discovery of about a dozen more elements took place. Sweden, with her long succession of brilliant chemists and mineralogists and her rich supply of ores, outstripped the other countries in these developments.

The discovery of most of the remaining elements, about 60 in all, occurred during the nineteenth century. A rather complete understanding of the concept of the chemical element, and also the birth of the periodic system of the elements emerged. In 1864 there was the important contribution of J. A. R. Newlands, who arranged the elements in the order of increasing atomic weights and noticed that the elements fall into natural families after intervals of eight. In 1869, at about the same time, J. L. Meyer and D. I. Mendelyeev independently developed the powerful correlation which is now known as the periodic system of the elements. Mendelyeev was particularly active in developing this concept. In the early part of the twentieth century the work of the English physicist, H. G. J. Moseley, served to place the periodic system classification on the soundest possible scientific basis. He showed that the more fundamental classification is one in which the elements are arranged in order of their atomic numbers rather than their atomic weights. With the concept of atomic number and the establishment of 92 as the atomic number of uranium, the heaviest element then known, it became clear that there could be only a limited number of elements between hydrogen and uranium.

Thus, by the second decade of the present century, after the discovery of two more elements, the rare earths europium and lutecium (or cassiopeium), the known list stood at a total of 85 with a clear understanding that there were places for only seven more elements between hydrogen and uranium. The following 20 years saw the positive identification of only three more: protactinium (number 91), hafnium (number 72), and rhenium (number 75). The remaining four gaps, corresponding to atomic numbers 43, 61, 85, and 87, were the subject of considerable research and publication. As a result of these investigations the name masurium (symbol Ma) was suggested for number 43, the two names illinium (Il) and florentium (Fr), on the basis of the work of two independent groups for number 61, the name alabamine (Ab) for number 85, and the names virginium (Vi) and (independently) moldavium (Ml) for number 87. Although these discoveries did not meet with universal recognition among scientists, various of these names found their way into the periodic tables and have there occupied places for a number of years. The methods which were used in these investigations were of such a nature that in every case the results implied that macroscopic or "ponderable" amounts of these elements must exist on earth [1].

THE QUESTION OF THE NATURAL EXISTENCE
OF THESE FOUR ELEMENTS

While it is beyond the scope of the present discussion to decribe in any detail the circumstances surrounding these disputed discoveries, it is pertinent to make a few general remarks concerning the prospects for their natural existence in macroscopic amounts. Such existence would imply that these elements are in the form of stable isotopes, or, if radioactive, as isotopes with very long half-lives. On the basis of increasingly intense investigation of radioactivity and nuclear science with its concomitant advance in the understanding of the nucleus of the atom, it was already becoming clear some ten years ago that all the isotopes of these elements should be unstable. At present there seems to remain no doubt that the elements numbers 85 and 87 are represented only by radioactive isotopes, and, further, that these are very unstable with half-lives so short that they cannot exist in ponderable amounts. As short-lived radioactivities they depend for their existence either on artificial production or on long-lived progenitors in the well-known natural radioactive families, and can manifest themselves only in submicroscopic, unweighable amounts by their radioactive properties.

In the case of the elements numbers 43 and 61 the deductions from the principles of nuclear science cannot be so conclusive because, although these predict the existence of only radioactive isotopes [2], the question as to half-lives cannot be certainly answered without more experimental work. On the basis of dependable correlations relating atomic numbers with the mass numbers of the corresponding stable isotopes, together with the well-known rule that the stable isotopes of the elements with odd atomic numbers have odd mass numbers, it can be stated that the "stable" isotopes of number 43 must be included among the mass numbers 95, 97, and 99, and for number 61 among the mass numbers 145, 147, and 149. However, from Mattauch's rule [3], which states that stable isobars of neighboring elements do not exist, together with the fact that molybdenum (number 42) and ruthenium (number 44) include among their stable isotopes the mass numbers 95, 97, and 99, and neodymium (number 60) and samarium (number 62) include mass numbers 145, 147, and 149, we conclude that all isotopes of element numbers 43 and 61 are radioactive.* All in all on the basis of these rules for nuclear stability and other evidence, it seems likely that these elements do not exist naturally in macroscopic amounts; nevertheless the possibility must be borne in mind that there may exist radioactive isotopes of sufficiently long half-life, or in such genetic relationship with conceivable long-lived neighboring elements [4], as to be present in detectable or even weighable amounts in nature.

ARTIFICIAL SYNTHESIS OF ELEMENTS

The clear recognition of the probability that these four elements do not exist in stable forms led various investigators in the nuclear fields, beginning some ten years ago, to instigate pro-

* Although Mattauch's rule is apparently violated by the existence of three or four pairs of stable neighboring isobars, it seems likely even in these cases that one of each of the pairs is radioactive and that further investigation with more sensitive means will show this to be the case, unless the half-lives are so long as to correspond to intensities of radioactivity too small to be measurable.

grams for their synthesis by artificial means. As a result of these studies, all four of these elements have been synthesized. We shall proceed with a description of the experiments, which certainly represent the first identification and, hence, the discovery of two or three of these elements.

Because it is a matter of long-established scientific custom that the discoverers of the various elements should have the right to give them their names, the later investigators who have succeeded in identifying these four elements in radioactive forms have suggested names for them which probably will replace the older ones mentioned earlier. It seems worth while at this point to describe the experimental work necessary to establish the discovery of an element, especially when a radioactive isotope in unweighable amount is involved. Under such circumstances, it appears that the central point defining the discovery of an element is the experimental proof, by the chemical method, that the element is different in properties, and hence is chemically separable, from all the other known elements. There should be no discrimination between naturally occurring and artificially produced isotopes. Of course, as a general principle, any method which first proves that the new isotope is different in properties from all other known elements is an acceptable proof, but in practice it is a chemical method which is likely to meet this requirement.

THE SYNTHESIS OF ELEMENT NUMBER 43

The first of the artificial or synthetic elements to be discovered was the one with the atomic number 43. The discovery was made in 1937 by C. Perrier and E. Segrè [5], working in their native Italy. The element molybdenum (number 42) was irradiated with 8-Mev deuterons in the University of California cyclotron of E. O. Lawrence and then sent to Perrier and Segrè. These investigators showed that two of the induced radioactivities, with half-lives of 62 days and 90 days [6], were chemically separable from all of the other 88 elements and hence, on the basis of the method of production, due to the element number 43. These radioactivities were not given isotopic assignments at that time, but later work [7, 8, 9, 10] suggests that the 90-day activity (half-life reported as 93 days and 95 days) should be assigned to the isotope 43^{97}, decaying by an isomeric transition to a very long-lived ground state of 43^{97}, and the 62-day activity (half-life reported as 52 days), decaying by orbital electron capture, should tentatively be assigned to 43^{95}.

Perrier and Segrè used these radioactive isotopes to study the chemical properties of element number 43 by the tracer technique, and their experiments showed that these properties resemble those of the heavier homologue rhenium to a much greater extent than they resemble those of manganese, the lighter homologue.* They waited nearly ten years to suggest a name, which in view of the evidence seems certain of adoption. Their suggestion [12] is "technetium" (symbol Tc) which is derived from a Greek word related to "technical," in recognition of the fact that this was the first element to be produced by technical or artificial means.

In an early continuation of the investigation of the radioactive isotopes of element number 43 (technetium), Segrè and G. T. Seaborg [13] produced by the deuteron and neutron bombardment of molybdenum the isotope Tc^{99}, which they observed to decay by means of an isomeric transition with a half-life of 6.6 hours to a lower isomeric state with a half-life greater than 40 years [14]. The upper isomeric state of this isotope was observed by Segrè and C. S. Wu [15] to be produced in the fission of uranium, and more recently D. C. Lincoln and W. H. Sullivan and also R. P. Schumann working on the Plutonium Project of the Manhattan District have independently observed the beta particles with a half-life of about 10^6 years due to the lower isomeric state [16]. Later work by E. E. Motta, G. E. Boyd, and Q. V. Larson [17] sets a more accurate value of 9.4×10^5 years for this half-life, while the mass assignment has been confirmed in the mass spectrographic experiments of M. G. Inghram, D. C. Hess, Jr., and

* It is interesting to note, as pointed out by F. A. Paneth [11], that although "masurium" was first reported as occurring in appreciable percentage with an early small amount of rhenium, no further amount has been reported even though kilograms of rhenium have been prepared in the meantime; on the basis of their great similarity in chemical properties these two elements would be expected to occur together and to be enriched together in the concentration process.

R. J. Hayden [18]. Since this isotope is formed in rather large amounts, namely, a fission yield of 6.2 per cent, in the slow neutron induced fission of uranium it is now possible to isolate technetium in weighable amounts and in rather substantial quantities. For example, a uranium pile operating at a power level of 10^5 kw. would produce about four grams of technetium, as the isotope Tc^{99}, per day. With such a long half-life the radioactivity associated with convenient amounts (some milligrams) would be so small in intensity as to create no problem provided reasonable care in handling were exercised. In fact, W. F. Peed, B. G. Saunders, and L. E. Burkhart [19] have recently used a sample of the long-lived Tc^{99}, isolated from uranium fission products by G. W. Parker and co-workers of the Clinton National Laboratory, to observe the $K\alpha$ and $K\beta$ X-ray lines of technetium by the use of an X-ray spectrograph in conjunction with an X-ray tube for excitation of the X rays of technetium in the standard manner. It is interesting to note that P. H. Abelson [20] was able a number of years ago to photograph the characteristic X-ray lines using the radioactive 6.6-hour 43^{99} as the source. Parker and co-workers [21] using the long-lived Tc^{99} isolated from uranium fission products, and Motta, Boyd, and Larson [17] using the same nuclear species isolated from the pile neutron irradiation of molybdenum ($Mo^{98} + n \rightarrow Mo^{99} + \gamma$; $Mo^{99} \xrightarrow{\beta^-} Tc^{99}$), have recently investigated the chemical properties of technetium using essentially pure material. S. Fried [21a] of the Argonne National Laboratory has prepared pure metallic technetium and a number of its compounds, while R. C. L. Mooney of the same laboratory has used this material to determine crystal structures by the X-ray diffraction method [22].

THE SYNTHESIS OF ELEMENT NUMBER 61

Early attempts toward the synthesis of elements number 61 were made by M. L. Pool, J. D. Kurbatov, L. L. Quill, and co-workers [23, 24, 25, 26] and also by Wu and Segrè [27]. These investigators irradiated the neighboring rare earths praseodymium and neodymium with cyclotron accelerated helium ions and deuterons and also with neutrons. This work led to the production of a number of radioactivities, some due to element 61 and some not due to element 61, but since these investigators made no chemical separations it was not possible to make any definite assignments at that time. The first of these groups [28] has recently suggested for element 61 the name "cyclonium" (Cy) in recognition of the essential role that the cyclotron has played in synthesizing new elements. More recently, W. Bothe [29] has irradiated neodymium with neutrons and observed a number of radioactivities some of which may be proved to be due to element 61. It was not possible to make definite isotopic assignment or even assignment of atomic number for any of these radioactivities until recently, when it was done on the basis of chemical identification experiments performed by others whose work will be described next.

The first positive identification of a radioactive form of element 61 came in 1945 in the experiments of J. A. Marinsky, L. E. Glendenin, and C. D. Coryell on the Plutonium Project [30, 16] of the Manhattan District. Following earlier exploratory work [16] by N. E. Ballou and also by B. L. Goldschmidt and F. Morgan, these investigators were able to show that the isotope 61^{147} with a half-life of 3.7 years (as measured by J. A. Seiler and L. Winsburg [16]) is formed in the neutron induced fission of uranium. They also showed that another fission product with a half-life of 47 hours should be assigned to 61^{149}. The salient point here is that Marinsky, Glendenin, and Coryell made, for the first time, *chemical identification* of radioactive isotopes of element 61. Their experiments used a technique involving the selective adsorption of a rare earth mixture on an ion exchange resin, coupled with subsequent selective elution (removal by dissolution) with aqueous solutions of chemical complexing agents. This new method for chemical separation provides very effective separations even of adjacent rare earth elements, with these elements being removed from the column in separate aqueous fractions in the inverse order of their atomic number, that is, as a sort of inverse "Moseley spectrum." The story of this marvelous development, involving a number of research teams on the Plutonium Project, has recently been summarized by W. C. Johnson, Quill, and F. Daniels [31].

The assignment of the 3.7-year activity to the mass number 147 has been confirmed and made certain in the mass spectrographic experiments of Hayden and L. G. Lewis [92], and the isotopic assignment of the 47-hour activity to the mass number 149 has been verified in the mass spectrographic experiments of Inghram, Hess, Hayden, and Parker [33].

The production of the isotope 61^{147} in the fission reaction with a fission yield of 2.6 per cent places this element among those which are now available in rather substantial weighable amounts. For example, the operation of a uranium pile at a power of 10^5 kw. will produce element 61, as the isotope 61^{147}, at the rate of about 1½ grams per day. The half-life of this element is sufficiently short to necessitate precautions in handling, but the radiation consists solely of soft beta rays (0.2 Mev), and therefore the problem of shielding is not difficult. In fact, element 61, as 61^{147}, has recently been isolated in substantial weighable quantities, with a purity not yet well determined, by Parker and P. W. Lantz [33a], using uranium fission products as the source, and also by B. H. Ketelle and Boyd [34] using as a source neodymium which had been strongly irradiated with pile neutrons

$$\left(Nd^{146} + n \rightarrow Nd^{147} + \gamma; \; Nd^{147} \xrightarrow{\beta^-} 61^{147}\right).$$

From the standpoint of production by artificial means it seems that Marinsky, Glendenin, and Coryell, in view of their first chemical identification of radioactive isotopes, should be considered the discoverers of synthetic element 61. However, there remains some question concerning the possible validity of the work on natural "illinium" (or "florentium"). Although some 20 years have passed since this early work was reported, no definite or convincing confirmation has been forthcoming, and thus it seems unlikely that natural element 61 has ever been found and identified in macroscopic quantities [35]. In fact, a number of exhaustive searches for macroscopic quantities of natural element 61 have given negative results [36]. In view of the definite possibility that their first discovery of a synthetic form represents also the actual discovery of the element, Marinsky, Glendenin, and Coryell have suggested the name "promethium" (symbol Pm) for this element [37]. This name is derived from that of the Greek god Prometheus, the giver of fire.

THE SYNTHESIS OF ELEMENT NUMBER 85

The first radioactive isotope of element number 85 was produced in 1940 by artificial means. D. R. Corson, K. R. MacKenzie, and Segrè [38] produced the radioactive isotope with mass 211 by means of the irradiation of bismuth with 30-Mev helium ions in the 60-inch cyclotron at the University of California. These investigators, employing the tracer technique, have used this isotope to study the chemical properties of element 85. They have found that it behaves in many ways like a metal and is more electropositive in character than is the case for the other halogens. This is not surprising in view of the pronounced trend in this direction as one approaches the heavier end of the halogen group, but the possible extent of this effect was apparently overlooked in the chemical searches which have been made for this element in its natural form.

The decay scheme of the isotope 85^{211} is very interesting. It undergoes a branching decay, going to a bismuth isotope (Bi^{207}) by alpha emission and to a polonium isotope (Po^{211}) by orbital electron capture. The Po^{211} is the well-known naturally radioactive AcC′ and decays to stable Pb^{207} by alpha-particle emission with a half-life of 5×10^{-3} sec. The Bi^{207} probably also decays to Pb^{207}, since Bi^{207} does not exist in nature as a stable isotope, but as yet no radioactivity corresponding to this decay has been found.

Corson, MacKenzie, and Segrè have recently exercised their right to suggest a name for the new element 85 and they propose [39] the name "astatine" (symbol At). This name is derived from a Greek word meaning "unstable" and, as is the case for a number of the halogens, this element is thus given a name which is descriptive of its properties.

It is interesting to note that a few years later, B. Karlik and T. Bernert, working in the Vienna Institute for Radium Research, obtained evidence for the occurrence of radioactive isotopes of astatine in all three of the heavy natural radioactive series. According to their evidence, not yet confirmed, it may be that the alpha emitters, AcA, ThA, and RaA, undergo a small branching decay with the emission of negative beta particles leading to the very short-lived alpha-emitting isotopes At^{215}, At^{216}, and At^{218}, respectively [40, 41, 42, 43]. The acceptance of these results has been subject to some question [44]. There had been previous claims [45, 46, 47] for the demonstration of the existence of isotopes of astatine in the heavy natural radioactive series, but since the reported radioactive properties of the isotopes involved were quite surprising and other work has not confirmed the observations [48], it seems certain that these previous claims are in error.

There is an interesting isotope of astatine known which was discovered through the research program on nuclear energy carried on during the war. In independent researches an American group [49] and a Canadian group [50] found among the decay products of the important new fissionable isotope of uranium, U^{233}, the alpha-emitting isotope At^{217}, which decays with a half-life of about 0.02 second. This is a member of the missing $4n + 1$ family, all the members of which have been discovered, starting with Pu^{241} and Am^{241} and ending with stable Bi^{209}; this radioactive family has been given the name "neptunium series" after its longest-lived member, in a manner similar to the naming of the uranium and thorium decay series.

THE DISCOVERY OF ELEMENT NUMBER 87

The first isotope of element number 87 to be discovered is a long overlooked member of the natural actinium family. M. Perey [51], working at the Radium Institute, Curie Laboratory, showed in 1939 that the beta-particle-emitting isotope Ac^{227} also undergoes a small proportion (about 1 per cent) of branching decay via alpha-particle emission. Earlier work had shown that purified actinium emits alpha particles [52]. Perey showed that this alpha-particle emission leads to a beta-particle-emitting substance with a half-life of 21 minutes. That this is the isotope

87^{223} was confirmed in her careful chemical experiments [53, 54] which showed that it has the chemical properties of an alkali metal. For example, it cannot be removed from solution by the precipitation of sulfides or of carbonates, but it can be crystallized from solution together with cesium perchlorate or cesium chloroplatinate. These early experiments have been confirmed by S. Peterson [55] in experiments performed on the Plutonium Project, and recently Perey has extended her study of the chemical [53] and radioactive [56] properties of this isotope.

Perey has recently exercised her right to name this element and has suggested "francium" (symbol Fr) in honor of her native land [53]. Since her work undoubtedly constitutes the first observation of an isotope of element 87, it seems certain that this name will be accepted. She had previously suggested the name AcK for the particular isotope 87^{223}.

It may be noted that the title of the present discussion includes francium as a synthetic element, a questionable procedure in view of its first discovery among the natural radioactivities. This element should not therefore, strictly speaking, be referred to as a synthetic element. There are, however, two facts which may make this nomenclature not completely inappropriate. The synthetic neptunium radioactive series [49, 50], which has already been mentioned, contains as one of its members an alpha-particle-emitting isotope of francium, Fr^{221}, which decays with a half-life of about five minutes. It is also interesting to note that even the isotope Fr^{223} may have its most important origin in the future from synthetic sources. In the research program already referred to, Peterson [55] has shown that the neutron irradiation of ordinary radium (the 1,600-year Ra^{226}) produces beta-particle-emitting Ra^{227} which leads to Ac^{227}. Thus, since Ac^{227} is rather difficult to extract directly from rare earth-containing natural ores, the neutron irradiation of readily available radium in uranium piles offers a better, and synthetic, source of Ac^{227} and hence of Fr^{223}.

As has already been mentioned, this work on the production and identification of radioactive isotopes of the elements with the atomic numbers 43, 61, 85, and 87, completes for the first time the entire periodic system of 92 elements. There now remain no new elements to be discovered in the entire range from the lightest, hydrogen, number 1, to the heaviest natural element, uranium, number 92.

THE TRANSURANIUM ELEMENTS

However, there have been a number of elements discovered beyond uranium. Already well known are the elements neptunium (symbol Np), plutonium (Pu), americium (Am), and curium (Cm), with atomic numbers 93, 94, 95, and 96, respectively, and these, together with those with higher atomic numbers which may yet be synthesized and identified, are referred to as the "transuranium elements." All of the transuranium elements are produced by artificial means from uranium, either directly or indirectly.

Even in some of the earliest periodic system classifications the possible existence of elements beyond uranium was recognized, and places were designated for them. A number of searches for such natural elements has been made, and, although success in their identification has been claimed in a few cases, we now feel quite certain that, except for minute amounts formed in uranium by neutrons of various origin, these elements do not exist in appreciable amount on the earth [57].

As understanding of the atomic nucleus and nuclear transmutations increased, especially with the discovery of the neutron and artificial radioactivity, it became clear that these elements would probably be radioactive with comparatively short half-lives and would have to be produced by artificial means. It is now well known that the first attempt in this direction was the neutron irradiation of uranium, and the beta-particle radioactivities which were produced in this manner were for a number of years interpreted on the basis of a transuranium hypothesis. Further work on these radioactive isotopes eventually led to their identification as fission products through the discovery by O. Hahn and F. Strassmann [58] in 1939 of the famous nuclear fission reaction, and thus there were still no transuranium elements known as late as the beginning of 1940.

The discovery of the transuranium elements has already been described in some detail on a number of occasions [59], and the salient facts may be briefly summarized here as follows.

Neptunium was the first transuranium element to be discovered. Using the neutrons from the Berkeley cyclotron, E. M. McMillan and Abelson [60] in 1940 were able to show with the help of their chemical work that the irradiation of uranium leads to the production of the isotope Np^{239}. This isotope, which has a half-life of 2.3 days, is the decay product of the 23-minute U^{239} formed by radiative neutron capture in U^{238}. Their experiments on the tracer scale of investigation enabled them to demonstrate that neptunium is similar in chemical properties to uranium.

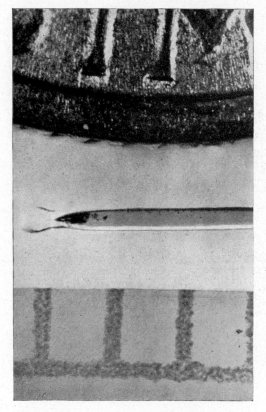

FIG. 23. Ten micrograms of neptunium oxide at bottom of capillary tube (*left center*), between edge of dime (*above*) and millimeter scale (*below*). $\times$ 20. Neptunium produced by use of cyclotron neutrons.

This was probably the most significant first evidence that the heavy elements do not have electron structures analogous to the elements immediately above them in the periodic table in which the 5d electron shell is being filled. The similarity of neptunium to uranium in chemical properties and its very great dissimilarity to rhenium, immediately above it in the periodic table, was the first convincing evidence that it is the 5f electron shell which is being filled in the heavy element region.

Another isotope of neptunium, Np^{237}, was discovered early in 1942 by bombarding uranium with fast neutrons, using the Berkeley cyclotron. This isotope is the decay product of the previously known 7-day beta-particle-emitting U^{237} which is formed as the result of an (n, 2n) reaction on U^{238}. The isotope Np^{237} is of particular importance because it has a very long life, emitting alpha particles with a half-life of 2.25×10^{6} years, and because it is available in weighable amounts (Fig. 23). Np^{237} is produced during the operation of the large uranium chain-reacting units, a very fortunate circumstance, for otherwise it is probable that the element neptunium would not be available for study in the macroscopic state. These studies have shown that the lower oxidation states of neptunium are more stable than those of the element uranium.

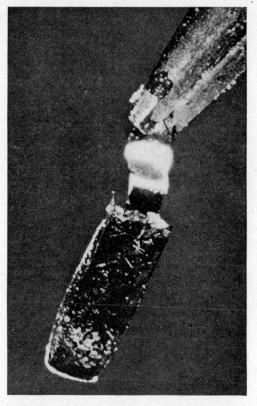

FIG. 24. First plutonium compound ever isolated appears as a golden incrustation (*bottom*) of platinum shovel, which is held by tip of forceps (*above*). Weight 2.77 micrograms.

Plutonium was the second transuranium element to be discovered. The first isotope to be discovered [61] was Pu^{238}, an alpha emitter of some 50 years' half-life, formed according to the reactions: U^{238} (d, 2n) Np^{238}, $Np^{238} \xrightarrow{\beta^-} Pu^{238}$. The chemistry of plutonium was first investigated by the tracer technique using this isotope. These and later experiments showed that the chemical properties of this element are similar to those of neptunium and uranium, differing in that the lower oxidation states of plutonium are more stable.

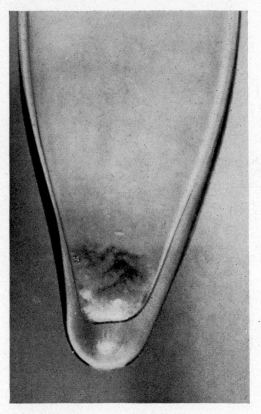

FIG. 25. Twenty micrograms of plutonium hydroxide in bottom of tube (*below*). It appears as a cloud-like mass. $\times$ 40.

The isotope of major importance is, of course, Pu^{239}. This isotope, which is an alpha emitter with a half-life of about 24,000 years, is the decay product of Np^{239}, and its tremendous importance arises from its property of being fissionable with slow neutrons [62], together with the fact that the problem of its mass production has been solved (Figs. 24, 25). The Plutonium Project of the Manhattan District was organized for the purpose of producing this isotope, the explosive ingredient for the atomic bomb.

Careful searches for plutonium in natural ores have shown the presence of extremely small amounts, about one part in 10^{14}, in pitchblende and carnotite. Apparently this plutonium is continuously formed as the result of the absorption of neutrons from various sources by the isotope U^{238} in the ores.

Americium, the element with atomic number 95, was the fourth transuranium element to be discovered, its first identification taking place late in 1944 and early in 1945. The first isotope of this element was identified in experiments of Seaborg, R. A. James, and L. O. Morgan at the Metallurgical Laboratory of the University of Chicago.

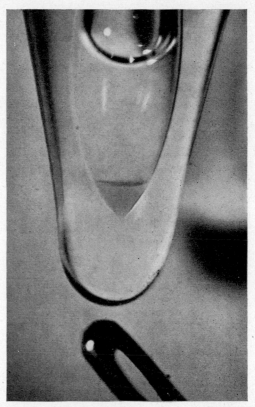

The bombardment of U^{238} with very high-energy (40 to 44 Mev) helium ions in the cyclotron leads to the formation of the isotope of americium with mass 241—that is, Am^{241}. The Am^{241} is the daughter of a relatively long-lived, beta-emitting Pu^{241} which is formed in the primary reaction of U^{238} and helium ions. The reactions therefore are as follows: U^{238} (a,n) Pu^{241}, $Pu^{241} \xrightarrow{\beta^-} Am^{241}$. The isotope Am^{241} emits alpha particles with a half-life of 500 years.

The availability of this isotope of americium made it possible first to study the chem-

FIG. 26. First americium compound in bottom of tube (*center*). Isolated January, 1946. Eye of sewing needle below indicates magnification.

ical properties of this element, using the tracer technique, and later to work with the pure element in weighable amounts (Fig. 26). Deductions from this work led to the conclusion that it probably exists in acid aqueous solution in only the one stable oxidation state, the III state. This is in line with the tendency toward the stabilization of the lower oxidation states in going to the heavier elements in this region.

Curium was the third transuranium element to be discovered. The first isotope of this element was the isotope Cm^{242}, which was identified in 1944 by Seaborg, James, and A. Ghiorso at the Chicago Metallurgical Laboratory after its production in the Berkeley 60-inch cyclotron by the following reaction: Pu^{239} (α,n) Cm^{242}. The isotope Cm^{242} is an alpha-particle-emitter with a half-life of about five months.

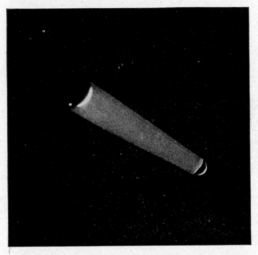

FIG. 27. Photograph of curium solution in tube, taken by its own light.

The availability of this isotope of curium has made it possible to study the chemical properties of this element, first by use of the tracer technique. Extensive investigations have led to the conclusion that curium also probably exists exclusively in the III oxidation state in aqueous solution. Both americium and curium are carried quantitatively by the rare earth fluorides in precipitation reactions and can be separated from them only with difficulty.

The isotope Cm^{242} is also formed as the result of the strong neutron irradiation of Am^{241}. The Am^{241} absorbs neutrons to form a short-lived (18 hours half-life) beta-particle-emitter Am^{242} which in turn decays to the Cm^{242}. These nuclear reactions may be summarized as follows: Am^{241} (n, γ) Am^{242}, $Am^{242} \xrightarrow{\beta^-} Cm^{242}$. This method has been used to produce a sufficient quantity of curium for its isolation (Fig. 27) and the study of its chemical properties in weighable amounts, and these observations again show that the III oxidation state is probably the only one that exists in aqueous solution.

These chemical studies on the transuranium elements have led to the elucidation of the electronic structure of the heaviest elements, the evidence indicating that these form a series of actinide elements, the added electrons for most of the 14 successive elements after actinium (number 89) going into the 5f, an inner electron shell, similar to the addition of successive electrons to the inner 4f shell in the case of the 14 previously known lanthanide (rare earth) elements.

It is interesting that of the 96 known elements it has been possible to isolate 94, all except astatine and francium, in quantities sufficiently large to see and weigh them. It seems doubtful that it will ever be possible to accomplish this with astatine and francium.

Any future elements which might be discovered must have atomic numbers greater than 96, that is, must lie in the "transcurium" region. It seems quite likely that it will be possible to produce and identify new elements in this region, but the major difficulty here is one of starting materials. Probably the most stable, or longest-lived, isotopes of the elements with atomic numbers 97 and 98 will be those with mass numbers perhaps as high as 247 and 248 and higher. Thus it is clear that the problem is one of starting materials, since the heaviest isotope now known is the Cm^{242}. The rather detailed understanding of the transition series which exists in this region makes it possible to make some good guesses about the chemical properties of such new elements, a fact which will be of considerable help in such a program.

For References see p. 307.

CHEMICAL ACHIEVEMENT AND HOPE FOR THE FUTURE

By LINUS PAULING

California Institute of Technology

THE past hundred years have witnessed the transition of chemistry from an essentially empirical and descriptive science to a largely exact and theoretical one. One hundred years ago the properties of many chemical substances had been investigated, the difference between elements and compounds had been recognized, analytical chemistry had been developed to such an extent as to be a reliable tool, many methods of synthesis of inorganic and organic substances had been discovered, and the foundations had been laid for an extensive chemical industry. However, the correct atomic weights of the elements had not yet been generally accepted, so that the formula of water was still written as HO by many chemists. The idea of valence had not yet been formulated: it was not until five years later that the statement was first made (by E. Frankland in England) that atoms have a definite combining power, which determines the formulas of compounds. The first structural formulas for molecules were not drawn until 1858, when Archibald S. Couper introduced the idea of the valence bond; in the same year August Kekulé, in Germany, showed that carbon is quadrivalent. During the next half century, chemistry developed very rapidly, to become the great science—and powerful art—that it is today.

HISTORY OF CHEMICAL THERMODYNAMICS

In 1847 J. Willard Gibbs, whom Wilhelm Ostwald has called the founder of chemical thermodynamics, was a child eight years old. The first law of thermodynamics—the law of conservation of energy—had not yet been accepted by physicists, although Joule had recently made his determination of the mechanical equivalent of heat. It was not until a year later, in 1848, that Hermann Helmholtz recognized the importance of Joule's work and followed its implications through various problems in chemistry, physics, and biology. The second law of thermodynamics had been formulated by S. Carnot in 1824, but it was not until 1851 that Lord Kelvin and Clausius combined it with the first law to produce the present science of thermodynamics, in its application to physical phenomena. Then, in the period between 1873 and 1878, Willard Gibbs published his great papers dealing with the application of thermodynamics to chemical phenomena. Gibbs' work put the science of chemical thermodynamics in nearly its final form; only one more great discovery remained to be made—that of the third law of thermodynamics, by W. Nernst at the beginning of the twentieth century.

Let us contrast the knowledge about a chemical reaction available in 1847 with that in 1947. In 1847 a reaction involving the conversion of certain reactant substances into certain products, such as nitrogen and hydrogen into ammonia, could be discussed only to the extent that direct experimental information, obtained by observing the reaction itself, was at hand. Only if the reactants had actually been observed to combine to form the products could the process be said to be a possible chemical reaction. The amount of heat evolved or absorbed during the reaction would have been known only if the reaction had actually taken place, and the heat evolution or absorption had been measured. The question of increasing the yield of the product could not have been discussed at all, for there was no knowledge as to whether increasing the temperature, increasing the pressure, or making other changes in the system would increase or decrease the amount of product obtained. In 1947 it is possible, from knowledge of the thermodynamic properties of the reactant substances and the products, to predict, for a reaction that has never been observed to occur, most of its important characteristics—the amount of heat that would be evolved or absorbed when the reaction takes place, and the extent to which it would take place, in its dependence on temperature, pressure, concentrations of the reactants, and other factors. There still remains, however, one most important question to which a definite answer cannot in general be given. This is the question as to the rate at which the reaction will take place under given circumstances. We are not yet able to make predictions about this rate of reaction, except for certain simple systems. The field of chemical thermodynamics is in nearly its final state of development; the field of chemical kinetics is just beginning to be developed.

Chemical thermodynamics, like nearly every other field of chemistry, has been influenced by the great progress that has taken place in the extension of our knowledge of atomic and molecular structure during the past few decades. The electron itself was discovered in 1897, and the atomic nucleus in 1911; since then, a penetrating and detailed understanding of the electronic and atomic structure of matter has been obtained, and chemists are now able to talk about the electronic and atomic architecture of molecules and crystals almost as confidently as architects can talk about the structural elements of skyscrapers and bridges. By the methods of spectroscopy, X-ray diffraction, and electron diffraction, accurate interatomic distances have been determined for thousands of substances. The magnitudes of the forces operating between the atoms have also been determined experimentally for very many molecules and crystals. Further information about the nature of substances has been obtained by the application of many different techniques of modern physics —the study of the diamagnetic, paramagnetic, and ferromagnetic properties of the substances, their electrical properties, and the spectroscopy not only of the visible, infrared, X ray, and ultraviolet regions, but even, in recent years, of the microwave and long-wave radio regions of the spectrum. The structural knowledge obtained in this way about molecules permits the calculation of thermodynamic properties for many substances.

A significant start has already been made on the task of formulating a complete system of chemical thermodynamics of pure substances. This task involves the determination for each substance at one temperature of its enthalpy, relative to the elements that compose it. It is further necessary to determine the entropy of the substance at one temperature, which can be done by any one of three methods: the measurement of a chemical equilibrium involving the substance and other substances of known thermodynamic properties, the measurement of the heat capacity down to very low temperatures and the application of the third law of thermodynamics, or the calculation of the entropy from structural data obtained by spectroscopic and diffraction methods. Knowledge of the heat capacity of the substance over a wide range of temperatures, obtained either by direct experiment or by calculation from known structural properties, then permits the extension of the tables of thermodynamic properties over this temperature range. It may well be expected that at some time in the distant future there will be available extensive tables of the enthalpy, entropy, and free energy of thousands of substances over wide ranges of conditions. There would then still remain, however, the problem of the thermodynamic properties of solutions, for which no such simple and inclusive set of data could be formulated.

It is interesting to note that, in a practical sense, the third law of thermodynamics differs from the first and second laws, in that it cannot be applied completely independently of structural considerations. In general, thermodynamic deductions are expected to be independent of any structural considerations, and to be reliable, provided only that true thermodynamic equilibrium has been approximated or achieved in the experiment. Investigations carried out during the past 25 years, especially by Professor William F. Giauque, have shown, however, that the applications of the third law of thermodynamics to the calculation of entropy values for crystalline substances by measurements of heat capacity made to low temperatures are often not reliable in practice, unless there is available some structural information about the residual entropy in the crystals at the lowest temperatures at which measurements are made. Thus simple substances, such as hydrogen, carbon monoxide, nitrous oxide, and nitrogen dioxide, have residual entropies of significant amount, caused by such structural features as a randomness of orientation of molecules in the crystal lattice. It may be said, with justice, that the experiments have not yet been carried out to sufficiently low temperatures, or that sufficient time has not been allowed for the crystals to achieve a state of true thermodynamic equilibrium; nevertheless, the practical problem still exists—the reliable application of the third law of thermodynamics requires a penetrating understanding of the structure of the crystalline substance under investigation.

The recent decades have seen an extraordinary development of the art of cryogenics, the production of low temperature. The pioneer work of Dewar was extended by Kamerlingh Onnes, whose feat of reaching a temperature as low as $0.71°$ K. seemed for many years to be incapable of significant betterment. Then, in 1924, William F. Giauque suggested and later put into practice the astounding new method of cooling by demagnetization, with which he and other investigators have been able to reach temperatures as low as about $0.001°$ K.

Although the production of low temperatures might well be considered to be a part of the science of physics, the fact that this final great achievement of reaching the temperature of $0.001°$ K. was made by a professor of chemistry, using a method invented by himself, justifies mention of it in this discussion. The work done by Professor Giauque illustrates the fact that the border line between chemistry and physics is a difficult one to define, as is also the border line between chemistry and biology. The logarithmic dependence of certain thermodynamic quantities on temperature is, of course, responsible for the great difficulty found in decreasing the temperature by successive factors of ten, and leads to the theorem of the impossibility of reaching the absolute zero itself. It has recently been pointed out to me by Professor Franz Simon at Oxford, however, that it is not true that there is an interesting portion of nature to which access is denied to man, namely, the portion of nature that deals with the properties of matter at temperatures lower than those that can ever be achieved in the laboratory. Professor Simon points out that the only low-temperature range that is inaccessible to man is that in which no interesting phenomena occur, because if any phenomena were to occur, they themselves could be used as the method of achieving the low temperature.

Let us now return to the basis of chemistry—the atoms of the chemical elements. The last hundred years have seen the systematization of the elements through the periodic system of Mendelyeev, the assignment of precise atomic weights to most of the known elements, the discovery of the elements predicted by the unfilled sequences in Mendelyeev's table, as well as the unanticipated series of noble gases, and, finally, in recent years, the development of modern alchemy, the conversion of one element into another, and the artificial production of new elements.* Now that four transuranium elements have been reported—neptunium, plutonium, americium, and curium—we may look forward with confidence to the announcement that still more new elements have been made, and that practical methods of manufacture in large quantities of the most rare of the lighter elements have also been developed. We may well expect that in the future world nuclear chemistry will be found of the greatest value in many ways, not only in the production of new elements and in the use of radioactive elements as tracers, but also in causing new chemical reactions through bombardment with high-energy particles.

INORGANIC CHEMISTRY

Inorganic chemistry has been making steady progress. The inorganic chemist of today has a great advantage over his fellow of preceding generations, in that he has a thorough understanding of the molecular structure of most of the substances with which he is working, and of the relation between the physical and chemical properties of the substances and their structures. An illustration of the usefulness of structural knowledge is provided by the recent development of substances that are similar to organic compounds, but with silicon atoms, which form the same tetrahedral bonds as carbon, in place of some or all of the carbon atoms.

The first substance of this nature was made half a century ago. It had not been found possible to make in large quantities

* See Chapters III and IV.

the substance diamond, which is a very useful material because it is the hardest of all known substances. However, it was found possible to make a new substance, with the same tetrahedral structure as diamond, but with half of the carbon atoms replaced by silicon atoms—the substance carborundum, which has now for many years found extensive use as an abrasive. Then it was found that other compounds of silicon could be made, the silicones, which have, in place of long chains of carbon atoms, chains of silicon atoms (usually with oxygen atoms interspersed, in a sort of ether linkage), with methyl groups or other side chains attached. The silicones have many very useful properties. They can be used as insulating lacquers, permitting electrical motors to be built for operation at much higher temperatures than with organic insulators. Silicone rubber can be made, especially for use at higher temperatures than those withstood by ordinary natural rubber or synthetic rubber. Some of the silicone oils have a very valuable property, that of changing their viscosity only a small amount with change in temperature—a property that seems to be due to the tendency of the molecules to coil into a roughly spherical shape at low temperatures, and hence to roll over one another relatively easily, whereas at higher temperatures, at which the molecules uncoil, they become entangled with one another, and thus overcome in large part the normal tendency of a liquid to show a pronounced decrease in viscosity with increase in temperature.

The chemistry of fluorine has made great progress in recent years. The valuable properties of new compounds of fluorine depend on the volatility of fluorine compounds and the low chemical reactivity of the carbon-fluorine bond. Useful fluorine compounds include the freons, such as CF_2Cl_2, which are used as the fluid in refrigerating machines and as nontoxic solvents for insecticides and other solutes, and the fluorine-carbon high polymers, such as the extremely unreactive plastic that is formed by the polymerization of tetrafluoroethylene.

An interesting recent development in inorganic chemistry is that of new techniques for growing large crystals for special purposes. During the war it was found possible to grow large crystals, weighing many pounds, of such substances as ethylene-diammonium tartrate, valuable because of their piezoelectric properties, which find use in radar and other fields of modern physics. In Germany, an interesting technique of growing large crystals of synthetic mica was developed, a technique which depends for its success on the orientation of the growing crystal in a strong magnetic field.

ORGANIC CHEMISTRY

The art of organic chemistry and the science of organic chemistry have moved along steadily hand in hand. Organic chemists develop a feeling for the chemical properties of the many substances with which they work which goes far beyond the systematized theoretical knowledge that they can express; but the theory of organic chemistry has nevertheless now developed to such a state that the science is no longer a mysterious one, purely an art whose practice depends on the application of empirical rules. It is now possible for the organic chemist to use his knowledge of molecular structure to predict, with some confidence, that certain reactions could be carried out to produce products with certain desired properties. One most interesting application of this new method in organic chemistry has been to the manufacture of high polymers, such as the new fibrous and plastic substances, which were synthesized in consequence of predictions of their properties made upon the basis of considerations of molecular structure.

The methods used by the organic chemist become more powerful from decade to decade. He now has at hand techniques of very high-pressure hydrogenation, the use of catalysts specific to certain reactions, powerful techniques of separation such as chromatographic analysis and molecular distillation, and new physical methods for structural studies such as X-ray diffraction and spectroscopy. A very interesting example of the interrelation between organic chemistry and other fields was provided during the war by the concerted attack on the problem of the structure of penicillin. The organic chemists who were working on the problem found it impossible to determine the correct structure by the conventional methods, because the molecule has some structural characteristics that had not appeared before in any known substances, and it remained for physical chemists and physicists, using the techniques of X-ray diffraction and infrared spectroscopy, to determine the structure for them.

CHEMISTRY IN RELATION TO BIOLOGY AND MEDICINE

It is the field of chemistry in relation to biology and medicine in which most striking progress has been made in recent decades, and which offers the most promise for the future. Biologists now are becoming chemists; they isolate vitamins, hormones, enzymes, acetylcholine in nervous processes, histamine in anaphylaxis and allergic responses, plant-growth factors, wound-healing substances, flowering substances, substances to hold the fruit on the trees and to ripen the fruit after it has left the trees. No longer is it possible for a chemist to achieve a feeling of superiority to the biologist simply by quoting some complex chemical formulas—nor, indeed, for the physicist to overcome the chemist by quoting some complex mathematics.

And in medicine, as in biology, a new future is drawing near—a future of great progress through ever closer cooperation with the basic sciences. There has been great progress in medicine during the past century. In 40 years the mean expectancy of life has increased from 49 to 65 years. Mortality from childhood diseases—diphtheria, scarlet fever, whooping cough—has decreased to 10 per cent of its previous value in 25 years. Other infectious diseases are in the main well under control by vaccines, serums, the sulfa drugs, and now penicillin. Shakespeare mentioned "the rotten diseases of the south, the guts-griping, ruptures, catarrhs, loads o' gravel i' the back, lethargies, cold palsies, raw eyes, dirt-rotten livers, wheezing lungs, bladders full of imposthume, sciaticas, lime-kilns i' the palm, incurable bone-ache, and the rivelled fee-simple of the tetter." Most of these diseases are no longer important: there are now no serious cases, so far as I know, of rivelled fee-simple of the tetter, but "incurable bone-ache," under which we might include arthritis, is a very serious disease, of which little control has been obtained. There are still virus diseases that are very troublesome—poliomyelitis, influenza, the common cold. Then there remains the problem of the degenerative diseases—cancer, heart disease, cerebral disease, nephritis—which, as control of other diseases is obtained, are becoming increasingly important. To attack these great medical problems new basic knowledge is needed about the nature of cells and of physiological processes, and about the chemotherapeutic action, as well as the normal physiological action, of chemical substances.

STRUCTURAL BASIS OF PHYSIOLOGICAL ACTIVITY

The greatest problem that remains to be solved is that of the structural basis of the physiological activity of chemical substances. When once this problem has been solved, and when it has become possible to determine in detail the molecular structure of the vectors of disease and of the constituents of the cells of the human body, we shall be able to draw up the specifications of the specific therapeutic agent to protect the body against a specific danger, and then to proceed to synthesize the agent according to the specifications. So far, we have only the hint that chemotherapeutic agents may act through competition with essential metabolites, as in the competition, pointed out by Woods and Fildes, of the sulfa drugs with p-aminobenzoic acid.

I believe that this problem, that of the nature of the competition of two substances presumably for specific combination with some part of a living cell, is very closely related to the general problem of the nature of the forces that lead to the striking specificity of properties shown by many biological substances, especially the native proteins and polysaccharides. I believe that these forces are also operative in the phenomenon of self-duplication shown by viruses, genes, and other biological entities.* I myself have been especially interested in the specific forces operating between an antibody molecule and the molecules of antigens or haptens with which it has the power of specific combination. My interest in this problem was developed over ten years

* See Chapters VII and IX.

ago in conversations with Dr. Karl Landsteiner, and the work that my collaborators and I have done has consisted largely in the extension and refinement of investigations initiated by Dr. Landsteiner.

Let us review briefly the basic phenomena of immunochemistry. When a foreign material of large molecular weight—a protein or polysaccharide, either pure or part of the structure of an animal or plant cell—is injected into an animal, such as a rabbit, the animal in the course of a few days may develop in its blood and within its cells substances, called antibodies, which have the power of specific combination with the injected material, the antigen. Thus, when a particular animal or plant protein is injected into a rabbit, the rabbit develops in its blood antibodies which are capable of combining with that protein, but not, or at any rate only very exceptionally, capable of combining with any of the tens of thousands of other proteins which exist in nature. For example, an antiserum made by injecting hemoglobin obtained from one animal into a rabbit is able to combine with that form of hemoglobin, but not with hemoglobin obtained from the red cells of other animals, except those of very closely related species. The act of combination of antibody and its homologous antigen may be shown by several different phenomena, such as the agglutination of cells, in the case of a cellular antigen, the formation of a precipitate on mixing a solution of antigen and its homologous antibody, the allergic response of a sensitized animal on receiving a subsequent injection of the antigen, and the lysis or other changed behavior of cells to which antibody has attached itself.

The phenomena of immunochemistry raise two great questions. The first concerns the nature of the forces between antibody and antigen, which lead to the power of selective combination of antibody and the homologous antigen and the rejection of other molecules, except those very closely related to the homologous antigen. The second problem is that of the mechanism of the manufacture of the antibody, and of its endowment with this power of specific combination.

The great versatility of living organisms in their production of specific antibodies was shown by the early work of Landsteiner with artificial conjugated proteins as antigens. Landsteiner found that it was possible to cause an animal to make antibodies with the power of specific combination with various chemical substances of known structure. He achieved this by attaching these chemical substances to a protein molecule, which was then injected into a rabbit. The rabbit, under the influence of the injected protein, produced an antiserum containing antibodies capable in general of combining with the particular protein that was used in making the artificial conjugated protein, and also capable of combining with the attached chemical substances. For example, an antiserum prepared by coupling diazotized p-aminobenzenearsonic acid with ovalbumin was found to form a precipitate with this particular azoprotein, and in addition to precipitate, in smaller amounts, ovalbumin itself and also any azoprotein made by coupling diazotized p-aminobenzenearsonic acid with another protein, such as sheep serum albumin. The precipitation by the antiserum of such an azoprotein, in which the protein part is completely different from that of the immunizing azoprotein, is evidence that some of the antibodies in the antiserum have a specific combining power with the benzenearsonic acid group. Landsteiner and his collaborators were able in this way to prepare antisera containing antibodies with the power of specific combination with scores of different chemical substances, many of which could hardly be considered to have any natural relation to the injected animal. These results showed that the versatility of the living organism in antibody production is very great, and made it probable that the antibody precursor was to be considered as a plastic material, able to be influenced by the injected antigen in such a way as to obtain directly from the antigen itself the property that leads to the power of specific combination with it.

Landsteiner and his collaborators also discovered and utilized an important phenomenon, that of hapten inhibition. They found that, for example, when benzenearsonic acid itself is added to an

antiserum made by injecting an azoprotein containing the
p-azobenzenearsonic acid group no precipitate is formed. Nevertheless, it can be deduced that combination has occurred between
the benzenearsonic acid and the antibody, because on addition of
an azoprotein containing the p-azobenzenearsonic acid group no
precipitate occurs, although a precipitate would be formed in
the absence of the benzenearsonic acid. The benzenearsonic acid
is thus shown to have the power of combining with antibody
homologous to this haptenic grouping, to form a soluble complex. Information about the strength of the combination of the
hapten and of the antibody can be obtained by seeing what concentration of hapten is necessary to prevent the precipitation of
the antiserum with a hapten-homologous azoprotein. Landsteiner and his collaborators in this way obtained a great amount
of qualitative information about the combining powers of various chemical substances with antibodies homologous to haptenic
groups of known structure. They found, for example, that not
only benzenearsonic acid but also various substituted benzenearsonic acids have the power of combining with anti-p-azobenzenearsonic acid serum, and that the strength of the combination
depends upon the nature of the group substituted in the benzene
ring and on the position in which it is substituted. Thus, in general, a group substituted in the para position in benzenearsonic
acid increases the combining power with anti-p-azobenzenearsonic acid serum, whereas the substitution of a group in the
ortho or meta position decreases the combining power with these
antibodies.

My collaborators * and I have continued and extended this
work, primarily by developing and using quantitative methods,
permitting the determination of approximate values for the
equilibrium constant of the reaction of combination of hapten
and antibody. We have also made use of a simplification in the
experiments, involving the elimination of one protein from the
precipitation test. Inasmuch as the structure of no protein is as

* Professor Dan H. Campbell, David Pressman, Carol Ikeda, Miyoshi Ikawa,
David H. Brown, John T. Maynard, Allan L. Grossberg, Stanley M. Swingle, John
H. Bryden, Leland H. Pence, and Frank Lanni.

yet known, a precipitation reaction involving two proteins, the antibody and the azoprotein, is an especially complicated reaction to study, and the possibility of obtaining information about the antibody might well become greater if the other protein could be eliminated. Landsteiner and van der Scheer observed that certain simple substances that they had prepared for use as hapten inhibitors themselves gave a precipitate with the hapten-homologous antiserums. These substances were dyes obtained by coupling two or more haptenic groups together; an example is resorcinol with two or three azobenzenearsonic acid groups attached to it. Many of our hapten-inhibition experiments have been performed with use of precipitating polyhaptenic antigens of this type, the system under study then containing only one substance of unknown structure, the antibody itself.

COMPLEMENTARINESS IN STRUCTURE

Landsteiner's results could be interpreted in terms of our modern knowledge of atomic and molecular structure to permit a definite conclusion to be reached regarding the nature of the specific forces between antibody and antigen and the structure of antibody molecule, and this conclusion has been strengthened by the additional information given by the experiments that my collaborators and I have performed in Pasadena. The conclusion is that the specificity of interaction of antibody and homologous antigen results from a detailed complementariness in structure, as was first suggested by Haurowitz and Breinl and by Jerome Alexander, and later emphasized by Stuart Mudd.

The complementariness in structure must be such as to permit a large portion of the surface of the antigen to be brought into juxtaposition with a corresponding portion of the surface of the antibody molecule. The weak forces that operate between any atom or small atomic group and adjacent atoms would then come into operation between each surface atom of the antigen and the immediately adjacent atoms of the antibody; these weak forces, integrated over the juxtaposed surfaces, would produce a resultant force strong enough to lead to the formation of an effective bond. Inasmuch as most of the weak forces operating between atoms and small molecules fall off very sharply with increasing distance, an effective bond would be formed only if the two molecules were in contact with one another, that is, if the surfaces of the atoms of antigen and antibody were to be no more than a very few angstroms apart. The specificity of the bond formed in this way would result from the detailed complementariness, not only in general surface configuration, but also in the positions of the groups capable of forming hydrogen bonds and in the positions of the positive and negative electrical charges. It can readily be seen that this mechanism does provide the possibility of very great specificity. Thus a combining region with area of perhaps 200 square angstroms, representing a surface of about 50 atoms, could be prevented from approaching to contact with the complementary region on the antibody simply by replacing a methyl group, say, on the antigen surface by a phenyl group, which would extend about 3 A. above the former surface, and would hence hold the antibody 3 A. farther away from the antigen, thus reducing the forces of attraction to such an extent as no longer to permit them to result in a significant bond.

The approximation of the antibody to the haptenic group of the immunizing antigen must be very close. A striking bit of evidence, from among the great amount that exists, is that of the cross reactivity of two closely related haptenic groups, the m-aminobenzoic acid group and the 4-chloro-3-aminobenzoic acid group, which differs from the first only in having a chlorine atom in place of the hydrogen atom. Landsteiner and his collaborators found that anti-4-chloro-3-aminobenzoic acid serum precipitates readily both with the hapten-homologous azoprotein and with an azoprotein containing the m-azobenzoic acid group. On the other hand, the anti-m-azobenzoic acid serum precipitates readily an azoprotein containing the m-azobenzoic acid group, but does not form a precipitate with an azoprotein containing the 4-chloro-3-azobenzoic acid group. The explanation that we propose of this cross reactivity between one antiserum and the substituted azoprotein, but not between the other antiserum and the different azoprotein, is that the phenomenon depends upon the fact that the chlorine atom is much larger than the hydrogen atom that it replaces, the van der Waals radius of chlorine being about 1.8 A. and that of hydrogen only about 1.2 A. If it is assumed that the combining region of an antibody fits tightly about the haptenic group of the immunizing antigen, the anti-4-chloro-3-azobenzoic acid antibodies would contain in the appropriate place a cavity into which a chlorine atom could fit, along with the rest of the haptenic group. This cavity, with radius 1.8 A., would be large enough to accept easily a hydrogen atom in the unsubstituted azoprotein, and the replacement of chlorine by hydrogen would have no effect other than to decrease slightly the force of attraction between the haptenic group and the antibody, as a result of the smaller van der Waals attraction of a hydrogen atom and of a chlorine atom for surrounding atoms. On the other hand, the cavity in the anti m-azobenzoic acid antibody is required only to be large enough to receive a hydrogen atom, with van der Waals radius 1.2 A. There might well then be a considerable amount of steric strain if the 4-chloro-3-azobenzoic acid haptenic group were to be forced into this cavity in the antibody, and the steric strain might be great enough to decrease the combining power to such an extent that no precipitate would be observed by the investigators.

This experimental result indicates that the fit of antibody to antigen is, in some cases at least, a very close one, so that a difference in atomic radius of 0.6 A. is significant. Our quantitative investigations in Pasadena provided a large amount of evidence substantiating this conclusion. One extensive series of investigations was made of the combination of antisera homologous to the o-benzenearsonic acid haptenic group, the m-azobenzenearsonic acid group, and the p-azobenzenearsonic acid group. It was found that in each case the substituted benzenearsonic acids with the substituent in the same position as the azo group of the immunizing azoprotein combine more strongly with the antibody than those with the substituent group in a different position, and the conclusion was reached from the values of the hapten inhibition constant that the surface configuration of the combining regions of the antibody molecules approximates that of the haptenic group to within closer than 1 A. A similar conclusion has also been reached by a study of the effect of electrical charge. The ratio of inhibiting powers of two similar haptens, one containing a positively charged group, the trimethylammonium ion group, and the other the uncharged group with the same size and shape, the tertiary butyl group, with antiserum made by injecting rabbits with sheep serum with attached p-azobenzene-trimethylammonium ion groups, could be interpreted to show that the positive charge of the charged haptenic group interacts with a negative charge in the antibody 7 A. away. Inasmuch as the positive charge in the phenyltrimethylammonium ion may be considered to be at the center of the nitrogen atom, and the radius of this ion (the distance from the center of the nitrogen atom to the surface of the methyl groups) is 3.5 A., and inasmuch as the minimum distance of approach of a negative charge to the surface of the antibody may be taken as the radius of an oxygen atom, 1.4 A., the minimum distance of approach of a positive charge in the hapten and a negative charge in the antibody is calculated to be 4.9 A. The fact that the value calculated from the hapten-inhibition data is only 2.1 A. greater than this again indicates that in general there is a very great complementariness in structure and closeness of fit of antibody and antigen.

It is my opinion that the general problem of the nature of specific biological forces has thus been solved, and that with the extension of our knowledge of detailed atomic structure of proteins and other biological substances we may hope that this understanding will permit a more effective attack to be made on many of the problems of biology and medicine.

NATURE OF ENZYMES

I should like now to discuss a closely related question: the nature of enzymes and of catalysts in general. In order to function, the living cell carries out many specific chemical reactions that do not take place when the reactants are simply mixed with one another. These reactions occur in nature because there are present molecules of a specific catalyst, the enzyme appropriate to the reaction. I believe that an enzyme has a structure closely similar to that found for antibodies, but with one important difference, namely, that the surface configuration of the enzyme is not so closely complementary to its specific substrate as is that of an antibody to its homologous antigen, but is instead complementary to an unstable molecule with only transient existence, the "activated complex," for the reaction that is catalyzed by the enzyme.

The mode of action of an enzyme would then be the following: the enzyme would show a small power of attraction for the substrate molecule or molecules, which would become attached to it in its active surface region. This substrate molecule, or these molecules, would then be strained by the forces of attraction for the enzyme, which would tend to deform it into the configuration of the activated complex, for which the power of attraction by the enzyme is the greatest. The activated complex would then, under the influence of ordinary thermal agitation, either reassume the configuration corresponding to the reactants, or assume the configuration corresponding to the products. The assumption made above that the enzyme has a configuration complementary to the activated complex, and accordingly has the strongest power of attraction for the activated complex, means that the activation energy for the reaction is less in the presence of the enzyme than in its absence, and accordingly that the reaction would be speeded up by the enzyme. My colleague Professor Carl Niemann and I are carrying out experiments on inhibition of enzyme activity designed to test this postulate, by the search for inhibitors that have a greater power of combination with the enzyme than have the substrate molecules themselves. This method of attack should, indeed, provide us with information about the nature of the active region of the enzyme, if we accept the postulate that it is complementary to the configuration of the strong inhibitors.

This picture of the nature of enzymes may well make us optimistic about the future of chemotherapeutics, for it predicts that for every enzyme, and in particular for the enzymes that are essential for bacterial growth, it would be possible to find an inhibiting molecule which is more closely complementary in structure to the enzyme than is the substrate itself, and which would accordingly be an effective inhibitor. The picture even presents us with an idea as to the nature of substances which would be effective inhibitors, namely, that these substances should closely resemble the activated complex, intermediate in configuration between the reactants and the products of the catalyzed reaction. A possible practical application of this concept is in relation to penicillin and its destruction by the enzyme penicillinase. Some of the organisms that resist the bacteriostatic action of penicillin may achieve their resistance through the manufacture of penicillinase, which destroys the penicillin as it approaches the organism. If it were possible to synthesize or to obtain by the degradation of penicillin itself a substance with molecular configuration such that it would combine with penicillinase more strongly than does penicillin, and thus would inhibit the action of the penicillinase, this specific inhibitor might be injected (or even taken by mouth) along with the penicillin, which might in this way increase its bacteriostatic action.

FORMATION OF SPECIFIC ANTIBODIES

We have far less evidence bearing in a detailed way on the problem of the process of formation of complex biological molecules than on the problem of the nature of specific biological forces. Nevertheless, a reasonable proposal can be made as to the process of formation of these molecules, on the basis of the information available on the nature of the forces themselves, and the assumption that the known laws of molecular physics are applicable to biological systems. I shall illustrate this proposal by discussing a possible mechanism of formation of specific antibodies [1].

The problem that we pose is the following: how is it possible for a cell to manufacture an antibody molecule with the power of specific combination with an arbitrarily chosen antigen? It might be that the difference in structure of the antibody molecule and a normal molecule of γ-globulin or an antibody molecule homologous to another antigen would result from a difference in the ordering of the amino acid residues in the polypeptide chains, as was suggested by Breinl and Haurowitz, and by Mudd [2]. However, a simpler assumption is that all antibody molecules produced by the same protective mechanism in the cell contain the same polypeptide chains as the normal globulin and differ from normal globulin and each other only in the configuration of the chain, that is, in the way the chain is coiled in the molecule. It is much easier to devise a mechanism for causing the polypeptide chain to assume the desired one of the alternative configurations than to devise a mechanism for producing great variations in the ordering of the amino acid residues. Moreover, the number of configurations accessible to a polypeptide chain containing a thousand or more amino acid residues is so great as to provide an explanation of the ability of the animal to form antibodies capable of specific combination with a very great number of different antigens.

Let us assume that a portion of a polypeptide chain (one end, say) which would be involved in the formation of a combining region of the antibody is of such a nature that it is able to coil into any one of a large number of alternative configurations, all of which have very nearly the same energetic stability, so that the choice among them may be determined by relatively small changes in the environment, tending to stabilize one or another of the configurations. In the absence of an antigen the polypeptide chain would fold into the configuration that happens to be the most stable in the environment in the cell, and would produce a molecule of normal γ-globulin. In the presence of the antigen, however, the folding of the polypeptide chain would take place in a way determined to some extent by the interaction of the chain with the atoms in the surface of the antigen molecule. This interaction would find expression in the formation of that configuration or those configurations of the polypeptide chain that permit the system as a whole to have the greatest stability. The greatest stability results, of course, from the formation of the strongest bond between the folded polypeptide chain and the antigen molecule. Accordingly, we have in this simple mechanism, involving the folding of a polypeptide chain into a structure whose nature is determined in considerable part by the presence of an antigen in the immediate neighborhood, a straightforward way of producing an antibody molecule with the power of specific combination with the particular antigen present, resulting from a complementariness in structure that is automatically assumed by the polypeptide chain that constitutes the combining region of the antibody molecule.

It is clear that the same mechanism, whereby one molecule present in the cell may influence the structure of another molecule that is being formed, may be invoked as an explanation of both hetero-catalytic and auto-catalytic activities of biological molecules in general. A gene may have the power of causing the synthesis of a certain protein molecule capable of acting as an enzyme catalyzing a particular chemical reaction through its possession of a structure essentially complementary to that of the active region of the enzyme molecule, and which can act as a template in the production of that enzyme molecule. The power of self-duplication of the gene might well have a similar explanation. In case that the gene happens to be complementary to itself, then it could serve directly as the pattern for itself; or it might produce the same result, the manufacture of replicas of itself, by working through an intermediate complementary to itself, which then serves as the pattern for the new gene, complementary to the intermediate and identical with the original gene. However, reliable information about the detailed nature of these fundamental molecular processes in biological systems must await further experimental study.

THE FUTURE

This discussion has been confined to the least interesting aspects of the developments of chemistry in the future. These least interesting aspects are those that can be predicted, that can be foreseen on the basis of our present knowledge. They consist primarily of the results of application and development of the discoveries that have already been made. The great discoveries of the future—those that will make the world different from the present world—are the discoveries that no one has yet thought about, the discoveries that will in fact be made as soon as the ideas underlying them take shape in the mind of some imaginative scientist. Who is there among us who ten years ago would have predicted that the field of nuclear structure and atomic energy would develop in the way that it has? Who can now say what the great discoveries of the next ten years will be?

I have spoken of hope for the future—but the discoveries that we cannot foresee may not all be obviously beneficial. Let me say, with Walt Whitman,

I know I am restless and make others so,
I know my words are weapons full of danger, full of death,
For I confront peace, security, and all the settled laws, to unsettle them. . . .

And the threat of what is call'd hell is little or nothing to me,
And the lure of what is call'd heaven is little or nothing to me;
Dear camerado! I confess I have urged you onward with me, and still urge you, without the least idea what is our destination,
Or whether we shall be victorious, or utterly quell'd and defeated.

Science cannot be stopped. Man will gather knowledge no matter what the consequences—and we cannot predict what they will be. Science will go on—whether we are pessimistic, or are optimistic, as I am. I know that great, interesting, and valuable discoveries can be made and will be made, of the sort that have been here described. But I know also that still more interesting discoveries will be made that I have not the imagination to describe —and I am awaiting them, full of curiosity and enthusiasm.

For References see p. 309.

CHROMATOGRAPHY AND SPECTROSCOPY IN ORGANIC CHEMISTRY AND STEREOCHEMISTRY

By L. ZECHMEISTER

California Institute of Technology

THE various branches of Chemistry as we know them today have developed at very different historical periods. Until the end of the eighteenth century only Mineral Chemistry existed, but at the beginning of the nineteenth century, as Liebig put it, "a new branch of science as inexhaustible as life itself budded from the healthy and strong stem of Inorganic Chemistry." This branch, Organic Chemistry, the chemistry of the carbon compounds, has finally come into close contact with biological sciences, although it has gone through a lengthy development and some detours.

At first organic chemistry lived up to its name exactly by investigating those compounds which are characteristic of animal and plant organs. The successful isolation of many naturally occurring substances produced as its main result the fact that, although these compounds show characteristics which markedly differentiate them from inorganic compounds, yet the chemical behavior in both classes is governed by the same laws. By about 1865 the gradual extension of organic research led to the concept of the tetravalency of the carbon atom and thence to structural chemistry. This new concept in itself contained all the impetus which was needed to bring about a radical change in the main direction of research. As soon as the human mind gained an insight into the architecture of organic molecules, it began to build up and to vary endlessly such structures. Simultaneously, interest in natural products began to fade.

During this second part in the history of organic chemistry, a period covering roughly the last half of the nineteenth century, synthesis was claimed to represent the ultimate level of research, whereas in reality it constitutes only a tool, although a powerful and ingenious one, in the study of nature. This fact was clearly recognized by men like Haber, who nicknamed the immense assembled knowledge of artifacts the "chemistry foreign to nature." It was a characteristic feature of this period that immediate practical application was made of almost every new discovery, especially in the fields of artificial dyes, pharmaceuticals, and explosives. Thus, organic synthesis on an industrial scale became one of the great factors which contributed to general welfare.

Again, the termination of this period was accelerated by its very success. The precise knowledge of many thousands of carbon compounds and of methods by means of which their interconversions can be studied, gradually lifted the art of organic experimentation to a level that permitted an attack on complex substances. Thus, the twentieth century is witnessing a revival of interest in the chemistry of natural products. However, whereas at the beginning of the nineteenth century the only outlet for such an interest was a kind of a chemical inventory of animal and plant products, at the present time we wish to know much more. The chemist desires to understand the biosynthesis, function, and ultimate disappearance of all those compounds whose interconversions constitute the processes of life.

An attack on such problems by chemical methods only would be hopeless. However, there is hope of success because of the rapid development of sensitive physical tools which are convenient enough for daily use by the average organic chemist. A century ago his only physical equipment was an analytical balance, but now many optical and electrical instruments are available, and the dexterity with which the chemist can manipulate them permits a rapid characterization of the polarimetric, refractometric, spectrophotometric, polarographic, and other properties of a carbon compound.

WHAT IS CHEMICAL PURITY?

As is well known, a fundamental concept in chemistry is the cause-and-effect relationship between the molecular structure and the properties of the compound. If a given sample consisted strictly of a single kind of molecule, it would have to be designated as "absolutely pure." Only in that ideal case could the true relationship between chemical structure and the physical, chemical, and biological properties be determined.

In practice, of course, even a "pure" compound contains a certain number of foreign molecules. The presence of relatively large amounts of such "impurities" would, if unrecognized, lead to gross errors in the determination of the physical constants, but even a minute quantity of contaminant might catalytically influence the chemical behavior of the compound.

An important task of the organic chemist is the preparation of compounds which are as pure as possible. Absolute purity can neither be attained nor tested, but the investigator will designate his substance as "pure" if no contaminants can be detected in it by means of the best available analytical procedure. If a new principle of purification is found or if the efficiency of existing methods improves, then the label "pure" may have to be changed.

The concept of maximum possible purification makes sense only if the degree of purity of an isolated natural product or of an artifact can be checked reliably. Most procedures simply consist of the repetition of certain operations until some characteristics of the sample undergo no change on further repetition. Since it has been known for a long time that contaminants generally depress the melting point of a carbon compound, the aim has been to raise the melting point to a constant value by repeated crystallizations which left impurities in the mother liquors. Then, when the melting point underwent no change on further recrystallization, the sample has generally been accepted as "chemically pure." Of course, it was pure only from the viewpoint of the test method applied. Although the constancy of the melting point probably indicates true purity in many substances, in principle it means only that the limits of efficiency of this particular purification method have been reached. In fact, instances are known in which the melting point remains constant through a number of crystallizations, although the sample is still a mixture which can be resolved by other procedures.

The example just given should also demonstrate that some "proofs" of homogeneity are based on a negative statement. One will have to find and apply several independent tests before a reliable positive claim of purity can be made.

FRACTIONAL ADSORPTION

It is generally known that very different physical conditions exist on the inside and on the surface of a solid particle or fiber. In the densely packed inside, the electrical charges are compensated from all directions, but on the surface there is no such compensation from the direction of the outside world. Strong electrical forces on the surface may manifest themselves by removing molecules from a solution and holding them firmly by forming an "adsorbate."

The importance of adsorption phenomena for the practical chemist lies in their highly differentiated selectivity. When several compounds are present in the same solution, each of them usually displays a different degree of adsorption affinity for a given solid particle. If only a limited surface area is available, then a "struggle for surface" may take place, and the compound with the strongest adsorbability will be held. In many instances the adsorption affinity of certain constituents of the solution will be negligibly small. For example, when diluted red wine is shaken with a little charcoal and filtered, the filtrate still contains many of those substances which lend their aroma to the wine, even though the latter is now colorless. The charcoal, however, has adsorbed the red anthocyanin pigment of the wine. This pigment can be removed from the surface by a treatment (elution) with another solvent such as pure alcohol.

When a solution streams in a predetermined direction through a large quantity of an adsorbent, then the deposition of the respective compounds will take place at different locations and in a chronological order, beginning with that particular compound whose molecules possess the strongest adsorption affinity.

That this principle of selective adsorption can well be applied to the resolution of mixtures was first recognized by the noted German physicist, Schönbein, as early as 1861. He observed such phenomena unexpectedly when investigating the conditions of ozone formation under the influence of electrical discharges. In order to detect ozone in a gas, he made use of paper strips which had been impregnated with reagents, such as a mixture of potassium iodide and starch. Keen observer that he was, Schönbein noticed that when one end of a filter paper strip was dipped into a solution the various components, which rose in the paper by capillary forces, reached different heights on the strip. He predicted about 80 years ago that this phenomenon "may assist the analyst as a qualitative tool in such cases in which other reagents are ineffective, for example, in the separation of dissolved organic dyes." Schönbein turned the problem over to his pupil, Goppelsroeder, who much later published a monograph on *Capillary Analysis*.

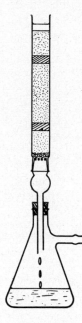

FIG. 28. Chromatographic apparatus.

This book was known to Tswett who in 1906 disclosed a new and efficient method of fractional adsorption, which is termed "chromatographic analysis" or "chromatography." He fractionated leaf pigments by forcing their solution through an adsorbent powder, closely packed in a vertical glass tube. Under such conditions each individual pigment forms a definite zone (Fig. 28). As Tswett stated it: "Like light rays in the spectrum, so the different components of a pigment mixture are resolved on the calcium carbonate column according to a law and can be estimated on it qualitatively and also quantitatively." Such separations can be effected in countless cases, after the extrusion of the column, simply by cutting the zones apart with a knife.

Although the majority of carbon compounds are colorless to our eye, this fact, of course, will not alter in principle the fractionation on the Tswett column. Under suitable conditions an invisible chromatogram will be formed, the zones of which must be found by some special methods. Location of the zones can often be achieved by noting the fluorescence produced by ultraviolet light (Karrer; Winterstein), or one may use strongly fluorescing adsorbents and locate the respective compounds by their quenching effect on the column fluorescence (Brockmann; Sease). In many cases the invisible zones can be detected by streaking the extruded column along its length with a brush dipped in a suitable reagent; color will appear where the brush crosses a zone. If all these methods fail, the column can be divided empirically and eluted, or the adsorbed substances can be washed fractionally into the filtrate. Each fraction can then be tested by some physical, chemical, or biological method. Such an empirical procedure must be used when colorless enzyme mixtures are studied, since their components can be detected and estimated by no other method than by the enzymatic action itself.

CHEMICAL STRUCTURE AND ADSORPTION AFFINITY

It would be of great interest to know exactly how the structure of an organic molecule determines the strength of adsorption; at present however, a theoretical basis for this unexplored field is almost nonexistent. We still do not know what happens on the active surface during adsorption nor how the adsorbed molecules are grouped or oriented in the adsorbate. It is, therefore, a general picture of the process rather than a precise description which can be given at the present time.

It seems that two factors are decisive in determining the behavior of a carbon compound in a given adsorbing system: first, the general shape of the molecule, and second, the presence or absence of certain atom groupings.

Evidently, the over-all shape of the adsorbed molecule must fit, to a certain extent, into the geometrical pattern of the surface. On the other hand, it would be unreasonable to assume that each part of the adsorbed molecule is equally responsible for the fixation process. In adsorption certain atomic groups will have a decisive function, and they may be conveniently termed "anchoring groups." This concept is similar to that which presumes that the fixation of a drug to an animal tissue or bacterial body takes place through a haptene group or groups. The relation of the dependence of adsorption affinity on the presence or absence of certain atomic groupings is more complicated than in other analogous problems. For example, we are able to predict with certainty that if a molecule contains an "asymmetric" carbon atom, that is, one whose four valencies carry four different substituents, optical rotatory power will appear; likewise, the presence of a long, conjugated double bond system will produce color in every case. However, it cannot be claimed with any general validity that the presence of a certain atomic group is a necessary and sufficient postulate for strong adsorption affinity. On the contrary, one and the same group may either decrease or increase the adsorbability depending on the nature of the system.

It was found, for example, that the introduction of a methyl group into certain thiophene derivatives markedly increased their adsorbability; in this instance, the methyl evidently had something to do with the anchoring process. However, as Kofler has pointed out, the adsorption affinity of some tocol derivatives (vitamin E) decreases upon the introduction of methyl groups into the ring, especially in a position adjacent to the phenolic hydroxyl group; methylation in a more remote position has much less or no effect. Obviously, the OH-group plays a part here in the anchoring of the molecule, but its effect is screened by neighboring methyls. In the presence of the latter, the anchoring section of the molecule does not seem to fit so well into the surface structures as was the case previous to the methylation.

It should also be emphasized that in various adsorption systems different parts of a complicated molecule may become operative in the anchoring. Hence the observed adsorption sequence of two compounds on a Tswett column is valid only under definite conditions. Those processes which take place during a chromatographic experiment are determined by the delicate interplay of three important factors: the dissolved substance, the solvent, and the column material. By changing the adsorbent or the solvent (or both) the sequence of two compounds may even be inverted. Impressive examples have been reported by Strain, LeRosen, Schroeder, and other investigators in this field.

SOME DEVELOPMENTS IN STEREOCHEMISTRY

One of the most ingenious concepts in organic chemistry, that of stereoisomerism, was introduced by van't Hoff and Le Bel in 1874. These pioneers as well as Wislicenus lifted organic-structural theories from a schematic and purely two-dimensional level into three-dimensional space. They predicted and proved that, if certain conditions are fulfilled, the molecules of one and the same compound may assume two or more forms that differ only in the spatial arrangement of their atoms. Such "stereo-isomers" possess identical chemical structures as expressed in terms of earlier concepts. The conditions mentioned may be of varied nature; however, we shall consider only a single, important type of stereochemical phenomena which is termed "cis-trans isomerism."

If in an open (noncyclic) chain of atoms there occurs a double bond such as $C = C$ or $C = N$ or $N = N$, then the adjacent atoms or atomic groups may occupy two different spatial positions ("configurations") as illustrated for azobenzene, $C_6H_5 — N = N — C_6H_5$, by the formulas (I) and (II).

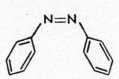

(I).   cis-Azobenzene.

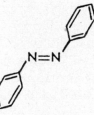

(II).   trans-Azobenzene.

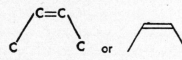

(III).   cis Configuration.

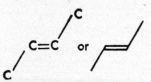

(IV).   trans Configuration.

There occur in the molecules of many natural and synthetic products carbon chains which contain a $C = C$ bond adjacent to single bonds on both sides, $C - C = C - C$. The two possible configurations correspond then to the models (III) and (IV). The shape of the carbon chain in the *cis* form reminds us of one half of a regular hexagon, whereas a Z-like pattern is characteristic of the *trans* form.

Important tasks in this field include the preparation of individual stereoisomers and the study of their physical properties as well as interconversions. Stereochemistry is, strictly speaking, not a branch of "chemistry" as commonly understood, since its main object is not the study of those deep-seated alterations which are termed "chemical reactions." When a compound is converted into its stereoisomer, no change occurs in the original number and distribution of its atoms or of their valencies.

Thus, stereochemistry is a very suitable field for studies of the dependence of physical or other characteristics on the shape of the molecule. When a *cis* compound assumes, by rearrangement (bending its carbon chain) *trans* configuration (III → IV) or vice versa, then its physical constants may undergo a surprisingly great change. For example, the melting points of *cis*-stilbene and *trans*-stilbene are 1° and 124°, respectively. The two spectra are also different. Likewise, the biological effect of some *cis-trans* isomeric compounds depends on their spatial configurations.

The progress of experimental stereochemistry, after having attained brilliant success, seemed to slow down somewhat because of difficulties in method. When consulting a standard work on this subject, *Stereochemie*, edited by Freudenberg, one will note that no system with many double bonds, and hence involving many steric forms, was studied previous to 1933. Furthermore, even in simpler systems, no convincing evidence has been offered in some instances that a steric form under investigation was actually free of small amounts of another stereoisomer.

A new impulse to stereochemical research was given by the work of various investigators who found that adsorption affinities depend so profoundly on the spatial configuration that the chromatographic technique is an excellent tool in the resolution of stereoisomeric mixtures and also in the purification and isolation of individual stereoisomers. For example, when an orange-colored benzene solution of both *cis*-azobenzene and *trans*-azobenzene is developed on an alumina column, the *cis* form will be more strongly adsorbed, and its zone, located near the top of the column, will become clearly separated by a colorless section from the zone of the *trans* isomer. If either of these two zones is cut out, eluted, and rechromatographed on a fresh column, it will form a single zone and thus show the absence of the other spatial form.

The same principle can be applied to the study of more complex systems, for which the carotenoids furnish a suitable example. Every year these yellow, orange, or red pigments are formed in the vegetable kingdom to the extent of hundreds of millions of tons. They are responsible for the coloration of countless petals, fruits, and roots. They are also present in every green plant organ, although their color is overshadowed there by that of the intensely green chlorophyll. Typical representatives of this class are β-carotene $(C_{40}H_{56})$, the main pigment of the carrot, and lycopene $(C_{40}H_{56})$, the main pigment of the ripe tomato.

The β-carotene molecule contains 11 carbon-carbon double bonds in alternation with single bonds. Like all of the double bonds of almost each naturally occurring carotene type pigment, those in β-carotene are in the *trans* configuration (IV). Two of its double bonds cannot rearrange, because they are fixed in ring systems; four other double bonds are, according to Pauling, spatially hindered from doing so. However, *trans* → *cis* rearrangement (IV → III) around the remaining five double bonds is able to produce 20 stereoisomeric forms of the β-carotene molecule, 13 of which actually have been observed. Some are formed, for example, when a small amount of iodine is added to a solution of naturally occurring β-carotene (the "all-*trans*" β-carotene). Under the influence of this catalyst and in the presence of light, the initial uniformity of the β-carotene molecules ceases to exist, and a mixture is produced in which many different spatial forms of the molecules are present. For the resolution of such mixtures no other method exists than chromatography. By means of this technique, several stereoisomeric β-carotenes have been obtained in pure state. They were used advantageously for a study of the dependence of (a) physical and (b) biological properties on the shape of the molecule.

(a) On the physical side, the influence of the spatial arrangement on the spectrum offers a broad subject for research. We know that the color of a carbon compound becomes manifest if the molecule contains in an open chain a system of alternating double and single bonds ("conjugated" double bonds) (V).

$$\ldots - CH = CH - CH = CH - CH = CH - CH = CH - CH = CH - \ldots$$

(V). Conjugated double bond system.

(The hydrogens may be substituted by other atoms or atomic groups.)

While it has long been recognized that the depth and intensity of the color is determined by the length of the conjugated system, recent experimentation has shown that the shape of such a molecule, that is, the presence or absence of *cis* double bonds, is also a determining factor.

A simple inspection of solutions shows that among all stereoisomeric carotenes the all-*trans* form is endowed with the greatest color intensity, and that this is less in any isomer in which a *trans* → *cis* rearrangement has taken place, around one or more double bonds. The same effect can be described more accurately by comparing the spectral curves of the isomers. The higher the maxima in such curves and the longer the wave lengths at which these maxima are located, the more intense will be the resulting color.

We find in Figure 29 the main spectral maxima of some stereoisomeric lycopenes. The uppermost (incomplete) curve represents the all-*trans* form as it is contained in the pigment of ordinary, ripe tomatoes; the other curves are those of some stereoisomeric lycopenes which occur in nature only in exceptional cases and contain four to seven of their double bonds in *cis* configuration. The differences between these curves are surprising indeed: not only are the heights and the locations of the maxima displaced, but also the amount of fine structure varies greatly. The all-*trans*-lycopene curve shows a very sharp fine structure (with steep slopes near the maxima); the other curves are much smoother and one of them reminds us rather of a semicircle. A theoretical evaluation of these features has not yet been made.

(b) The carotenes belong to the provitamins A, and are converted in the animal body into vitamin A proper, which is important for life. When young rats have been depleted of this vitamin, they cease to increase in weight. However, their growth is resumed if a β-carotene is added to the diet. Then the required curative dose can be determined for a stereoisomeric form. Such bioassays, which were performed by Professor H. J. Deuel, Jr., and his colleagues of the University of Southern California, in collaboration with our group, have shown that a bending of the β-carotene molecule decreases the bio-potency to one half or one third of the initial value. The individual stereoisomers administered had been pre-

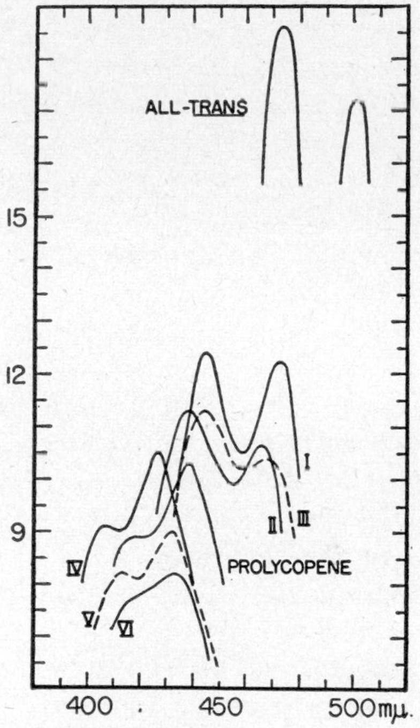

FIG. 29. Spectral maxima, in hexane solution, of some stereoisomeric lycopenes. (The uppermost curve represents the all-*trans* form as it occurs in ordinary tomatoes, and the other curves correspond to stereoisomeric lycopenes which have four to seven double bonds in *cis* configuration.) Abscissa, wave length; ordinate, $E_{1cm.}^{mol.}$ From *Jour. of the Am. Chem. Soc. 69,* 1930 (1947). (With J. H. Pinckard.)

pared chromatographically, and their stereochemical purity had to be checked by spectral readings; the experimental procedure included in this case a combination of adsorption and optical methods as well as animal tests.

AN EXAMPLE OF COLLABORATION OF THE GENETICIST WITH THE ORGANIC CHEMIST

Chromatography of numerous plant extracts revealed that, below the colored carotenoid zones, a colorless compound was adsorbed which exhibited intense, greenish-gray fluorescence when exposed to ultraviolet light in a dark room. This phenomenon had been observed earlier by Strain in some instances. We found that the fluorescence is generally caused by the first known representative of the colorless carotenoids, phytofluene ($C_{40}H_{64}$), whose conjugated system is too short to bring about visible color. That phytofluene occurs also in lower organisms was a welcome fact which aided in the investigation of some mutation phenomena of a red yeast, *Rhodotorula rubra*, in collaboration with my colleagues, Professor J. Bonner, Dr. Y. W. Tang, and Dr. A. Sandoval. I shall describe the observations as they were made (a) without and then (b) with the use of modern techniques.

(a) It has been known for some time that if a suspension of a few hundred red yeast cells in water is exposed to ultraviolet light, most of the cells will die; however, some of the survivors will emerge with markedly changed properties because of mutation. When plated out on agar, they will produce orange or yellow or white cultures which represent various mutants. That is the story as it can be told without application of spectroscopy and chromatography.

(b) By means of these methods the observations were completed as follows. An extract of the original red yeast was chromatographed, and the spectra of all zones were taken. They showed that this organism is a master in producing several conjugated double bond systems of various lengths. The original *Rhodotorula* pigment is a mixture that includes an intense, purplish-red carotenoid, the well-known torulene with 13 conjugated double bonds; several orange and yellow components with 9 to 11 such bonds; and, finally, colorless phytofluene containing 7 double bonds of which 5 are conjugated. Their spectral curves appear in Figure 30.

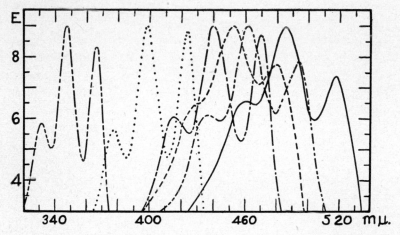

FIG. 30. Spectral curves of carotenoids (in petroleum ether) which occur in the red yeast, *Rhodotorula rubra*, before mutation: ——, Torulene; — · · —, γ-Carotene; — — —, β-Carotene; — · — ·, Pigment "A"; . . . ., Pigment "B"; and — · · · —, Phytofluene. From *Arch. Biochem., 10, 113, 1946.*

The pigment composition in an orange-colored mutant proved to be very different. This mutant contained very little red pigment, but increased amounts of the orange and yellow carotenoids. The sum of all pigments, including phytofluene, had not been essentially altered by mutation in this case. However, in a white (albino) mutant only traces of any pigment were present and, significantly, the phytofluene was missing too. All molecules of the colorless, orange, and purplish-red representatives of this class of compounds are built on the same general pattern, but they differ from each other essentially in their hydrogen content. The less hydrogen that is present, the more double bonds there will be contained in the molecule, and the more intense will be the color in most cases.

We may assume with some probability that the pigment biosynthesis in the red yeast follows a scheme as represented in Figure 31.

Starting from colorless precursors and phytofluene, a stepwise elimination of hydrogen ("dehydrogenation") takes place, which is terminated by the formation of purplish-red torulene. In the orange mutant this normal process is genetically blocked just before the last step. However, in the albino mutant such a blocking occurs at a much earlier stage of the biosynthesis, before even phytofluene could accumulate. So far no mutant has

	Block in albino mutant ↓		Block in orange mutant ↓	
Unknown precursors	⟶	*Phytofluene* (colorless) ⟶ *Yellow and orange pigments*	⟶	*Red pigments*

FIG. 31. Suggested stages in the biosynthesis of the red yeast.

been observed in which blocking occurred just after the phytofluene stage had been reached; this would produce a colorless mutant whose extract would fluoresce strongly. However, such mutants (and other new types) may well be detected in the future.

This is the picture of the red yeast mutation as obtained by means of spectroscopic and chromatographic methods.

CONCLUSIONS

In the foregoing sections an incomplete survey of some aspects in the development of organic chemistry is presented and illustrated by a few arbitrarily chosen examples. However, even such a brief treatment shows that at the present time organic chemistry is undergoing a re-orientation in its relationship to other branches of science. Like many other disciplines, it is developing more rapidly now that it is coming into contact with ways of thought and techniques other than those familiar to chemists one or two generations ago.

In the study of artificial or natural products more and more subtle heterogeneities are being revealed, and thus, in many instances, preparations which had been held earlier to be chemically and stereochemically homogeneous now appear to be complex mixtures. This progressively deeper insight into the composition of organic matter requires laboratory methods which are more delicately differentiating; among these methods physical procedures offer the greatest precision. With their help a quantitative attack on many problems connected with life is now possible. Accordingly, some main lines of research in modern organic chemistry are physical in their methods and biological in their outlook.

For References see p. 309.

VIRUS RESEARCH: ACHIEVEMENT AND PROMISE

By W. M. Stanley

Rockefeller Institute for Medical Research, Princeton, N. J.

RESEARCH in the field of the viruses was for some time retarded, while it remained, too long, within one compartment of science. Eventually it expanded, not into a single adjoining compartment, but into compartment after compartment, until today virus research can almost be regarded as the study of natural science. As the techniques of the different sciences were brought to bear on the viruses, spectacular advances were made. Some of these advances yielded knowledge which resulted in the stimulation of new aspects of research within a particular field. Most of the advances would never have been made if virus research had remained solely within a single compartment of science.

DISCOVERY AND PROPERTIES OF THE VIRUSES

Viruses were discovered, independently, by Iwanowski in 1892 and by Beijerinck in 1898 when they noted that the agent responsible for the mosaic disease of tobacco would pass through fine filters which retained all living organisms then known. This infectious, disease-producing agent is now known as a virus and, since the original discovery, well over 300 different viruses, capable of causing disease in man, animals, and plants, have been discovered. Among the virus-induced diseases of man are smallpox, yellow fever, dengue fever, poliomyelitis, certain types of encephalitis, measles, mumps, influenza, virus pneumonia, and the common cold. Virus diseases of animals include hog cholera, cattle plague, foot-and-mouth disease of cattle, swamp fever of horses, rabies, fowl pox, Newcastle disease of chickens, and certain benign as well as malignant tumors of rabbits and mice. Plant virus diseases include tobacco mosaic, peach yellows, aster yellows, potato yellow dwarf, alfalfa mosaic, curly top of sugar beets, tomato spotted wilt, corn mosaic, cucumber mosaic, and sugar cane yellow stripe. Bacteriophages, which are agents capable of causing the lysis of bacteria, are now regarded as viruses.

The viruses are characterized by their small size, by their ability to reproduce or multiply when within the living cells of a given host, by their ability to change or mutate during multiplication, and by their inability to reproduce or grow on artificial media. The sole means of recognizing the existence of a virus is provided by the manifestations of disease which result from the multiplication of the virus. This fact has not proved a severe handicap, although it has resulted in the binding of all of virus research firmly to biological tests for virus activity. Each and every treatment of a virus preparation must be followed by a test for virus activity, for this is the only way to determine whether the integrity of the virus has been altered.

Viruses spread from diseased to normal, susceptible hosts by different methods. Some are transferred by direct contact, as when an infected leaf is caused to rub against a healthy leaf by a gust of wind, or as when a normal person or animal comes into direct contact with a diseased person or animal. Such viruses can usually be transferred by indirect contact via the medium of nonspecific animate or inanimate agents. Some viruses cannot spread by direct contact, but require an intermediate host, such as a mosquito, louse, or leaf hopper. In some cases a highly specific intermediate host is necessary, and a period of incubation within this host may be required before it can pass on the virus. These relationships, which are of the greatest importance from both practical and theoretical standpoints, have not received the attention they deserve. Studies on these relationships must be intensified and broadened in the future.

Reproduction, mutation, and metabolic activity have long been regarded as unique and special properties of living organisms. When viruses were found to possess the ability to reproduce and to mutate, there was a general tendency to regard them as small living organisms, despite the fact that the question of metabolic activity remained unanswered. Because of their small size they could not be seen by means of the ordinary light microscope. Although this fact puzzled some investigators, it was pushed to the background, and for over 30 years interest in virus research centered about the discovery of new virus diseases and studies on the pathological manifestations of viruses. Although notable advances were made, virus research remained in a very narrow scientific channel. Then, about 1930, Elford began his important work on the filtration of viruses through graded collodion membranes. He demonstrated that different viruses possessed different and characteristic sizes, and that, whereas some viruses were as large as 300 mμ, others were as small as 10 mμ. It was soon realized that the acceptance of a virus 10 mμ in size as an ordinary living organism presented certain inherent difficulties, especially with respect to metabolism. Grave doubts were expressed that the complicated processes of respiration and digestion and other metabolic functions of life could be contained within structures as small as 10 mμ, especially since protein molecules larger than 10 mμ were known.

The true nature of viruses was soon shrouded with all of the elements of a first-class mystery. What were these small infectious disease-producing agents, some of which were larger than certain small living organisms, others of which were smaller than certain protein molecules, and all of which possessed the ability to reproduce and to mutate when within certain living cells? A chart illustrating the relative sizes of several viruses and certain reference materials is shown as Figure 32. The fact that, with respect to size, the viruses overlapped with the organisms of the biologist at one extreme and with the moleules of the chemist at the other extreme, only served to heighten the mystery. The closing of the gap between the molecules of the chemist and the organisms of the biologist, which had existed for years, was a major scientific achievement, but it presented new problems, which, at the time, appeared almost insoluble. Were viruses merely very small living organisms, or were they molecules endowed with new and unusual properties? Were some organismal in nature, and others molecular in nature? Or did the viruses represent a new type of entity, wholly unfamiliar to scientists?

	Diameter or width X length in mμ
Red blood cells	7500
B. prodigiosus (Serratia marcescens)	750
Rickettsia	475
Psittacosis	450
Canary pox	260 x 310
Myxoma	230 x 290
Vaccinia	210 x 260
Pleuro-pneumonia organism	150
Pseudo rabies	150
Herpes simplex	150
Rabies fixe	125
Influenza	115
Newcastle disease	115
Vesicular stomatitis	100
Staphylococcus bacteriophage	100
Fowl Plague	90
T₂ coli bacteriophage	60 x 80
Chicken tumor I	70
Equine encephalomyelitis	50
T₃ coli bacteriophage	45
Rabbit papilloma (Shope)	44
Pneumonia virus of mice	40
Tobacco mosaic and strains	15 x 280
Latent mosaic of potato	10 x 525
Gene (Muller's est. of max. size)	20 x 125
Southern bean mosaic	31
Rift valley fever	30
Tomato bushy stunt	26
Poliomyelitis (Lansing)	25
Hemocyanin molecule (Busycon)	22
Yellow fever	22
Hemocyanin molecule (Octopus)	20
Louping ill	19
Tobacco ring spot	19
Japanese B encephalitis	18
Alfalfa mosaic	17
Tobacco necrosis	16
Foot-and-mouth disease	10
Silkworm jaundice	10
Hemoglobin molecule (Horse)	3 x 15
Egg albumin molecule	2.5 x 10

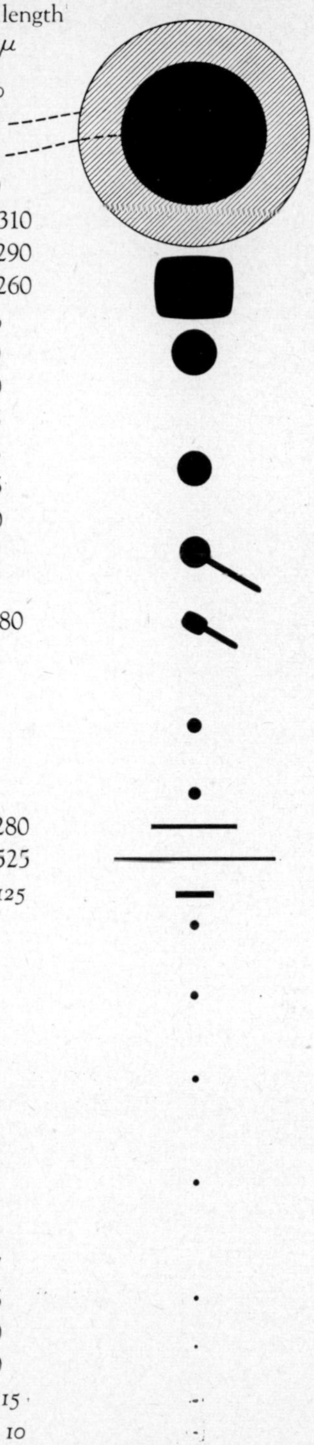

Fig. 32. A chart showing approximate sizes of viruses and reference materials. (From W. M. Stanley, *Chem. and Eng. News*, 25, 3786, 1947.)

Could they best be worked with by biological or by chemical methods? For a short time, there was a reluctance to accept the challenge which was presented by the viruses, for no approach seemed quite equal to the task.

It was in this atmosphere of mystery and indecision that I was first introduced to viruses by Dr. Simon Flexner and Dr. L. O. Kunkel. These men were convinced that the approach through chemistry had not been explored sufficiently, and they asked me to assume this task. I accepted this opportunity, because I was attracted by the unusual challenge which it presented, and because I was aware of recent achievements of chemistry in which certain hormones and enzymes had been shown to be proteins.

SELECTION OF TOBACCO MOSAIC VIRUS FOR CHEMICAL STUDY

Tobacco mosaic virus was selected for the initial studies because it appeared to offer several unusual advantages. Large amounts of highly infectious material were readily available, and the virus was known to be unusually stable. Furthermore, it was possible to titrate or measure the amount of this virus in a preparation with ease and rapidity and with great accuracy. Evidence was soon obtained that tobacco mosaic virus was either a protein, or closely associated with a protein, which could be digested by pepsin. Then, by means of the methods, or modifications of the methods, that had been used in the isolation of the protein hormones and enzymes, there was obtained from extracts of mosaic-diseased tobacco plants a crystalline material which seemed to possess the properties of tobacco mosaic virus. Crystals of this material are shown in Figure 33. There was, of course, great skepticism that this crystalline material, which proved to be a nucleoprotein, was really tobacco mosaic virus. Many workers, imbued with the idea that viruses were living organisms, were frankly opposed to accepting the idea that a virus could be a crystalline nucleoprotein. However, the fact that the crystalline nucleoprotein was available as a definite, tangible entity made it possible to subject the hypothesis that virus activity was a specific property of the nucleoprotein to rigorous test by experimentation.

If studies on this crystalline nucleoprotein had been restricted to the use of techniques of only one field of science, there might still be considerable doubt regarding the relationship between tobacco mosaic virus and the nucleoprotein. However, because

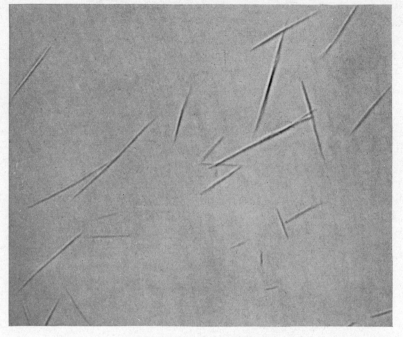

FIG. 33. Crystals of the tobacco mosaic virus nucleoprotein. X 1200. (From W. M. Stanley, *Am. Jour. Bot.*, *24*, *59*, *1937*.)

of the great importance of the problem, it was obvious that every technique capable of yielding significant information should be employed. Accordingly, the nucleoprotein isolated from mosaic-diseased tobacco plants was subjected to a barrage of forces from many fields of science. Nucleoprotein preparations isolated from different lots of diseased plants and at different times of the year were found to possess the same specific virus activity. Repeated crystallization of the nucleoprotein was not found to affect the virus activity appreciably. Fractionation of the nucleoprotein by crystallization, by means of centrifugation at different hydrogen ion concentrations, by means of filtration, by means of absorbing agents, or by means of electrophoresis, yielded no evidence for the presence of an impurity, for the specific virus activity of all fractions remained unchanged. Solutions of the nucleoprotein were found to be homogeneous with respect to rate of sedimentation and with respect to rate of electrophoretic movement. The rate of sedimentation of the infectious principle was demonstrated to be the same as that of the nucleoprotein. The injection of rabbits with a solution of the nucleoprotein resulted in the production of antibodies which gave a specific precipitin reaction with the nucleoprotein. More important, the antiserum was found to neutralize virus activity. The nucleoprotein was found to possess a characteristic ultraviolet absorption spectrum. This absorption spectrum coincided with the destruction spectrum of virus activity. The range of stability of the nucleoprotein and of virus activity at different hydrogen ion concentrations was found to be the same. The disintegration of the nucleoprotein in strong solutions of urea was accompanied by loss of virus activity. The nucleoprotein was shown to be unusually resistant to digestion by enzymes. The rate of proteolysis by pepsin was found to be about 1 per cent of that of ordinary proteins. Trypsin and ribonuclease were found to cause loss of virus activity, but this was shown to be reversible and hence not due to hydrolysis.

Then, in 1938, a rather important experiment on the nucleoprotein was conducted with the assistance of Dr. Ross. It was shown that treatment of the nucleoprotein with formaldehyde resulted in a decrease in amino groups and in groups which react with Folin's reagent, presumably the indole groups of tryptophane, and that these reactions were accompanied by loss of virus activity. By appropriate treatment it was found possible to reverse these reactions and cause an increase in amino groups and in groups which react with Folin's reagent. Of great significance was the fact that the reversal of the reactions was accompanied by an increase in virus activity. Although complete reactivation was not secured, the activity of partially inactivated preparations was generally increased about tenfold by the reactivation process, and completely inactivated preparations were reactivated to an appreciable extent. The results left no doubt that definite and measurable changes in the chemical structure of the nucleoprotein molecules were accompanied by definite and measurable changes in specific virus activity. This provided good evidence that the virus activity was a specific property of the nucleoprotein and, hence, that the nucleoprotein was really tobacco mosaic virus. Thus, many kinds of experiments yielded results which all led directly to the conclusion that tobacco mosaic virus was, in fact, a crystallizable nucleoprotein. Although additional evidence hardly seemed necessary at this point, more evidence of a different nature was soon forthcoming.

Tobacco mosaic virus has an unusually wide host range. It can cause disease in many different kinds of plants, such as tobacco, tomato, petunia, spinach, and phlox plants. If the conclusion that the crystallizable nucleoprotein was tobacco mosaic virus was correct, this same nucleoprotein should be present in different kinds of mosaic-diseased plants. This approach possessed a special interest, for it had been shown by serological methods that the proteins of certain susceptible plants differed completely from the proteins present in other kinds of susceptible plants. Was it really possible that two different kinds of cells, such as those of the Turkish tobacco and phlox plants, which normally produce serologically distinct proteins, could be caused to produce the same unusual nucleoprotein merely as a result of the introduction of a few molecules of this nucleoprotein into these cells? The test was soon made by subjecting the extracts of mosaic-diseased Turkish tobacco and phlox plants to the isolation procedure. Preparations of crystallizable nucleoproteins were obtained and, by all tests yet applied, were found to be identical. This result provided information of considerable significance. Naturally it was the result to be anticipated if the nucleoprotein was really tobacco mosaic virus. In addition, it indicated that the virus was constructed, not from large units such as serologically active proteins, but from small serologically inactive units, perhaps even from amino acids. The result also demonstrated that vastly different metabolic systems, systems geared to the production of quite different end products, could be diverted by the mere presence of the virus nucleoprotein to produce the same end product.

Still another approach was provided by the fact that plant pathologists have recognized that tobacco mosaic virus exists in the form of many strains, and that, by means of special techniques of their science, they have been able to segregate these virus strains. The different strains cause different symptoms of disease, such as, for example, those shown in Figure 34. It was, therefore, of considerable interest to determine the nature of the nucleoproteins present in different plants of the same kind infected with different strains of tobacco mosaic virus. Would such plants yield nucleoprotein preparations, and, if so, would these be identical with tobacco mosaic virus nucleoprotein, or would each differ in a characteristic manner? The first test was made about ten years ago, when nucleoprotein preparations were obtained from Turkish tobacco plants infected with tobacco mosaic virus and with a yellow mottling strain known as aucuba mosaic virus. It was soon found that, although the general properties of these two nucleoprotein preparations were very similar, they nevertheless differed in a significant manner. For example, the isoelectric point of the aucuba mosaic virus nucleoprotein was found to be more alkaline than that of the tobacco mosaic virus nucleoprotein. This fact made possible a rather significant experiment. When the two purified nucleoproteins were mixed at pH 7 and the solution was then gradually made more acid, the aucuba mosaic virus nucleoprotein came out of solution first. It thus became possible to separate the two nucleoproteins. When this was done, and the two preparations were used to infect separate lots of Turkish tobacco plants, one group came down with tobacco mosaic and the other with aucuba mosaic. This experiment demonstrated, in a striking manner, that the two nucleoproteins were different and that a given type of biological activity remained associated with a characteristic nucleoprotein. Subsequently, many strains of tobacco mosaic virus were obtained in the form of purified nucleoproteins. Although these were all

FIG. 34. Leaves of Turkish tobacco plants showing symptoms typical for each of 6 strains of tobacco mosaic virus. TMV, tobacco mosaic virus; YA, yellow aucuba; GA, green aucuba; M, Holmes' masked strain; J14D1, a derivative, isolated by Dr. L. O. Kunkel, of Dr. J. H. Jensen's J14 virus; and HR, Holmes' rib grass strain. The leaf showing the masked strain (M) is practically indistinguishable from a normal leaf, although it contains an appreciable amount of virus. The J14D1 and HR viruses differ from the other strains shown in giving distinct primary lesions on the inoculated leaves as well as typical secondary symptoms. In each of these cases, the first leaf shows characteristic primary lesions and the second leaf the secondary symptoms. (From W. M. Stanley and C. A. Knight, *Cold Spring Harbor Symp. Quant. Biol.*, 9, 255, 1941.)

found to possess quite similar general properties, they could, nevertheless, be distinguished from each other by means of certain distinctive properties. The results demonstrated, therefore, that different strains of tobacco mosaic virus existed in the form of similar, yet distinctive, nucleoproteins.

As a whole, the experimental results that have been described permit only one conclusion. Tobacco mosaic virus is a characteristic, crystallizable nucleoprotein which is present at all times in all kinds of tobacco mosaic-diseased plants. Attention was therefore directed toward finding out as much as possible regarding this characteristic nucleoprotein.

PROPERTIES OF THE VIRUS NUCLEOPROTEIN

The virus nucleoprotein was found to consist of 6 per cent of nucleic acid and 94 per cent of protein. The components of the nucleic acid were found to be similar to, or identical with, those of yeast nucleic acid. However, by heat treatment, a virus nucleic acid was obtained which was highly asymmetric and possessed a molecular weight of about 300,000, a value much larger than any previously reported for the yeast type of nucleic acid. This nucleic acid decomposed spontaneously to form less asymmetric particles having a molecular weight of about 60,000. Treatment of this material with cold alkali yielded particles having a molecular weight of about 15,000 and an axial ratio of 10. The latter material is similar to yeast nucleic acid with respect to size and shape. The composition of the protein component of the virus has been studied quite extensively. As will be described in a subsequent paragraph, the amino acid content of the protein component has been determined, either completely or almost completely.

Extensive studies on the diffusion, viscosity, electrophoretic, and sedimentation behavior of solutions of the virus nucleoprotein were made. The viscosity and rate of sedimentation were found to vary with the concentration of the nucleoprotein. For a time, the use of physicochemical data to calculate particle weight, size, and shape was questionable, because it was not possible to assess the relative contributions of hydration and asymmetry. The virus was too small to be seen by the light microscope, and the electron microscope was not yet available; hence, it was not known whether the virus molecules were spheres, plates, or rods. However, over ten years ago, Takahashi and Rawlins noted that the juice of mosaic-diseased plants exhibited stream double refraction, and that the entire flowing stream of juice was double refracting. They concluded that the virus was composed of, or associated with, rod-shaped particles. Since solutions of the purified nucleoprotein were found to exhibit the same phenomenon, it seemed likely that the virus nucleoprotein was rodlike in shape. Calculations of particle weight and size became possible, but these were still rendered ambiguous because of lack of information regarding the density of the virus in solution.

About this time, a significant contribution was made by Bernal and associates through X-ray studies on the virus nucleoprotein. They found that the virus preparations possessed certain definite intramolecular, as well as intermolecular, spacings. They concluded that the individual virus molecules were essentially crystalline in nature, and that these could arrange themselves in the form of para-crystals with perfect hexagonal symmetry with respect to cross section, but with no regularity with respect to length. The distance of closest approach between the virus molecules, namely, 15.2 mμ, was regarded as representing the diameter of the virus molecule. The constancy of the intramolecular spacings has been regarded as providing evidence that water does not exist within the virus molecules, and, for a time, the virus was considered to consist of anhydrous rods. Recently, however, Schachman and Lauffer studied the sedimentation behavior of the virus in serum albumin solutions of different densities, and concluded that the density of the virus in solution was 1.13 and, hence, that the virus contained 65 per cent water by volume. This information made it possible, for the first time, to calculate in an unambiguous manner the size and shape of unhydrated virus nucleoprotein particles from physicochemical data. These calculations indicated that the virus particles were 15 by 280 mμ in size, with a molecular weight of about 40 million. In the meantime it had become possible to secure good pictures of the virus particles by means of the electron microscope, and these provided abundant, direct evidence that the particles were 15 by 280 mμ in size. Recent studies by light scattering methods have also provided indirect evidence for the existence of particles of this size. The fact that it was possible to arrive at the correct size and shape of the tobacco mosaic virus nucleoprotein by indirect methods constituted a major triumph for theoretical physical chemistry.

HYDRODYNAMIC BEHAVIOR OF VIRUS PARTICLES

During the past several years, a great many theories relating hydrodynamic behavior to particle size and shape have been proposed. These theories became important because of the recent great interest in high polymer research, especially that involving rubber; yet it was not possible to subject the theories to a proper experimental test, because of the lack of a suitable test material. Because of its unique size and shape and its unusual homogeneity with respect to particle size, tobacco mosaic virus nucleoprotein has served as an admirable material with which to test these theories. The successes achieved with tobacco mosaic virus will doubtless result in the acceptance and wide use of these theoretical relationships. Another unique use of the virus nucleoprotein, based on its unusual size and shape and not on its virus activity, is in studies of liquid flow. Solutions of the nucleoprotein exhibit double refraction of flow, and they can, therefore, be used to study the nature of the flow currents in machines, such as pumps and hydraulic rams, or the intensity and direction of flow when objects, such as boats or projectiles, move through a liquid. Solutions of the nucleoprotein are also being tested to determine if they can serve as a model for the atmosphere and thus aid in studies of the air currents surrounding the earth.

During the course of X-ray studies on the virus nucleoprotein, Bernal and associates secured good evidence for the existence of long-range forces effective between the rodlike virus particles. They found that, as the virus rods were brought closer together in solution, for example, by the evaporation of the solution, the rods assumed positions exactly, or almost exactly, parallel to each other, even when the distance between them was as much as 80 mμ. The assumption and maintenance of parallel positions at such great distances provide good evidence for the existence of unusual forces operative at long range. The existence of long-range forces is now generally accepted, but the nature of these forces has been and remains a matter of much controversy. Long-range forces are obviously of great importance in biology, for they may be responsible for many intracellular events, such as, for example, chromosome duplication. Tobacco mosaic virus provides an admirable experimental material with which to study the nature of long-range forces, and this is a field of research which may yield very significant results in the future.

Another remarkable phenomenon exhibited by the virus rods consists of their end-to-end aggregation. Although electron micrographs of fresh, untreated extracts of diseased plants and of the contents of hair cells of diseased plants have provided good evidence that the virus exists in the form of rods 15 by 280 mμ in size within the cells of diseased plants, preparations of the virus rods have been obtained in which the rods are joined together, end to end, to form long strands. This type of aggregation has been found to be partly reversible and partly irreversible. Aggregation can be caused by certain salts and, when it occurs, it is accompanied by a decrease in specific virus activity, since the number of infectious units is decreased. How the ends of the rods find each other, and why they are able to form a union of great strength, remain unknown. The virus rods are known to follow an alternating electric field; hence, they can act as dipoles. However, this fact does not provide an adequate explanation for their unusual behavior with respect to end-to-end aggregation. Treatment of aggregated or unaggregated virus preparations with high-intensity sound causes a breakage of the rods. Breakage of rods 15 by 280 mμ in size by sonic treatment is accompanied by loss of virus activity with the formation, first, of half lengths, then quarter lengths, and eventually eighth lengths. The immuno-chemical properties of these fragments have been found to be similar to those of the intact virus. These inactive fragments can be caused to aggregate end to end again; but when they do so, there is no tendency to form, predominately, lengths of 280 mμ, and virus activity is not regained. The aggregation of tobacco mosaic virus or of fragments of the virus rods provides another example of the existence of unusual, specific forces which demand elucidation.

PURIFIED FORMS OF OTHER VIRUSES

Many of the interesting properties of tobacco mosaic virus nucleoprotein derive from its unusual size and shape and not from the fact that the nucleoprotein possesses virus activity. However, the latter fact is of the utmost importance, and, with its establishment, interest naturally was directed toward the isolation of other viruses in purified form. Would these prove to be crystallizable, rodlike nucleoproteins? The question was soon answered, for several viruses were obtained in purified form in the laboratories at Princeton, and others were obtained in other laboratories in this and in other countries. Some proved to be crystallizable nucleoproteins, either rodlike or spherical in shape. Some were found to be nucleoproteins which have not as yet been crystallized. Others proved to be large particles consisting of nucleoprotein, lipid, and carbohydrate and possessing in some cases a degree of morphological differentiation hardly characteristic of structure at the molecular level and more characteristic of organisms. Still others have so far defied isolation, possibly in some cases because of extreme instability.

Electron micrographs have been obtained of the individual particles of several purified virus preparations, and these provide an excellent idea of the amazing array of sizes and shapes that exist. Figure 35 shows electron micrographs of eight different virus preparations at the same magnification. At the upper left is a picture of vaccinia virus, which exists in the form of brick-shaped particles about 210 by 260 mμ. These appear to possess a composition similar to that of bacteria. They have a limiting membrane and are apparently semiorganized, for they have definite areas of increased density. Next is an electron micrograph of the Lee strain of influenza virus. These particles are spheres about 115 mμ in diameter and consist of nucleoprotein, lipid, and polysaccharide. Although the influenza virus particles are affected by osmotic influences, evidence that they possess a definite limiting membrane is still lacking. Of considerable interest is the fact that, in marked contrast to tobacco mosaic virus, the influenza virus appears to possess an antigenic component which is characteristic of the host from which the virus was obtained. The significance of this finding, which may be of considerable im-

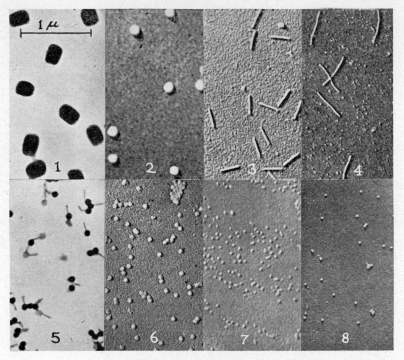

FIG. 35. Electron micrographs of 8 purified virus preparations. 1. Vaccinia virus; 2. Lee strain of influenza virus; 3. Tobacco mosaic virus; 4. Potato X virus; 5. T₂ coli-bacteriophage; 6. Rabbit papilloma virus; 7. Southern bean mosaic virus; 8. Tomato bushy stunt virus. (From C. A. Knight, *Cold Spring Harbor Symp. Quant. Biol.*, *12*, 115, 1947.)

portance in virus research, represents a problem for the future. The next is an electron micrograph of tobacco mosaic virus, which shows the particles 15 by 280 mμ in size. As described earlier, these particles consist solely of nucleoprotein and are characterized by an inner structural regularity of such a nature that each particle can be regarded as a crystal. These particles can, of course, combine to form large, needle-shaped para-crystals that are readily visible with a low-power microscope. At the upper right is a picture of X virus, also known as latent mosaic of potato virus. This virus is a crystallizable nucleoprotein, the particles of which are about 10 by 525 mμ in size. This virus is of interest because it occurs in almost all of the potato plants grown in the United States. It causes practically no damage to the potato plants, and, because of this fact and because of its almost universal presence in potato plants, it has come to be called the healthy potato virus. It might almost be regarded as a normal constituent of potato plants in this country. It is interesting to note that, if one worked only with potato plants of this country, it would be impossible to demonstrate that this infectious agent existed. Contemplation of this fact causes one to wonder whether other infectious, self-reproducing units may not exist and, as yet, have escaped our notice.

The picture at the lower left shows particles of a coli-bacteriophage. The particles are sperm-shaped with a head about 60 mμ in diameter and a tail about 80 mμ in length. These particles have a definite limiting membrane and consist of nucleoprotein and lipid. The next picture shows particles of the rabbit papilloma virus. These are about 44 mμ in diameter and consist of nucleoprotein and little or no lipid. This virus is highly specific and can infect and cause disease only in certain kinds of rabbits. Of considerable interest is the fact that the papillomas induced in domestic rabbits by this virus usually progress and become cancerous, and, when this happens, the virus disappears as an infectious agent. However, good evidence that the virus is still present in the cancerous cells has been obtained. Knowledge of the characteristics of the rabbit papilloma virus and of the healthy potato virus can be used as the basis for much speculation regarding malignant growths in general. As a matter of fact, knowledge such as this, together with presently available knowledge of the properties of the mouse mammary cancer virus, provide a basis for a most promising experimental approach to the problem of cancer. The next picture shows particles of the southern bean mosaic virus. This virus is a crystallizable nucleoprotein and is spherical in shape with a diameter of 31 mμ. The picture at the lower right in Figure 35 shows particles of tomato bushy stunt virus. These are spherical in shape and are about 26 mμ in diameter. This virus is a nucleoprotein which can be obtained in the form of the crystals shown in Figure 36.

VIRUS REPRODUCTION AND MUTATION

The viruses here described are more or less typical of the viruses that have been obtained in purified form. It is obvious that they range from simple nucleoproteins, some of which are

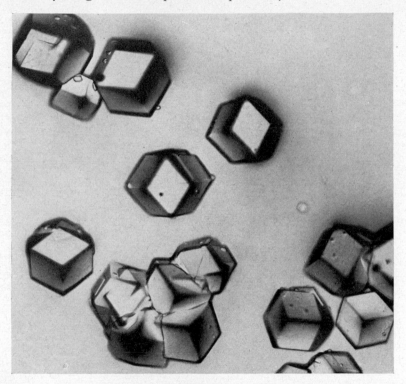

FIG. 36. Crystals of the tomato bushy stunt virus nucleoprotein. X 224. (From W. M. Stanley, *Jour. Biol. Chem.*, *135*, 437, 1940.)

crystallizable, up through a series of structures of gradually increasing complexity. Chemical structure appears to give way to a type of morphological differentiation characteristic of organisms. Yet all of these diverse structures are bound together by one all-important property. They all possess virus activity, which implies the ability to reproduce and mutate when within certain living cells. The nature of virus activity is a great and fundamental problem and, at the present time, it is a complete mystery. It is not known whether viruses reproduce by division, after the manner of simple organisms, or by means of some new and, as yet,

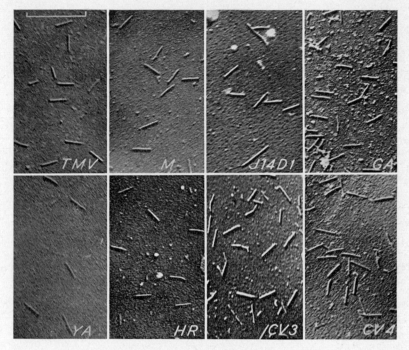

FIG. 37. Electron micrographs of 8 strains of tobacco mosaic virus. TMV, ordinary tobacco mosaic virus; GA, green aucuba; YA, yellow aucuba; HR, Holmes' rib grass; CV3, cucumber virus 3; CV4, cucumber virus 4. The micrographs are of contents of hair cells from appropriately diseased Turkish tobacco plants, except in the cases of CV3 and CV4 which were obtained from hair cells of diseased cucumber plants. The mounts were prepared with gold by the shadow casting technique. The line of the micrograph of TMV represents 1 micron. (From C. A. Knight and G. Oster, *Arch. Biochem.*, *15*, 289, 1947.)

unknown process. Just before the war an attempt was made to determine if any of the substance of infecting virus particles would appear in their progeny. Tobacco mosaic virus marked by radioactive phosphorus was used, and, although the marked phosphorus of the virus was stable *in vitro*, it was not found to remain solely with the virus when the virus was placed within

living cells; hence, the experiment failed to provide definite information regarding the nature of virus reproduction. However,
it seems likely that similar experiments will eventually yield
definite and important information.

Another approach to the problem of the nature of virus reproduction was provided by the existence of purified preparations
of several strains of tobacco mosaic virus. As described earlier,
these possessed similar, yet nevertheless, distinctive properties.
For example, as can be seen from Figure 37, the particles of
several of these strains have a similar size and shape. Presumably
these strains arose from tobacco mosaic virus by a process similar
to that of mutation in organisms; hence, it seemed likely that
information regarding the nature of the differences between
these virus strains would be important, not only in connection
with the problem of virus reproduction, but also in connection
with basic problems in genetics. Attention should be directed to
the fact that there is a striking similarity between the properties
of viruses and those that have been ascribed to genes, the bearers
of hereditary characteristics. Both genes and certain viruses may
be regarded as large nucleoproteins that have the ability to multiply and perpetuate themselves within, and only within, certain
specific cells. Both may undergo sudden changes, apparently
either spontaneously or as a result of external factors, and these
changes are then faithfully reproduced in subsequent generations. So far as is known, these changes or mutations occur only
during the reproduction of the active agents within living cells.
The magnificent work of Beadle and of Tatum on *Neurospora*
has demonstrated, in a striking manner, that definite biochemical
reactions are controlled by genes, and this work is providing very
significant information concerning the nature of gene action.*
However, because there are great obstacles to making studies on
the nature of the chemical differences between genes, the approach using purified preparations of virus strains appeared to
offer certain advantages.

Seven distinctive strains of tobacco mosaic virus were selected
for study, and purified preparations of these were subjected to

* Cf. Chapter IX.

amino acid analyses by Dr. Knight. From the results, which are presented in Table I, it can be seen that definite differences in the amino acid content of certain strains were demonstrable. These results indicate that the mutation of a virus can be accompanied by a change in the concentration of one or more amino acids in the virus structure, by the introduction of one or more

TABLE I

Amino Acid Contents of Highly Purified Preparations of Some Strains of Tobacco Mosaic Virus

Amino Acid				Strain					
	TMV	M	$J_{14}D_1$	GA	YA	HR	CV_3	CV_4	MD*
Alanine	5.1	5.2	4.8	5.1	5.1	6.4		6.1	0.2
Arginine	9.8	9.9	10.0	11.1	11.2	9.9	9.3	9.3	0.2
Aspartic Acid	13.5	13.5	13.4	13.7	13.8	12.6		13.1	0.2
Cysteine	0.69	0.67	0.64	0.60	0.60	0.70	0	0	
Cystine	0		0		0	0		0	
Glutamic Acid	11.3	11.5	10.4	11.5	11.3	15.5	6.4	6.5	0.2
Glycine	1.9	1.7	1.9	1.9	1.8	1.3	1.2	1.5	0.1
Histidine	0	0	0	0	0	0.72	0	0	0.01
Isoleucine	6.6	6.7	6.6	5.7	5.7	5.9	5.4	4.6	0.2
Leucine	9.3	9.3	9.4	9.2	9.4	9.0	9.3	9.4	0.2
Lysine	1.47	1.49	1.95	1.45	1.47	1.51	2.55	2.43	0.04
Methionine	0	0	0	0	0	2.2	0	0	0.1
Phenylalanine	8.4	8.4	8.4	8.3	8.4	5.4	9.9	9.8	0.2
Proline	5.8	5.9	5.5	5.8	5.7	5.5		5.7	0.2
Serine	7.2	7.0	6.8	7.0	7.1	5.7	9.3	9.4	0.3
Threonine	9.9	10.1	10.0	10.4	10.1	8.2	6.9	7.0	0.1
Tryptophane	2.1	2.2	2.2	2.1	2.1	1.4	0.5	0.5	0.1
Tyrosine	3.8	3.8	3.9	3.7	3.7	6.8	3.8	3.7	0.1
Valine	9.2	9.0	8.9	8.8	9.1	6.2	8.8	8.9	0.2

The values given in the table represent percentages of the indicated amino acids. In order to facilitate comparison, the values which are considered to differ significantly from those of *TMV* are underlined.

TMV, tobacco mosaic virus; *M*, Holmes' masked strain; *GA*, green aucuba; *YA*, yellow aucuba; *HR*, Holmes' ribgrass; *CV₃*, cucumber virus 3; *CV₄*, cucumber virus 4.

* Mean deviation (*MD*) of the values of single determinations from the averages given in the table. Three to 5 preparations of each strain were analyzed for each amino acid, with the exception of cysteine, and the results were averaged to give the figures presented in the table.

(From C. A. Knight, *Jour. Biol. Chem.*, *171*, 297, 1947.)

new amino acids into the virus structure, or by the elimination of an amino acid from the virus structure. This work has provided the first information regarding the nature of the structural changes which accompany mutation. Presumably, changes of this type are responsible for the alterations of genes, for the conversion of a mild to a killing strain of poliomyelitis virus, and for the conversion of virulent yellow fever virus into a mild strain which has proved useful as a vaccine. Recently, studies of this nature were extended to more highly organized viruses. Examination of purified preparations of two kinds of influenza virus revealed differences in amino acid composition similar to those found among strains of tobacco mosaic virus.

The results already obtained provide a basis for speculation regarding the nature of mutation. For example, it seems unlikely that changes of the nature that has been described could have resulted from alterations of fully formed virus structures. It is more likely that the changes in virus structure which accompany mutation result from a diversion of the synthetic process by means of which a virus multiplies. Because of important implications with respect to medicine, to the nature of virus reproduction and mutation, and to the nature of gene action, research work on the structural differences between virus strains should be pursued vigorously. In view of the significant results already obtained and the vast amount of experimental material awaiting exploitation, the future of this aspect of virus research offers great promise.

The fact that changes in chemical structure, corresponding to mutations in higher organisms, can occur in structures as simple as those of certain viruses provides a definite experimental approach which offers a great challenge to organic chemistry. If it should prove possible to cause different and reproducible changes in the chemical structure of a virus by means of known, definite, chemical reactions in the test tube, the way would be opened, not only to the production of a variety of new virus strains, some of which might prove useful as vaccines, but also to a direct study of the exact chemical structure necessary for virus activity. A few years ago such an approach would have appeared utterly fantastic, but when the knowledge of the nature of the structural differences between virus strains, and the knowledge that tobacco mosaic virus could be inactivated and reactivated became available, the approach appeared eminently feasible. Studies of this type were therefore inaugurated, and it was soon found possible to prepare a variety of chemical derivatives of tobacco mosaic virus. Unfortunately, the inoculation of these chemical derivatives to healthy Turkish tobacco plants resulted in the production of the ordinary tobacco mosaic disease, and the virus isolated from the diseased plants was indistinguishable from ordinary tobacco mosaic virus. The results indicated, therefore, that the chemical derivatives were converted into ordinary virus following their introduction into the cells of the plant, or, more probably, that the infecting molecules may not necessarily function as exact patterns for reproduction. The results also indicated that the changes in chemical structure, characteristic of the derivatives that have been prepared, are not sufficiently great, or are not of the correct kind, to represent heritable changes. However, certain of the chemical derivatives of tobacco mosaic virus were found to have an altered virus activity with respect to one kind of test plant, although the virus activity with respect to other kinds of test plants was unchanged. It is believed that this result provides the first example of the modification of virus activity by means of definite, known, and reproducible changes in the chemical structure of a virus. This result lends encouragement to the belief that eventually heritable structural changes will be achieved in the chemical laboratory. The accomplishment of this objective will be accompanied by implications of far-reaching significance in many fields of science. Perhaps it could even be said that knowledge of this type could affect the destiny of all living things.

The great progress in virus research which has been made during the past few years resulted from the application of techniques characteristic of several different fields of science. Progress in virus research would have been seriously impeded if viruses had been studied solely from the standpoint of the pathologist, or of the bacteriologist, or of the chemist. Significant contributions have come from a variety of fields, and, as so often happens in the pursuit of knowlege, achievement in one sphere has resulted in the stimulation of other spheres. With the possible exception of nuclear energy, there is, perhaps, no other research problem which has drawn from so many fields of science as has virus research.

The progress that has been made is symbolized by our knowledge of tobacco mosaic virus. Not until 1935 did this virus nucleoprotein become available for study; yet it is highly probable that more is known about the properties of this material than about the properties of any other protein. Despite recent achievements in virus research, it seems almost certain that the most important problems still lie ahead. How do viruses reproduce? How do they mutate? What chemical structure is necessary for virus activity? What is the nature of the long-range forces that operate in strong solutions of tobacco mosaic virus, and are they related to forces responsible for events within cells? These are some of the problems which make the future of virus research bright with promise.

For References see p. 310.

VIII

THE TUBERCLE BACILLUS AND TUBERCULOSIS

By René J. Dubos

Rockefeller Institute for Medical Research, New York

TUBERCULOSIS illustrates well the problems of parasitism, because it presents a situation where the infective agent, the tubercle bacillus, can live in apparent equilibrium with the infected host for prolonged periods of time, often causing only limited clinical signs of disease. The pathologist has described with extraordinary thoroughness the histological aspects of the response of the host to the parasite, from the initiation of the infection, to the establishment of the lesion, and its arrest or progression to fatal outcome. The clinician has learned to recognize, predict, and to some extent control the manifestations of the disease. The epidemiologist has accumulated data describing the natural course of the disease in new and in immune populations, and the influence of environmental factors on morbidity and mortality. The bacteriologist has learned to grow the bacillus, and knows much of its peculiar chemistry. But despite this immense background of theoretical and practical knowledge of the disease and of the causative organism, little is known of the mechanisms by which tubercle bacilli become established in a new host and cause disease, or of the processes used by the infected host to overcome the infection. In other words, we know much of the ecological aspects of host-parasite relationships in tuberculosis, but hardly anything of the means used by the bacillus to behave as a parasite.

THE EVOLUTION OF TUBERCULOSIS

In the early part of the nineteenth century, tuberculosis reached epidemic levels in Europe and North America and became the largest cause of disease and death. Thus, spread over the century, one recognizes the names of Friedrich Schiller, John

Keats, Percy B. Shelley, René Laennec, Anne, Charlotte, and Emily Brontë, Frédéric Chopin, Honoré de Balzac, Alfred de Musset, Elizabeth Browning, Henry David Thoreau, Waldo Emerson, Marie Bashkirtseff, Robert Louis Stevenson, Cecil Rhodes, all of whom died of the disease or suffered from it. Indeed, so many of the famous children of the nineteenth century

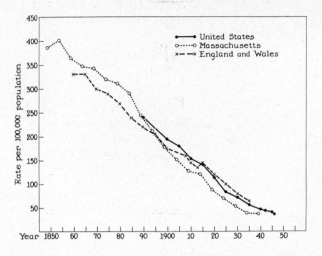

FIG. 38. Mortality rates of tuberculosis in Massachusetts, the United States, and England and Wales. (Drawn from official data obtained through the courtesy of Dr. C. E. Palmer, Tuberculosis Control Division, U.S.P.H.S., and Dr. A. S. Pope, Division of Tuberculosis and Sanatoria, Commonwealth of Massachusetts.)

lived and died tuberculous that one came to postulate the existence of some tragic and mysterious relation between tuberculosis and genius. It is more likely, however, that tuberculosis was so prevalent at the time, that it affected with equal severity all intellectual and social strata, probably in all age groups; tuberculosis was then, truly, the White Plague of the Western World.

Available mortality records indicate that, toward the end of the eighteenth and the beginning of the nineteenth century, "consumption" accounted for some 20 per cent of the total deaths in western Europe and on the eastern seaboard of the United States [22a]. Although the lack of convincing diagnostic criteria renders these early statistics somewhat questionable, there is little doubt that annual tuberculosis mortality rates of 500 to 1,000 per 100,000 population were common in our cities. It is estimated that in London 320 persons per 100,000 population died of the pulmonary form of the disease in 1847. This mortality rate had decreased to approximately 230 in 1875, and to 80 in 1925. Mor-

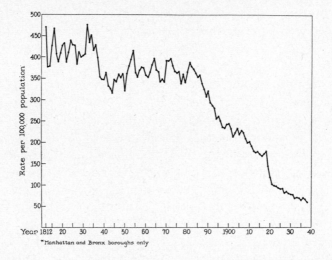

FIG. 39. Pulmonary tuberculosis death rate since 1812: New York, Philadelphia, and Boston. (Drawn-from data supplied by Miss Mary Dempsey, statistician, The National Tuberculosis Association, New York.)

tality statistics suggest that pulmonary tuberculosis reached even higher levels in Massachusetts, but here again, it is evident that the disease has shown since 1849 a steady decline, which is illustrated in Figure 38, along with approximate mortality rates for the United States, and for England and Wales, during the same period. The course of the decline is illustrated in greater detail in Figure 39, which shows the combined mortality rates for Boston, New York, and Philadelphia from 1812 to 1939. It is unfortunate that trustworthy records of mortality rates during the nineteenth century are not available for most parts of the world. Moreover, the early statistics recognize only the pulmonary form of the disease. Nevertheless, there is little doubt that the dramatic change in the relation of the tubercle bacillus to man which is revealed in Figures 38 and 39 also took place over most of the Western World during the same 100-year period. In other words, there is evidence that mortality rates began to decrease in Europe and North America around 1850 and that they have continued to decrease steadily ever since, except for short and local interruptions in the downward curve during and after the first and second World Wars. Recent and more reliable mortality rates provide convincing demonstrations of the occurrence of this phenomenon during the twentieth century.

The data presented in Figure 38, for example, illustrate the dramatic fall in tuberculosis mortality which occurred in the United States between 1890 and 1946. This downward trend has even been bettered in a few other countries; in Denmark, for example, the mortality rate was 34 per 100,000 population in 1944, and this despite the privations and sufferings caused by the second World War.

The facts reported above give reason to hope that civilization is winning the fight over tuberculosis. One must emphasize, however, that, at the same time as the disease is on the retreat in most of the civilized world, it is still increasing, often at an alarming rate, in certain parts of Latin America and in most tropical countries, where it is responsible for mortality rates exceeding in certain areas 500 per 100,000 population. The disease exhibits an equal prevalence and severity in Greenland, Alaska, China, Japan, etc., indicating that climate is not a determinant factor in its spread [37]. Even in the most favored countries, in the United States, for example, tuberculosis still attacks a large percentage of the population and remains today the greatest single cause of death in the age group 15 to 40. Whether measured in terms of human or economic values, the losses and misery which it causes are not exceeded by any other disease [31, 33]. Equally disturbing, from another point of view, is the fact that the forces which determine the decrease in mortality rates in our communities have not yet been clearly and convincingly identified. One may wonder, therefore, whether these forces will keep on operating in the future as they have in the past, and whether our understanding of the epidemiology of the disease is sufficient to plan adequately for its eradication or at least its control.

The natural evolution of tuberculosis in our communities constitutes a lesson in humility for the student of infection. The slope of the downward trend of tuberculosis mortality had been so constant for several decades that, about 1930, epidemiologists became bold enough to extrapolate from it and to predict the early eradication of the disease from our midst, on the assumption that the number of tuberculous individuals would soon become so small as to break the chain of infection. Although it is true that only a small percentage of the population of the United States suffer from clinical tuberculosis, it is equally certain that, even today, approximately one half of the population exhibit convincing evidence of contamination with tubercle bacilli [31, 33]. This contrast between prevalence of the infection and relative rarity of severe clinical disease emphasizes our ignorance of the factors which condition the manifestations of tuberculous infections and should be a warning against complacency.

It will be noticed that the rate of decrease of tuberculosis mortality had already reached its maximum slope around 1900, long before any specific immunization or therapeutic measures were available, indeed long before the antituberculosis campaigns in their various forms had gained full momentum. This fact should not lead one to minimize the influence of antituberculosis measures in decreasing the toll taken by the disease in our communities at the present time. First, it must be emphasized that even before the demonstration of the germ theory of disease (about 1875) and before the discovery of the tubercle bacillus (1882), there had grown an increasing consciousness of public health problems, forced upon the social conscience by the appalling misery in industrial cities. In consequence, many of the sanitary measures which are now advocated so forcefully by the antituberculosis campaigns, on the basis of factual knowledge of the mode of spread of the bacilli, had received some application during the nineteenth century. Hygiene began then to be projected from the individual to the public plan on the basis of an empirical awareness of the contagiousness of the disease. Although it is not possible to estimate the influence of these early measures on the evolution of the epidemic, there is reason to believe that it was not negligible.

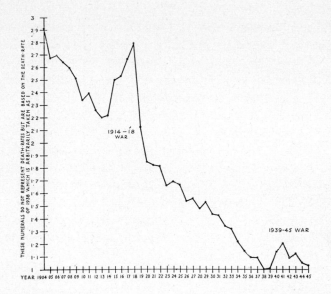

FIG. 40. Comparative mortality indices (base year, 1938): Tuberculosis all forms, under 15 years, England and Wales, 1904–1945. (Reprinted from *Tubercle*, 29, 69, 1948.)

More direct evidence of the effectiveness of the many-sided antituberculosis campaigns in recent times is given by the fact that tuberculosis mortality increased immediately wherever the public health program was disrupted as a result of the first and second World Wars. This tragic phenomenon, illustrated in Figure 40, for England and Wales, occurred in an even more dramatic manner in many other European countries. Of equal interest is the fact that tuberculosis mortality resumed its downward course as soon as public health measures were restored to their former level of efficiency. There is no doubt, therefore, that in Europe—and in this country as well—man lives in a state of unsteady equilibrium with tuberculous infection, and that this equilibrium can be readily disturbed in favor of the disease. Although tuberculosis morbidity and mortality have decreased in a spectacular manner, the bacillus is still in our midst, as ubiquitous and as virulent as ever, ready to initiate a new White Plague if circumstances ever render man and society less resistant to it.

Granted the importance of public health measures in holding the disease in check, it must be emphasized that equally important forces have been at work for three quarters of a century and have had a major influence in curbing the devastating effect of the disease in much of the Western World. What are these forces, how can we harness them to better advantage, and how long will they remain effective? These are some of the most important questions in the study of tuberculosis.

Many hypotheses have been formulated to account for the variations in prevalence and severity of tuberculosis during historical times. Since all students of the disease agree that the bacillus itself has not changed and that its ability to cause disease has remained unimpaired, we must look for some modifications in the receptivity of man and society to infection.

It has been pointed out that, during the first part of the nineteenth century in Europe and North America, and at the present time in Latin America, the Industrial Revolution resulted in the migration to large cities of rural populations which became exposed to increased chances of infection while living under most unfavorable hygienic conditions, a state of affairs favorable to the establishment of a widespread epidemic. It is probable that the most susceptible members of the population were the first to become the prey of the disease, often dying too young to leave any progeny. Hence, one may assume that a process of selection slowly took place favoring the survival and the multiplication of those endowed with a higher degree of natural resistance. On the other hand, many epidemiologists also believe that, as a result of the widespread distribution of the disease, most individuals have the opportunity of coming in contact repeatedly with doses of tubercle bacilli too small to cause clinical tuberculosis, but sufficient to establish subclinical infections capable of eliciting resistance against further tuberculous disease; in other words, a process of immunization would be constantly taking place in the population. Finally, it is accepted that the growth of industrialization was accompanied by an improvement in living standards, in industrial areas at least—a fact which probably had a favorable effect in controlling the epidemic. Indeed, epidemiological evidence indicates that less crowding and better housing decrease the chances of infection, and that better nutrition increases natural resistance to clinical tuberculosis. As already mentioned, it is also probable that a certain awareness of the value of public health for the community began to permeate the Western World during the middle of the nineteenth century and probably played some part in controlling the spread of the disease.

This picture of the epidemiological pattern of tuberculosis appears plausible enough. Unfortunately, it is based on a number of assumptions for which no objective evidence is available. Whether the general level of natural hereditary resistance has increased in our populations cannot be demonstrated at the present time because there is no known technique to measure it or even to recognize it. Granted that better nutrition increases resistance to clinical tuberculosis it is regrettable that, despite many claims to the contrary, no information is available concerning the dietary factors involved; in fact the possible influence of the nutritional state has never been convincingly separated from nonspecific environmental and physiological effects. Similarly, the part played by acquired immunity must remain problematical at the present time. Although much progress has been made in the analysis of the nature and mechanism of the allergy elicited by tuberculous infections, nothing is known of the immune mechanisms by which the host attempts to protect itself against invasion or injury by the bacillus. It may be said in passing that we are equally ignorant of the nature of the components and products of the bacilli which may elicit protective mechanisms, an ignorance which greatly limits the development of new immunization procedures or the improvement and standardization of those which, like the use of BCG, appear to possess a limited degree of effectiveness.

Attempts to elucidate these various problems by experimental methods have been handicapped by difficulties inherent in the peculiar mode of growth of tubercle bacilli in artificial media, and in the character of the disease produced in experimental animals. We have deemed it worth while, therefore, to reëxamine the methodology of the study of experimental tuberculosis, and to attempt in particular an analysis of the factors which affect the proliferation of the bacillus *in vitro* and *in vivo*.

THE GROWTH OF TUBERCLE BACILLI *IN VITRO*

One of the most striking characteristics of tubercle bacilli is the hydrophobic nature of their cell surface. This property is responsible for the fact that, in the usual aqueous media used by the bacteriologist, mammalian tubercle bacilli grow in the form of heavy pellicles or large clumps which are not (or only little) wetted by the water phase. This peculiar mode of growth complicates technical operations aiming at the accurate sampling or enumeration of the bacilli and often necessitates mechanical grinding (resulting in a certain amount of injury to the cell) for the preparation of finely dispersed bacillary suspensions. Of greater importance than this technical difficulty, however, is the fact that the bacilli situated inside the clumps or pellicles are living under physicochemical conditions very different from those prevailing at the periphery. In consequence, cultures of tubercle bacilli grown *in vitro* in the classical media consist of organisms which have been exposed to all degrees of asphyxiation and starvation, and which exhibit therefore many different physiological states. In fact, these cultures often contain a large percentage of dead cells having suffered all degrees of autolytic changes. This heterogeneity of the bacterial population adds greatly to the difficulties of quantitative studies concerned with the enumeration of the bacilli, the analysis of their immunological structure, the measurement of their metabolic activity, the determination of their nutritional requirements, the discovery of growth inhibitory effects, etc.

We have attempted to overcome the hydrophobic character of the bacterial surface by adding wetting agents to the culture media. Although most surface active substances exert a marked inhibitory effect on the growth of tubercle bacilli, certain non-ionic agents can wet the bacterial surface even when used in concentrations sufficiently low to cause no toxic effect. Two classes of non-ionic wetting agents have been found particularly useful in this respect. One class consists of polyoxyethylene derivatives of sorbitan esters of long chain fatty acids (commercially known under the name of Tween), which are particularly nontoxic when they are used in a purified form free of nonesterified fatty acid [2, 3, 8, 10, 14, 15, 16]. There is indirect evidence that at neutral pH and in aqueous media Tween becomes adsorbed through its own lipophylic chain on the hydrophobic surface of the bacillus and surrounds the latter with a hydrophilic atmosphere consisting of ethylene oxide chains [9, 26]. In practice, fairly well-dispersed and homogeneous cultures of tubercle bacilli can be obtained after one-week incubation in culture media containing 0.01 to 0.05 per cent of Tween 80.

As Tween 80 is an ester of oleic acid, it is susceptible to hydrolytic destruction by esterases and lipases [3, 4, 7, 19], a fact which limits its usefulness in media containing animal tissues or body fluids rich in these enzymes. Fortunately we have recently found another type of non-ionic wetting agent of low toxicity which can also wet the surface of tubercle bacilli, and which is resistant to lipolytic action, because it does not contain any ester linkage. This wetting agent, commercially known under the name of Triton A20, is an arylalkyl polyether of phenol and remains active in bacteriological media containing components of animal tissues [17].

Although Triton A20 disperses cultures of tubercle bacilli, it does not appear to increase their rate of growth or their metabolism, as measured by oxygen intake. On the contrary, in addition to its wetting effect on the bacterial cell, Tween 80 enhances growth probably by supplying oleic acid in a nontoxic, water-soluble form available for metabolic utilization. It is a remarkable fact that under the proper conditions certain long-chain fatty acids and alcohols, and even hydrocarbons, are much more effective than glucose or glycerine in stimulating the respiration of tubercle bacilli [34]. Furthermore, the yields of avian and human mycobacteria grown in serum albumin media containing palmitic, stearic, or oleic acids (either in the form of the sodium soaps or of the water dispersible esters), linoleic, linolenic, arachidonic, or lignoceric acids, increase in direct proportion with the concentration of the fatty acid in the medium [10, 11].

While capable of enhancing the growth of tubercle bacilli, long-chain fatty acids also exhibit marked toxicity for these organisms. This toxic effect, however, can be neutralized by addition of serum albumin to the medium, the amounts required being of the order of 1 mol of albumin per 6 to 8 mols of oleic acid [4, 5, 6, 14, 16]. It appears that fatty acids form, with the albumin fraction of serum, complexes in the form of which they are no longer toxic, although they remain available for metabolic utilization. Serum albumin also neutralizes the toxic effect of a large variety of substances which occur as impurities in laboratory media and which exert an inhibitory effect on the growth of tubercle bacilli [1, 5, 6]. In consequence, addition of 0.1 to 0.5 per cent albumin to culture media greatly facilitates growth, not necessarily by supplying nutritional factors, but by exerting a protecting effect on the organisms and thus permitting the initiation of growth from small inocula.

Evidence is now accumulating that other tissue components are capable of exerting a stimulating effect on the growth of tubercle bacilli. For example, the phospholipid sphingomyelin permits the growth of small inocula even in the absence of serum albumin, and at the same time increases markedly the yield of growth within a given period of incubation [11]. This dual effect can be analyzed in terms of two independent properties. On the one hand, sphingomyelin, like albumin, can detoxify long-chain fatty acids and thereby exerts a protective effect on the bacilli. On the other hand, it acts as a source of nutrient, probably by virtue of the lignoceric acid which is present in amide form in its molecule. Other tissue factors of as yet unidentified nature have been found to enhance and modify the growth of tubercle bacilli *in vitro*. It appears likely, therefore, that as more is learned of the requirements of these organisms, it will become possible to reduce considerably their generation time *in vitro*, which is now reckoned to be of the order of 30 hours in the classical media [38].

This result would be of theoretical and practical importance, especially in view of the fact that the generation time of tubercle bacilli *in vivo* may be much shorter than is usually assumed.

TABLE I

The Effect of Lipids, Albumin, and Wetting Agents on the Growth of Tubercle Bacilli

Added to the basal medium (final concentration)					Growth 10 days after inoculation with H37Rv (mg./cc. medium)			Avian Camden 3 (mg./cc. medium)
Tween 80	Triton A20	Oleic Acid	Sphingo-myelin	Albu-min	2×10^{-4}	2×10^{-6}	2×10^{-8}	2×10^{-6}
%	%	%	%	%				
0	0	0	0	0	3 g	1 g	0	1
0	0	0	0	0.5	6 g	4 g	2 g	1
0.05	0	0	0	0	3 fd	0	0	5
0.05	0	0	0	0.5	8 fd	5 fd	3 d	8
0	0.05	0	0	0	3 d	2 d	0	1
0	0.05	0.02	0	0	0	0	0	0
0	0.05	0	0	0.5	5 d	4 d	3 d	1
0	0.05	0.02	0	0.5	8 d	6 d	3 d	6
0	0.05	0	0.05	0	8 d	5 d	2 g	5
0	0.05	0	0.05	0.5	8 d	6 d	4 d	8
0	0	0	0.05	0	4 g	3 g	2 g	5
0	0	0	0.05	0.5	7 g	4 g	3 g	7

The amount of growth is recorded in terms of an arbitrary scale from 0 (no growth) to 8 (growth corresponding to approximately 0.4 mg. dry weight of bacilli per cc. of medium).

fd indicates that growth was finely dispersed, exhibiting no large clumps on microscopic examination.

d indicates that the growth was dispersed but consisted of clumps readily seen with a hand lens.

g indicates granular growth consisting of large clumps or flakes.

It is not possible to present here the experimental data on which are based the preceding statements concerning the factors which modify the growth of tubercle bacilli *in vitro*. The few results recorded in Table I will serve to illustrate the effects of oleic acid, sphingomyelin, serum albumin, and of the wetting agents Tween 80 and Triton A20, on the growth of two strains of tubercle bacilli: H37Rv (human) and Camden 3 (avian).

Some of the findings and principles outlined above have been utilized in the formulation of several types of culture media adapted to different experimental and diagnostic purposes [16, 21, 25]. Suffice it to say here that addition to a simple basal medium of small amounts of the wetting agents Tween 80 or Triton A20 permits dispersed growth of the bacilli, and that initiation of growth of very small inocula (containing but a few cells) can be obtained if albumin or sphingomyelin are added as protective agents. The basal medium consists of inorganic salts, buffered at pH 6.8, and of enzymatic hydrolysate of casein as source of nitrogen. An additional source of energy can be added in the form of glucose or glycerol when large yields of bacteria are desired. Magnesium may then become one of the limiting factors of growth; addition of citric acid is a convenient method of maintaining large concentrations of magnesium in solution.

Although dispersed growth is of great advantage for many types of experimental work, it is not a requirement or even an advantage in diagnostic procedures; for this purpose, the wetting agent can be replaced in the medium by small concentrations of oleic acid (0.005 to 0.01 per cent). It is of particular interest that tubercle bacilli can be readily cultivated directly from pathological materials in media which are so poor in the usual sources of energy, carbon, and vitamins that they are unable to support the proliferation of staphylococci, streptococci, pneumococci, or meningococci, and allow only scant growth of colon bacilli. It appears possible that the peculiarity in the nutritional requirements of tubercle bacilli, in particular their marked affinity for various types of lipids, is of significance in the pathogenesis of tuberculosis.

Of special interest also is the fact that all surface active substances which facilitate dispersed growth of tubercle bacilli by wetting their hydrophobic surface increase the susceptibility of these organisms to a variety of antibacterial agents (triphenyl-methane dyes, p-amino salicylic acid, streptomycin, subtilin, penicillins). For example, strains of mycobacteria which can grow in oleic acid albumin medium (in which their surface is strongly hydrophobic) in the presence of 100 micrograms of penicillin or of subtilin per cc. are inhibited by 5 micrograms of these substances in media containing the proper wetting agent [12, 13, 21, 22]. Whether this is due to the more dispersed state of the cultures in media containing the wetting agents or to the fact that the latter substances facilitate access of the antibacterial agent by modifying the bacterial surface is as yet unsettled. In any case, the important conclusion can be drawn from these facts that the resistance of tubercle bacilli to inhibitors which are effective against other microbial species need not be the consequence of peculiarities in the metabolic equipment of the former organisms. It may be due merely to the hydrophobic character of their surface, which retards or prevents the contact between the inhibitor and the susceptible cellular substrate.

FACTORS AFFECTING THE SUSCEPTIBILITY OF MICE TO EXPERIMENTAL TUBERCULOUS INFECTIONS

There is clinical and epidemiological evidence suggesting that susceptibility to tuberculosis in man exhibits a familial pattern and is governed by hereditary factors [32]. Similarly, it has been possible, by selective breeding, to develop strains of rabbits and guinea pigs possessing increased or decreased susceptibility to the disease [20, 36]. These hereditary differences in susceptibility are manifested in a particularly striking manner by various strains of mice. Of the 20 strains of mice so far compared for this purpose in our laboratory, the most susceptible appear to be line 1 dba (a dilute brown agouti strain developed at the Jackson Memorial Laboratory, Bar Harbor, Maine). Injection of a few bacilli by the intravenous or intracerebral route establishes in these mice a pulmonary infection which progresses to destruction of lung tissue and to death. Larger infective doses may cause an acute infection resulting in death within a week without any gross destructive lesions. In general, the standard laboratory albino mice exhibit a much higher degree of natural resistance. Other strains of mice are intermediate [29, 30]. The difference in susceptibility between albino mice and dba line 1 mice is illustrated in Table II and in Figure 41.

Both in the susceptible and in the more resistant strains, the

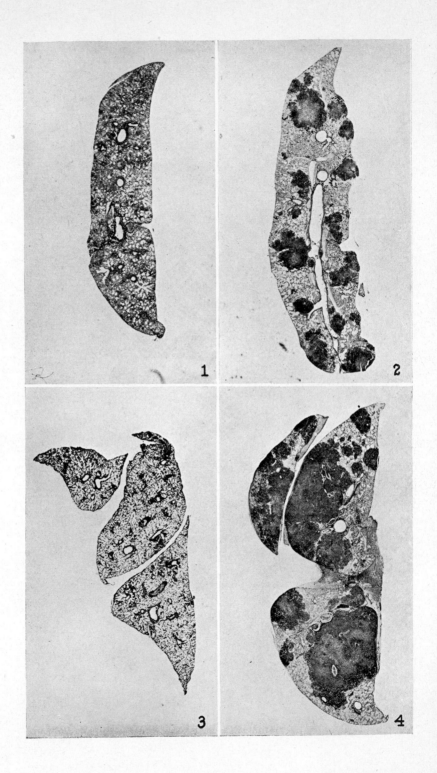

course and outcome of the disease are markedly affected by the environmental conditions under which the animals are kept during the infectious process. Thus, the susceptibility of mice to tuberculosis can be greatly modified by changing the composition of the diet fed the animals during, or before, initiation of the infectious process (Table II). Although investigation of this problem is still in the preliminary stage, the following conclusions appear justified. (a) It is possible to devise a diet (consisting of cornmeal, butter, salts, and vitamins) on which noninfected mice can be maintained in adequate health, although with little gain in weight, but which renders the animals extremely susceptible to tuberculous infection. (b) Addition to this diet of various amino acids (tryptophane, tyrosine, lysine, etc.), of water soluble vitamins, of yeast extract, and of fat soluble vitamins, does not increase resistance to infection. (c) Addition of milk to the cornmeal-butter diet restores the animals to optimal resistance [17a].

FIG. 41. Difference in susceptibility to tuberculosis between albino mice and dba line 1 mice. Lung sections stained with hematoxylin-eosin. X 8.5.
1.   Mouse strain: Swiss albino
    Inoculum: 0.003 cc. $H_{37}Rv$ (intravenous).
    Autopsy: 3 weeks after infection.
Note many small areas of parenchymal and subpleural lesions. Occasional epithelioid cells are visible in these lesions at higher magnification.
2.   Mouse strain: dba
    Inoculum: 0.003 cc. $H_{37}Rv$ (intravenous).
    Autopsy: 3 weeks after infection.
Note large, sometimes confluent parenchymal, peribronchial, and subpleural lesions. Central necrosis is evident. Many epithelioid cells are visible in these lesions at higher magnification.
3.   Mouse strain: Swiss albino.
    Inoculum: 0.01 cc. $H_{37}Rv$ (intravenous).
    Autopsy: 3 weeks after infection.
Note several small, dark areas in the parenchyma. Higher magnification reveals these to consist of inflammatory lesions without necrosis, which are usually perivascular.
4.   Mouse strain: dba.
    Inoculum: 0.01 cc. $H_{37}Rv$ (intravenous).
    Autopsy: 3 weeks after infection.
Note massive consolidation of most of the lung with large areas of necrosis.
(These illustrations are reproduced from Pierce et al., *Jour. Exp. Med.*, 86, 159, 1947.)

TABLE II

Effect of Diet on Albino Swiss and Line 1 dba Mice Infected i.v.
with 0.000015 mg. Mammalian Tubercle Bacilli

Strain of Mice	Diet ad lib.	Survival (S) or Death (indicated by number of days after infection)								Average Weight of Uninfected Controls *		
										Initial	3 Weeks	14 Weeks
Albino Swiss	BM	S	S	S	S	S	S	S	S	gm. 22.0	gm. 24.2	gm. 27.5
	CGB	64	67	72	79	80	S	S	S	22.3	17.2	19.3
Line 1 dba	BM	26	39	47	47	66	66	74	86	17.5	16.7	21.3
		Average Survival 58 days										
	CGB	20	27	27	27	30	30	30	44	17.3	13.0	16.6
		Average Survival 29 days										

BM. Bread and milk.

CGB. Cornmeal, gelatin, butter, and vitamins.

* All uninfected animals were living and well at the end of experiment (14 weeks after infection).

Although these findings may be accounted for by the existence of a nutritional factor specifically concerned with resistance to infection, it is also possible and, indeed, likely that the loss of resistance determined by the change of diet may be related to some metabolic or physiological disturbance, rather than being due to a specific nutritional deficiency.

Concomitant infections with other pathogens can also decrease the resistance of mice to tubercle bacilli. The tuberculous process in the mouse lung can be augmented significantly when a minimal infection with certain filtrable viruses is initiated even as late as three weeks after the injection of relatively small amounts of tubercle bacilli. This effect was secured with two different pneumotropic viruses, namely, PVM (strain 15) and influenza A (strain PR8), using virus inocula sufficiently small to induce little or no definite virus pneumonia. In this manner it is possible, by experimental means, to convert a mild and slowly progressing tuberculous infection, normally leading under the conditions employed to the development of gross pulmonary lesions in only a small proportion of animals, into a distinctly more serious and rapidly progressive disease causing gross pulmonary lesions, and often death, in a large proportion of animals [85].

CORRELATION BETWEEN VIRULENCE AND MORPHOLOGY OF MAMMALIAN TUBERCLE BACILLI

It is likely that progress in the development of immunization techniques against tuberculosis would be greatly facilitated if knowledge were available of the particular functions and structures of the bacillus which endow it with the ability to invade animal tissues and against which the immunity process must be directed to be effective against infection. Unfortunately, nothing is known as yet of the immune mechanism by which the host reacts with the parasites or their products to prevent or retard the spread of tuberculosis. Nevertheless, some observations have been made which point to the existence in human and bovine tubercle bacilli of a cellular structure which is correlated with virulence.

It is well known that virulent strains of tubercle bacilli can give rise by variation (mutation) to avirulent variant forms. Experimental pathologists have established many fundamental facts describing the comparative behavior of the virulent and avirulent forms in resistant and susceptible animals. For the present, only those facts will be considered which pertain to the behavior of the bacteria toward phagocytosis. Following their introduction into the animal (or in tissue cultures or other *in vitro* phagocytic systems), both virulent and avirulent bacilli are rapidly taken up by polymorphonuclear leucocytes and find their way into mononuclear cells a few hours later. It is the course of events subsequent to phagocytosis which differentiates the two forms of bacilli. The avirulent forms may survive intracellularly for prolonged periods of time, but fail to multiply to a significant degree. On the contrary, the virulent organisms rapidly increase in numbers in the susceptible animals and soon become detectable both within and outside the phagocytic cells. Whether bacterial multiplication occurs extracellularly, intracellularly, or both, is a question which has not been convincingly answered, and which cannot be discussed here.

Very recently, my colleague, Dr. Hubert Bloch, has made a few observations which may contribute to our understanding of the relation of virulence to phagocytosis. By studying the peritoneal exudate at intervals of time after injection of bacilli into the peritoneal cavity of the mouse, he could confirm that both avirulent and virulent forms were rapidly engulfed by phagocytic cells. He further gained evidence that engulfment of the virulent bacilli often resulted in the death and disruption of the phagocyte, a fact not observed with the nonvirulent forms. These observations, if substantiated, suggest the important conclusion that virulence may be correlated with the ability of the bacillus to cause injury to the phagocytic cell. It seems legitimate to wonder whether this cytotoxic effect does not result in the liberation of cellular products that favor the further growth of the bacilli [13].

Comparison of the mode of growth of the virulent and avirulent variants in the classical synthetic media, as well as in media containing different concentrations of wetting agents or oleic acid, has revealed striking morphological differences between the virulent and avirulent forms of human and bovine strains [13, 18, 26, 28]. In all virulent variants so far studied the cells exhibit a marked tendency to adhere to one another in the direction of their long axis; this tendency results in the formation of cords or strands of bacilli, which can be very long and, at times, extend over several microscopic fields, and which are several cells in thickness. In contrast to this serpentine pattern of growth, the avirulent forms exhibit either random growth or perhaps a rosette arrangement of the cells (Fig. 42). These microscopic morphological differences are reflected in the macroscopic appearance of the cultures in liquid and on solid media, the virulent forms tending at first to give rise to thin films of growth spreading by the outward progression of the long strands or cords of cells, whereas the nonvirulent variants tend to multiply in the form of heaped masses of bacilli [26]. It is of interest that these fundamental morphological characteristics are maintained in animal tissues and therefore are not artifacts due to cultivation in the culture media. For example, very striking morphological differences of the type described above can be recognized in the drawings made by Maximow in the course of a study of the comparative behavior of a virulent bovine strain and of the avirulent BCG strain growing in animal cells in tissue cultures [23, 24].

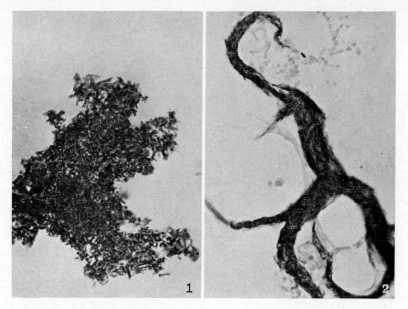

FIG. 42. Comparative morphology of avirulent (H37Ra) and virulent (H37Rv) human tubercle bacilli.

1. H37Ra. Ziehl-Neelsen stained smear of a 7-day-old culture in liquid medium containing 0.02 per cent Tween 80 and 0.5 per cent serum albumin. Note the lack of orientation in the arrangement of the cells of this avirulent strain. X 1000.

2. H37Rv. Ziehl-Neelsen stained smear of a 7-day-old culture in liquid medium containing 0.02 per cent Tween 80 and 0.5 per cent serum albumin. This culture was recently isolated from an experimentally infected mouse. Note the tendency to the formation of cords. X 1000.

On the basis of present information, therefore, it appears that the substance which tends to make the virulent bacilli adhere to each other and which causes their spreading mode of growth is in some obscure way correlated with virulence, if not responsible for it. Knowledge of its nature would probably throw some light on the processes by which tubercle bacilli can establish themselves in animal tissues and might suggest ways to combat the infection. Unfortunately there is as yet no convincing information concerning the chemical nature of the substances which determine the tendency of the virulent bacilli to grow in the form of "cords," and it can only be stated that this tendency is overcome by the addition to the culture medium of certain types of non-ionic wetting agents. It is possible that the morphological differences between virulent and avirulent bacilli are not of a qualitative but only of a quantitative nature and may be due to the production by the virulent forms of larger amounts of a certain hydrophobic substance, much less abundant in the avirulent form, which is wetted by the non-ionic surface active agents [17].

CONCLUSIONS

Virulent tubercle bacilli exhibit sufficient peculiarities to warrant the hope that the analysis of the factors which condition their morphological characteristics, their type of growth, and their metabolic behavior, will yield a better understanding of the mechanisms of infection and immunity in tuberculosis. Furthermore, it is apparent that experimental tuberculous infections of mice provide an opportunity to recognize, under controllable conditions, many of the factors which have been assumed to influence the evolution of tuberculosis in the human race: the hereditary character of natural susceptibility and resistance, the conditioning effect of environment on the course and severity of infection, the development of some measure of acquired immunity as a result of previous exposure to the bacillus, etc.

Needless to say, tuberculosis in man is a vastly more complex problem than the experimental infection of mice. Many pathologists will even question the wisdom of studying human tuberculosis through the artifice of an experimental infection which differs appreciably from the human disease in its pathogenesis and pathology. It has appeared to us, however, that it is the very spirit of the experimental method to dissociate complex natural phenomena into a set of simpler situations instead of attempting to reproduce them in their total complexity. It is our hope that the experimental techniques which we are developing for the study of the properties and behavior of the tubercle bacillus *in vitro* and *in vivo*, will facilitate the identification of the cellular structures and reactions at the level of which the animal and bacterial economy influence each other.

For References see p. 311.

GENES AND BIOLOGICAL ENIGMAS

By G. W. Beadle

Kerckhoff Laboratories of Biology

California Institute of Technology

"What is life?" is a question that has had irresistible appeal to man from the time in the long course of his evolution that he first became a rational being. In attempting to answer it, the biological sciences have described in the minutest detail the multitudinous variations among those living systems that now inhabit the earth. At the same time they have attempted to abstract from the resulting vast array of facts certain generalizations and to search out those denominators common to all things that live. What is the result? In the hierarchy of sciences in which, as we proceed from mathematics to physics, to chemistry, and on to biology, we include increasing numbers of concepts of decreasing generality, what is it that biology has that the physical sciences do not have? Is it a Driesch entelechy or merely a new order of organization?

Our answers to these questions, like the attempts of the three blind men to describe the elephant, have been greatly influenced by our approach. We have quite naturally tended to start with a consideration of ourselves. This is unfortunate in many respects because we represent the climax of a tremendously long process of evolutionary specialization and accordingly possess many characteristics that are not of a fundamental biological nature even though they are of the greatest importance to us. Thus the possession of a central nervous system sufficiently advanced to make reason possible is not basic biologically, for many organisms do very well without it. As we work down the evolutionary scale we see that many additional biological properties that we hold dear are dispensable. Movement is not essential. Irritability and ability to adjust to environment are useful but not indispensable. Even cellular structure can be taken away.

But finally we find as common denominators two properties: reproduction and mutability. It is these that set the living and the nonliving worlds apart. They are the basis of pride in ancestry and of hope for posterity, concepts that have no meaning outside of biology.

During the present century it has become increasingly evident that the hereditary units, first clearly conceived by Mendel and now known as genes, may well be the ultimate units of reproduction and mutation in living systems. Our knowledge of them as embodied in the theory of the gene—incidentally, the subject of Thomas Hunt Morgan's Silliman Lecture series of 20-odd years ago [50]—represents one of the two great advances in biology of the last century. Darwin's concept of common descent with modification—organic evolution—is the other outstanding achievement, and, as every schoolboy knows, the two are inseparably bound together, in that genes provide the basis of the heredity and variation that underlie the evolutionary process.

It is my purpose here to review in a very brief way the evidence which leads us to the conclusion that genes are the basic dies or templates from which new generations of organisms are built, and to indicate how these units are to biology what molecules, atoms, neutrons, protons, and electrons are to chemistry and physics. I intend also to say something about what genes are, what they do, how they act, and how they are related to some of the many unsolved problems of biology that we are now prepared to formulate. To attempt to do all these things is a very large undertaking, and I am keenly aware that I can hope to do it only in a limited and imperfect way.

That genes are basic units in the process of reproduction and in directing the development and functioning of organisms may be inferred from three main lines of evidence. The first is based on the direct investigation of heredity by the methods of classical and chemical genetics. The second comes from a study of the sequence of events that characterizes the evolutionary specialization of parasitic forms, while the third involves speculative considerations of the manner in which life first originated on earth and of the nature of the first living systems.

THE METHODS OF CLASSICAL AND CHEMICAL GENETICS

The Mendelian laws of heredity are now generally taught in high school courses in biology and there is little need to review them in great detail here. They were first formulated by the Austrian monk Gregor Mendel in 1865 as a result of his careful breeding experiments with garden peas, in which he investigated the manner of transmission of specific characteristics, like height, shape of seed, and color of seed leaves, from one generation to another. The truly basic significance of his findings is eloquently confirmed by the fact that they have since been found to be applicable to such a great variety of organisms that it is quite safe to say that in principle they hold for all the hundreds of thousands of species of bacteria, protozoa, algae, fungi, and other forms of plant and animal life.

Both because they serve well to illustrate the principles of Mendelian inheritance and because it will be desirable to refer to them in other connections later, I shall here mention briefly several genetic traits in man and in other organisms.

Phenylalanine Metabolism in Man

The black urine disease. One of these is a rare disease in man that appears to have been known for 300 years. Its most readily observed symptom is blackening of the urine on exposure to air. Almost a century ago the German biochemist Bodecker found that this unusual behavior of the urine of patients with the black urine disease is due to the presence in the urine of relatively large amounts of a specific chemical compound which is not excreted by normal individuals. Bodecker isolated it and determined by the usual methods of organic chemistry that it was acetic acid with a partially oxidized benzene ring substituted for one of its hydrogen atoms. This modified excretory substance, chemically known as 2, 5-dihydroxyphenylacetic acid, has the following structural formula:

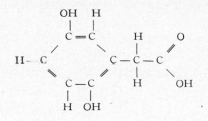

in which the C's, H's, and O's represent atoms of carbon, hydrogen, and oxygen and the dashes symbolize the chemical bonds
that hold these atoms together to form molecules. This substance
is also known as alcapton, from the Arabic and Greek roots meaning "alkali" and "to seize," because the darkening of urine containing it is accelerated by the addition of alkali. It is from alcapton that the medical name of the disease, alcaptonuria, literally
"alcapton in the urine" is derived.

Alcaptonurics exhibit the symptoms of the disease from birth.
They apparently suffer no seriously harmful effects and appear
to have a normal life expectancy. In later years the characteristic
dark pigment derived from the oxidation of alcapton may be
deposited in cartilaginous tissues, giving a bluish tinge to the ears,
the nose, and also other parts of the body where such tissues are
abundant.

Shortly after the rediscovery in 1900 of Mendel's now classical paper, the English biologist Bateson, who deserves much of
the credit for making the world aware of the great significance
of Mendel's discoveries, and his collaborator Punnett pointed
out that alcaptonuria seemed to be inherited as a recessive Mendelian trait, an interpretation that has since been confirmed. This
means that there exist alternative forms of a specific hereditary
unit or factor, the normal form of which is essential for normal
metabolism in which alcapton is not excreted. If an individual
receives from both his parents a defective form of this unit, or
gene as we now call it, his metabolism is altered in such a way
that alcapton is excreted.

One representative of the "black urine" gene is contributed

to a new individual by the mother through the egg, and another by the father through the sperm. The fertilized egg therefore carries two representatives of this particular gene. All the cells that are descended from the fertilized egg and that go to make up a fully differentiated individual are like one another and like the fertilized egg in this respect. If, following a convention of genetics, we designate the defective form of the black urine gene by the mnemonic symbol *bu* and its alternative form by *Bu,* we can write down formulas for the three possible genetic types of individuals as far as this trait is concerned. These are

> *Bu Bu,* a purely normal individual
> *Bu bu,* a "hybrid" normal individual
> *bu bu,* an alcaptonuric.

That the hybrid individual is normal is the evidence for the recessive nature of alcaptonuria.

It is now a simple matter to diagram the results of a mating between any two types of individuals. If, for example, a pure normal and an alcaptonuric have children, the result will be as follows:

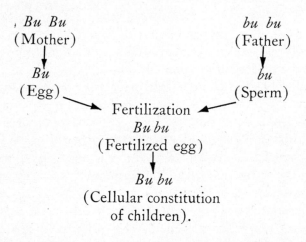

The children will be normal—but not pure normal—genetically.

If two such "hybrid" normal individuals have children, there are four possibilities as follows:

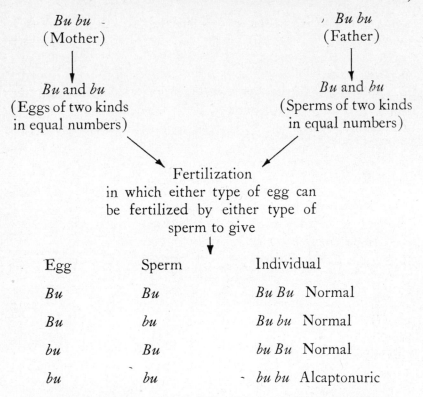

Of the four possible types, three will have normal urine and one will excrete alcapton. It is matings of this type that give the well-known 3 to 1 Mendelian ratio.

In other connections we shall have further occasion to refer to alcaptonuria.

Phenylpyruvic acid idiocy. Within the past ten years medical men and geneticists have learned about another rare inherited disease in man in which idiocy or a lesser degree of feeble-mindedness is a characteristic symptom. Not all hereditary feeble-mindedness is of this type; in fact in Norway, where extensive studies have been made, only between 1 and 2 per cent of the inmates of institutions for the mentally defective are of this kind [21]. This trait is further characterized by relatively large amounts of phenylpyruvic acid in the urine, an organic chemical compound with the formula

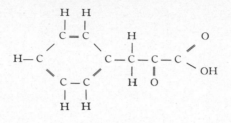

All individuals who habitually excrete large amounts of phenylpyruvic acid in the urine—and this can be determined readily by means of a simple qualitative color test in which iron chloride is used—appear to be mentally defective. This suggests a relatively simple causal relation between the metabolism of this substance and the functioning of the central nervous system. It is clear, however, that there are other causes of mental deficiency, for as indicated above, only a small proportion of mentally defective individuals excrete phenylpyruvic acid.

Fölling [20], Penrose [54], and others [21] have shown that phenylpyruvic acid idiocy, known medically as *Oligophrenia phenylpyruvica,* is inherited as a Mendelian recessive character according to exactly the same principle as those applicable to alcaptonuria. It is another example in which a hereditary unit can be said to direct a specific metabolic process.

Albinism. Most higher animals such as reptiles, birds, and mammals have in their skins and its appendages characteristic dark pigments known as melanins. It is these pigments that give color to our hair, eyes, and skin. They are concerned in the tanning reaction that occurs in response to ultraviolet light. One form of albinism in man is inherited as a simple recessive trait. If the gene concerned is present in defective form only, no pigment is formed. Again, it obeys simple Mendelian laws.

Interrelations of alcaptonuria, phenylpyruvic acid idiocy and albinism. The three diseases just mentioned are metabolically related in that alcapton, phenylpyruvic acid, and melanin all appear to be derived from an amino acid, phenylalanine. Phenylalanine is one of the some 20 amino acids that are the building blocks out of which the proteins of protoplasm are built. Unlike plants, man and most other animals are unable to make amino acids from simpler compounds but must obtain them from an ex-

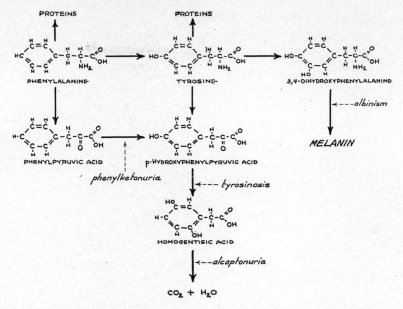

FIG. 43. Phenylalanine tyrosine metabolism in man showing relation of inherited defects to specific chemical reactions. (Based on Haldane [26a].)

ternal source, ordinarily from dietary materials such as meat or vegetable proteins. Once supplied with a particular set of nine of them, man is able to reshuffle their parts to make the remaining ones that he needs. Phenylalanine is one of those that cannot be made from others and is therefore a dietary essential. Several things may happen to it in the human body: it may be rebuilt into any of a large number of proteins, it may be oxidized to form the related amino acid tyrosine, or it may undergo oxidative deamination in which its amino group is replaced by an oxygen atom. These possibilities, together with further chemical changes that may occur in its derivatives, are shown in Figure 43. In this scheme of phenylalanine metabolism, the roles of the genes concerned with the three hereditary diseases discussed above are indicated. In an alcaptonuric, the gene that directs the breakdown of alcapton is defective; alcapton cannot be further metabolized and is therefore excreted in the urine. In phenylketonurics, phenylpyruvic acid cannot be oxidized because of a gene defect and, like alcapton in an alcaptonuric, is excreted in the urine. The precise chemical reaction controlled by the gene concerned with albinism is not known. In the disease tyrosinosis, para-hydroxyphenylpyruvic acid and tyrosine are excreted. Whether the disease is hereditary is not known, for it has been observed in but a single individual.

In the case of the gene that controls the oxidation of alcapton, there is a suggestion as to what the mechanism of control is. Alcaptonurics appear to lack an enzyme that is present in the blood of normal individuals and that catalyzes the oxidation of alcapton [25]. This suggests that the normal form of the gene acts by directing the formation of this enzyme and, through it as an intermediary, controls the specific chemical reaction by which alcapton is oxidized. It is probable that the other genes known to be concerned with phenylalanine metabolism in man function in a similar way.

This concept of gene action was suggested almost 40 years ago by A. E. Garrod in a stimulating book entitled *Inborn Errors of Metabolism*. This remarkable work, revised in 1923 [22], has until recent years received little attention from geneticists. J. B. S. Haldane is to a large extent responsible for reviving interest in it among students of heredity.

Other Examples of Gene-controlled Chemical Action

An important question to which one would like an answer is, how general are relations of this kind between genes and chemical reactions? Biology is not yet in a position to give a complete answer, for the simple reason that most inherited characters are too complex to be described in terms of known chemical reactions. This is of course not at all remarkable, for we have so far gone only a very short way in the process of understanding even the simplest organisms in terms of the chemical reactions by which they develop and function. But it is gratifying that the list of instances in which gene control can be expressed in terms of specific chemical reactions is growing rapidly and at an accelerating rate. For example, the genetic control of the chemical reactions by which the yellow, red, and blue pigments that give color to flowers and other plant parts are synthesized and differentiated is now reasonably well understood [38]. Coat colors in guinea pigs, eye pigmentation in insects, particularly *Drosophila*, formation of cyanogenetic glucosides, and other instances can be cited in which it appears that genes direct chemical reactions, presumably through directing enzyme specificities [6].

The Red Bread Mold Neurospora

In an attempt to find out in a systematic way whether gene control of known chemical reactions could be demonstrated, studies on the red bread mold *Neurospora* were initiated several years ago by Dr. E. L. Tatum and the writer. *Neurospora* was deliberately chosen as material for work of this kind for several reasons. It has advantages over most animals in being able to synthesize protoplasmic constituents like amino acids, vitamins, etc. from a defined medium containing sugar, inorganic salts, and the vitamin biotin. It has a short life cycle—about 10 to 12 days from sexual spore to sexual spore—that is well suited to genetic investigations. In addition to reproducing sexually, *Neurospora* multiplies vegetatively, a distinct advantage if one desires large amounts of genetically homogeneous material for biochemical investigation. It is heterothallic, that is, comes in two sexes or mating types which may be multiplied separately by asexual spores or crossed at will to give sexual spores. The nuclei of the mycelium of the mold are haploid, that is, have only a single set of seven chromosomes and accordingly carry only one set of genes. In this respect the phase of the organism that is observed and investigated biochemically corresponds to the gametes of higher animals and the gametophytes of higher plants. Because of the haploid nature of the organism, genetic characters express themselves without the complications of dominance and recessiveness being evident. Another very important feature of *Neurospora* from the standpoint of its use for genetic studies is that all products of the reduction divisions may be recovered as sexual spores and in the order in which they are formed.*

For having recognized the advantages of *Neurospora* for genetic studies we are indebted to Dr. B. O. Dodge. He and Dr. C. C. Lindegren have been largely responsible for working out the basic principles of inheritance in it.

Producing and detecting mutations in Neurospora *affecting biosynthesis.* Comparative biochemistry has taught us that protoplasm is pretty much the same wherever it is found. It contains proteins, built up of about 20 amino acid building blocks, 10 or so vitamins of the B group, and many other biologically significant compounds. One difference between bread mold and man is that the mold is able to synthesize most of its protoplasmic constituents from simpler components like sugar, nitrates, phosphates, sulfates, and other inorganic salts, while man must have these building blocks supplied ready made in his diet. If the synthesis of these component parts of protoplasm are genetically controlled in *Neurospora,* one should be able to induce mutations in the genes concerned and thereby produce a series of strains, each dependent on an external supply of one or more of the basic building blocks. This has in fact been done on a large scale by exposing the mold to various mutagenic agents—X rays, ultraviolet radiation, neutrons, and mustard gas; establishing single ascospore strains on a medium supplemented with a large number of amino acids, vitamins, and other compounds of known biological importance; and then testing for ability of the strains to grow on the original basal medium. *Neurospora* lends itself admirably to a procedure of this kind. The details of how the experiments are carried out have been described elsewhere [7, 8].†

In this way several hundred mutant strains have been found that are deficient in ability to synthesize known chemical sub-

* A simplified life cycle is given in Figure 52, p. 173, *Science in Progress,* Series V.

† They are diagrammed in Figures 53 and 54, pp. 176, 177, *Science in Progress,* Series V.

stances. Usually a given strain requires a single substance to make it grow normally; that is, it has lost the ability to make this substance and must now obtain it from the medium. It can be determined how such strains differ genetically from the original strain in a very simple manner. A cross between a strain defective in synthetic ability—say, one unable to make the vitamin pantothenic acid—and an original strain of the opposite sex is made. From the mature fruiting bodies produced in this cross, spore sacs are taken and the sexual spores removed in serial order and planted in tubes containing a medium to which pantothenic acid has been added.

All eight spores will now germinate and give rise to mycelia that grow. If asexual transfers are made to a basal medium in which there is no pantothenic acid and it is found that four grow and four do not, it is concluded that the mutant strain differs from the original wild-type strain by a unit of inheritance, that is, a gene, concerned with pantothenic acid synthesis.

This type of experiment has been carried out many times for many different strains, and it has been found that in many instances there is a one-to-one relation between a gene and the ability to carry out a specific reaction [7, 8].

Methionine synthesis. By studying a series of mutant strains of *Neurospora* in which different steps in a series of related reactions are interrupted, it is often possible to find out more about the mechanisms by which a given metabolic end result is achieved. This principle was made use of in determining the course of phenylalanine metabolism in man. Or, stated another way, genetics was used as a tool by the biochemists in studying this system of metabolism. Several examples in which this has been done successfully in *Neurospora* could be cited [5]. One of these that has recently been reported involves the synthesis of the sulfur-containing amino acid methionine [32, 63]. The situation is summarized in Figure 44. For each of the six chemical reactions shown, a gene is known.

Cystathionine as a shuttle mechanism for transferring the sulfur atom from the three carbon amino acid cysteine to the homologous four carbon amino acid homocysteine was demonstrated by growing a mutant strain in which gene 2 is defective in a medium supplemented with methionine. This strain attempts to carry out the synthesis of methionine but cannot carry it beyond cystathionine. In much the same way in which an alcaptonuric accumulates alcapton, this strain accumulates cystathionine. This can be isolated from the mycelium or the medium, identified chemically as cystathionine, and demonstrated to be a precursor of methionine by determining that it will substitute for methionine or homocysteine in promoting the growth of a mutant strain in which gene 3 is carried in the mutant form.

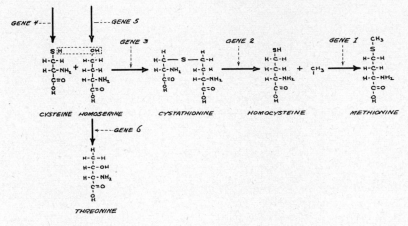

FIG. 44. Postulated genetically controlled steps in the biosynthesis of methionine and related amino acids in *Neurospora*. (Based on work of Horowitz [32] and of Teas, Horowitz and Fling [63].)

Tryptophane and nicotinic acid synthesis. A number of mutant strains of *Neurospora* are known in which the synthesis of the amino acid tryptophane is interrupted [62]. Three genetically different strains are known that cannot synthesize the amino acid nicotinic acid [11]. In both instances our knowlege of the mechanisms by which these indispensable components of protoplasm are synthesized has been extended through a study of these strains. A significant relation has been shown to exist between these two systems of synthesis, which at first glance would seem to be independent. That tryptophane and nicotinic acid may be closely related was first suggested by the observation that in several animals nicotinic acid deficiency symptoms (pellagra in man) could be abolished if sufficient tryptophane were added to the diet. A similar relation is suggested in *Neurospora* by the existence of a mutant strain that can be induced to grow normally by supplying *either* tryptophane or nicotinic acid. Through a

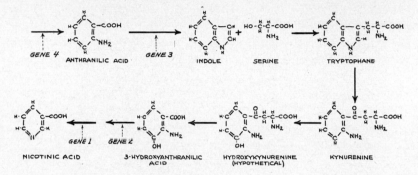

FIG. 45. Postulated biosynthesis of tryptophane and nicotinic acid in *Neurospora*. In addition to the four genes indicated in the diagram, three others have been reported [10]. The precise steps controlled by these genes have not been determined. There is, in fact, reasonable doubt as to the correctness of the scheme given here [10]. (Based on work of Mitchell and Nyc [47], Bonner [10], and others.)

study of this and biochemically related mutant types it has been found that tryptophane is probably a normal precursor of nicotinic acid and can be converted into it through kynurenine and hydroxyanthranilic acid [47, 10]. Our present concept of tryptophane and nicotinic acid biosynthesis is given in Figure 45. While it has not yet been experimentally established that the conversion of tryptophane to nicotinic acid in the mammal follows the same course as in *Neurospora*, it seems probable on theoretical grounds that it does. This relation constitutes another of many striking examples in which it is clearly evident that many of the basic metabolic processes that are carried on in protoplasm are essentially the same wherever they occur—in bread mold or in man.

The tryptophane-nicotinic acid interrelation just outlined is of great interest from the standpoint of our understanding of the cause and cure of pellagra in man. It has been recognized for many years that this disease is of dietary origin, but knowledge of its relation to nicotinic acid dates back only to 1937, when Elveh-jem and his co-workers found that this vitamin would cure canine black tongue, the dog analogue of pellagra in man. Previous to this there were at least three hypotheses, viz. (1) that pellagra is due to "poor quality" in the protein of the diet, (2) that it results from lack of a water-soluble vitamin, and (3) that it is caused by a pellagragenic factor in maize. The experimental evidence was conflicting and the debates that resulted were many. Nicotinic acid seemed at first to be the final answer, for here was a known chemical compound that in very small amounts brought about spectacular cures of black tongue in dogs and pellagra in man. The other hypotheses were largely forgotten and the con-flicting evidence disregarded. With the new knowledge of the interrelation between tryptophane and nicotinic acid, it is now understandable why individuals who eat plenty of "good qual-ity" protein—that is, who obtain plenty of tryptophane—do not suffer from pellagra. The protein quality hypothesis, after all, turns out to be correct. Even more amazing, there is now good evidence that Indian corn does in fact contain a chemical com-pound sufficiently closely related to nicotinic acid to interfere with it in metabolism. In the presence of this competing sub-stance, more nicotinic acid is needed than in its absence. Indian corn favors pellagra in those who make it an important part of the diet, for three reasons: it is low in nicotinic acid, its proteins are relatively low in tryptophane, and it contains a pellagragenic factor that actually increases the nicotinic acid requirement. Solu-tions to medical problems, at best difficult, are not often so sim-ple as they seem at first.

The Gene-enzyme Hypothesis

The manner in which genes control vital chemical reactions like those mentioned above is not difficult to understand if it is assumed that in these instances genes serve as permanent models in the image of which enzyme proteins are constructed. Enzymes are the organic catalysts that accelerate essential chemical re-actions of living systems. These reactions would otherwise not take place or would proceed at intolerably low speeds. So far as we now know, all enzymes are either proteins or contain protein components that are responsible for their specific catalytic properties. In general, for every type of chemical reaction that goes on in an organism there is a specific enzyme. The gene-enzyme hypothesis, in its simplest form, assumes that each of these enzyme proteins has its master pattern present in a gene. If a gene from which an enzyme protein is copied becomes modified by mutation, the enzyme protein copied from it will be altered and will in all probability be enzymatically inactive or less active than its normal counterpart. If a gene is completely destroyed, the enzyme whose protein is copied from it will not be present at all. In the event of either drastic alteration of an enzyme or absence of it, the specific chemical reaction catalyzed by it will fail.

The gene-enzyme hypothesis is not new. Bateson discussed a form of it during the early part of the present century. A. R. Moore elaborated it in considerable detail in 1910 [49], and Garrod [22], Goldschmidt [23], Troland [64], Wright [66], Muller [52], and many others have since given it serious consideration. But its formulation in terms of protein specificities is new, and necessarily so, for it was not until 1926 that the protein nature of an enzyme was incontrovertibly established by Sumner's crystallization of urease. Another five years or more elapsed before chemists and biologists generally accepted Sumner's work and, indeed, it is only within the last ten or a dozen years that the proteinaceous nature of enzymes has received full recognition in biological thinking.

Blood Group Inheritance

In addition to instances of gene-directed enzyme specificities such as those discussed above, there are other large molecular weight substances whose specific configurations seem to depend fairly directly on genes. Notable among these are substances that possess antigenic activity. Many proteins and at least some high molecular weight polysaccharides have the property of inducing the formation of so-called antibodies when injected into an animal to which they are strange. Thus if hen's egg albumin, the protein that makes up most of the white of the egg, is injected into a rabbit, the animal will, if conditions are right, form in the blood specific proteins capable of combining with and precipitating hen's egg albumin. It is of course this ability to form antibodies that enables many animals to build up immunity to disease-producing organisms or the toxins produced by them.

Red blood cells in man and other mammals contain antigenically active substances, and, if these cells are transferred to an animal of another species or even to another individual of the same species, antibodies may be formed which are capable of clumping or destroying the blood cells of the type that led to their production. The antigenically active components of the blood cells may vary from individual to individual, and, when they do, their presence or absence can usually be shown to be correlated with genetic constitution. To take a specific example, there are two antigens in man known as M and N. All people so far tested have one or the other or both of these present in their red blood cells. By injecting a rabbit with blood cells of a person carrying only the M antigen, antibodies specific to such cells will be developed. By removing unwanted antibodies to miscellaneous other antigens, an anti-M test serum can be made. It will clump the blood cells of a person who has the M antigen but not of one who lacks it. In an analogous way an anti-N serum can be made. It will clump cells that carry the N antigen, but not clump those that lack it. Using these two test sera, it is a relatively simple matter to classify all persons with regard to the presence or absence of the M and N antigens.

From the standpoint of gene action, it is significant that persons possessing only M antigen differ genetically from those having only N, and each differs from those individuals whose blood cells carry both antigens. Inheritance studies show that M and N antigens are gene-directed. One particular gene, present in all persons, exists in two forms. One form conditions the presence of M antigen and the other is invariably associated with N antigen. For convenience, the two forms, or alleles, of this gene are designated *M* and *N* to indicate correspondence with the antigens that accompany them. Since every person carries two alleles of this gene in each of his cells, one from the mother and one from the father, there are three and only three genetic types of individuals possible, namely, *MM*, *NN*, and *MN*. The first will be of M blood type, the second N, and the third MN. The results of the six types of matings with respect to the M and N blood types are found to be as follows:

Mother	Father	Children
M *(MM)*	M *(MM)*	All M *(MM)*
N *(NN)*	N *(NN)*	All N *(NN)*
MN *(MN*	MN *(MN)*	¼ M *(MM)*: ½ MN *(MN)*: ¼ N *(NN)*
N *(NN)*	M *(MM)*	All MN *(MN)*
M *(MM)*	MN *(MN)*	½ M *(MM)*: ½ MN *(MN)*
N *(NN)*	MN *(MN)*	½ N *(NN)*: ½ MN *(MN)*

where genetic constitutions are shown in parentheses. Reciprocal matings—that is, those in which genetic constitutions of mothers and fathers are the reverse of those shown—will give exactly the same results.

There are other blood cell antigens known in man, for example, those responsible for the A-B blood groups, which are controlled by another gene that is not in the same chromosome as the *M-N* gene. This gene exists in three forms or alleles and there are therefore six genetic constitutions possible. The alleles may be designated *A*, *B*, and *O*. The possible genetic constitutions and their corresponding blood groups are as follows:

Genetic Constitution	Blood Group
OO	O
AA	A
AO	A
BB	B
BO	B
AB	AB

A and *B* alleles are responsible for A and B antigens, respectively, while allele *O* is inactive. Both *A* and *B* alleles are dominant over *O*, but when both are carried by one individual, each produces its characteristic antigen.

In both of these examples it is seen that there is a one-to-one correspondence between gene and antigen. It is commonly supposed that in these instances genes act by serving as models or dies from which antigens are copied, in much the same way as enzymatic proteins are thought to be copied from gene protein patterns.

A gene-directed blood cell antigen in man that has achieved considerable scientific fame and much medical notoriety in recent years is the so-called Rh antigen. This antigen, so designated because the red cells of the Rhesus monkey carry it, is present in some individuals of the human species and absent in others. Presence of Rh antigen is dominant, and there are three genetic types as follows:

Genetic type	Rh Antigen
Rh Rh	Present
Rh rh	Present
rh rh	Absent

The medical notoriety comes from the fact that a mother of *rh rh* genetic constitution, and therefore lacking the Rh antigen, may have an *Rh rh* child that carries the Rh antigen. The father would be genetically either *Rh Rh* or *Rh rh*. Antigens developed by the child in the fetal stage of development may leak through the placental connections into the mother and induce the formation of antibodies capable of destroying red blood cells carrying Rh antigens. Thus the mother may be immunized against her own child. The antibodies responsible may persist until a subsequent pregnancy and then leak back through the placenta to the fetus. If this developing child is Rh positive (*Rh rh*, genetically), the antibodies may interact with the Rh antigens and destroy red blood cells, leading to a condition known medically as *erythroblastosis fetalis*. This disease may cause either prenatal or postnatal death. In its milder forms it is not lethal, and affected babies may recover completely spontaneously. Blood transfusion with Rh-negative blood is often resorted to with beneficial results. It should be noted that the father is invariably

Rh-positive. The baby carries antibodies that will interact with his cells, and his blood should therefore never be used for transfusion in such instances, a fact that has only recently become appreciated.

Actually the Rh antigen situation is more complex than the simplified version just given [19]. While these complexities are of very great importance genetically and medically, the facts as far as known are still consistent with the hypothesis that genes and antigens are related in the model-copy manner indicated.

Gene-antigen relations of the type described for man are known in a number of other animals. Cattle are heterogeneous for some 40 or more cellular antigens, enough to make it highly probable that any two individuals, even siblings, will be different antigenically [35]. Here again the immunological and genetic evidence indicates that antigenic differences result from differences in genetic constitution. The known facts are likewise consistent with the one-to-one gene-antigen hypothesis. Extensive studies by Irwin and his associates on dove-pigeon species and their hybrids indicate a similar conclusion, with the reservation that in some hybrids, so-called hybrid cellular antigens appear that are not found in either parent. The significance of these apparent exceptions to the general rule is not yet entirely clear.

Hemophilia

Hemophiliacs or bleeders have been known with certainty to medical science since the beginning of the nineteenth century [13], but it was not until after the discovery of the sex-linkage of white eye in the vinegar fly *Drosophila* in 1910 that the manner of inheritance of the disease was understood. It then became evident that, like the white eye character in the fly, hemophilia is a simple sex-linked recessive. The gene by which hemophiliacs are differentiated from normal individuals is carried in the X chromosome. Its inheritance is well illustrated by the descendants of Queen Victoria of England, who was a carrier, and who transmitted it directly to her son Leopold and through two of her daughters, as indicated in Figure 46.

Haldane [26] has estimated that on the average about one male in 50,000 has the disease. Since males have only a single X chromosome, this is a direct measure of the frequency of the recessive form of the gene in the entire population of human X chromosomes. If males with hemophilia had the same probability

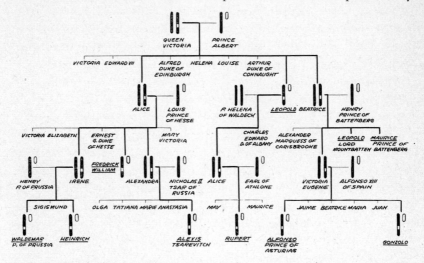

FIG. 46. Inheritance of hemophilia among descendants of Queen Victoria. Y chromosomes represented by short open rods, X chromosomes by long black rods. X chromosomes carrying the normal allele of the hemophilia gene are solid, those carrying the mutant allele are indicated with a white gap. Heavy lines indicate descent of mutant gene. Names of persons who inherited hemophilia are underscored. Lines of descent in which hemophilia is unknown are omitted. This pedigree is necessarily incomplete in that daughters who inherit hemophilia from their mothers can be distinguished from their noncarrier sisters only if they have sons with hemophilia. Many carriers are unidentified either because by chance they have only normal sons or because they have no sons at all. (Based on pedigree given by Haldane [26a].)

of reproducing as normal males, the chance of the character appearing in a female would be the product of the probabilities of the mutant gene occurring in her two X chromosomes, i. e., $\frac{1}{50,000^2}$. Thus only one female in 2,500,000,000 would be expected to be a hemophiliac. Since males with the disease do not often live to reproduce, the expected frequency in women is even less than this. It is not surprising, therefore, that no well-established case of the disease in women has ever been recorded.

Investigations made within the last few years [37] have indicated that coagulation of the blood of hemophiliacs is abnormally delayed because of a deficiency in a blood protein of the globulin type. This protein may be supplied hemophiliacs either through transfusion of normal whole blood or by the injection of a specific blood protein fraction. This may greatly reduce the blood coagulation time of the patient and arrest bleeding. Unfortunately, however, hemophiliacs may become refractory to such treatment, apparently because of the production of antibodies against the coagulation-promoting globulin. An individual who suffers the disease apparently becomes immunized against and destroys the very substance that would otherwise make him normal.

The evidence suggests that the hemophilia gene is concerned with the production of a specific blood protein, the normal form conditioning its presence, and the mutant or defective form being unable to direct its formation. Here, again, it appears that the structure of a protein responsible for its specificity is intimately related to a gene, presumably because the gene serves as a model in its synthesis.

Chemical Nature of Genes

The view that genes are the basic pattern molecules from which specific proteins and possibly other molecules of comparable size and complexity are copied implies that the genes themselves are large molecules, probably proteins, with high degrees of specificity. Direct experimental evidence as to the chemical constitution of genes is not easy to obtain. Chromosomes, which are known to be the carriers of genes, have been isolated and analyzed chemically [46], and they are found to be largely if not entirely nucleoprotein in nature. Nucleoproteins are high molecular weight substances made up of proteins and nucleic acids. The nucleic acid components of nucleoproteins are themselves of high molecular weight and of incompletely understood structure. Unfortunately, such direct study of the chemistry of chromosomes does not constitute conclusive evidence that genes themselves are nucleoproteins, for there is good evidence that chromosomes contain a high percentage of nongenic material.

A second type of evidence bearing on the nature of genes is provided by the ultraviolet action spectrum of gene mutation. As will be pointed out later, gene mutations are induced by ultraviolet radiation. When the effectiveness of ultraviolet radiation of various wave lengths in inducing gene mutations is investigated, it is found that this is highly correlated with the absorption of ultraviolet radiation of different wave lengths by nucleic acid. Since only absorbed ultraviolet radiation can be effective in producing chemical change of any kind, this close correlation constitutes evidence that nucleic acid is the effective absorbing agent. The simplest interpretation is that nucleic acid is a component part of the genes which are affected. This is of course consistent with the hypothesis that genes contain nucleic acid combined with proteins in the form of nucleoproteins.

Still a third line of evidence is based on the analogy between genes and viruses. There are good reasons for believing these two entities to be fundamentally similar. These reasons will be discussed later. It is sufficient to say here that all viruses that have so far been isolated in highly purified form have been found to be made up largely or wholly of nucleoproteins [60]. In view of similarity of genes and viruses in other essential respects, it seems probable that such similarities have a common basis in chemical structure—that is, that genes, too, are nucleoproteins.

Nucleoproteins are known to have chemical and physical properties that will account for their high degree of specificity. Until recently it has been commonly assumed that gene specificity resides in the protein moiety. With the recent demonstration of numerous variations in biological specificities of the nucleic acids of different immunological types of Pneumococcus bacteria [4], it now seems likely that the specific properties of genes may reside in either the protein or the nucleic acid components, perhaps in both.

Gene Duplication

Genes are transmitted from one cell generation to the next and, in higher forms, from one whole organism to its descendants. They are obviously able to duplicate themselves. If, as many of us believe, they are the irreducible molecular patterns of the organisms of which they are a part, this process of self-duplication is clearly one of the most significant of all biological problems. It is also one toward the solution of which little real progress has been made. If genes are indeed composed of nucleoproteins, then it is evident that it is impossible to understand in any very complete way how one of them directs the synthesis of a copy of itself, until it is first known how simple proteins and nucleic acids are synthesized in living cells. There is a long way to go before achieving these goals.

It is true that we are a discouragingly long way from an understanding of how proteins and nucleic acids are synthesized in terms of the specific chemical reactions and energy relations involved, but we have, nevertheless, learned some things about gene duplication. Genes are integral parts of all living systems. They direct and take part in the many chemical reactions the pattern of which determines, first, that the system will be alive, and, secondly, what manner of being it will be. Genes exist and multiply in the presence of large numbers of chemical reactions and reaction products. They are constructed of parts synthesized by reactions which they themselves direct. The entire complex of genes of an organism must therefore function as a unit if the system is to be maintained. In multiplying itself, a given gene requires many building blocks—amino acids, with which proteins are built, as well as purines, pyrimidines, and phosphates used in the construction of nucleic acids. The fabrication of these units must involve hundreds of reactions, each catalyzed by a specific enzyme, the specificity of which is in turn referable to a gene. Thus before even one gene can multiply, many others must have done their work. Also, since genes are made of relatively few building blocks that are common to all, it is evident that a gene concerned in a reaction on which a given building block depends will be essential for the duplication of all those genes of which this unit is a part. But, as Sewall Wright [68] points out, the synthesis of a gene cannot depend on the prior synthesis of *specific* components common to many genes, for then a mutational change in one gene would be expected to result in secondary mutations in other genes. This is not observed. The specificity of a gene seems to be conferred either by the last step in its synthesis or a step unique to it. This specificity-conferring step may well be a complex one by which many component parts are held in position against the parent model gene while their chemical union takes place [16].

Mutability of Genes

The fact that complex living systems have originated is in itself sufficient evidence that the self-duplicating units out of which they are built are mutable, for without such mutability organic evolution could not have occurred. Mendel's discovery of genes as hereditary units likewise could not have been made if genes were immutable. By the conventional methods of classical genetics a gene can only be discovered and worked with if it exists in at least two forms. Granting the principle of common descent, one form of a given gene must ultimately have been ancestral to the others. We know that the reaction by which normal persons metabolize alcapton is gene directed, only because alcaptonurics carry a defective form of this gene.

While all genes are probably capable of undergoing mutational changes that modify their action without destroying their capacities for self-synthesis, the frequency with which such changes occur spontaneously may be exceedingly low. For example, the normal allele of the gene for hemophilia in man is calculated to mutate to a recessive allele, which is ineffective in directing the synthesis of a globulin protein necessary for normal blood clotting, once in about 50,000 generations. Stated differently, this means that a single line of descent of this gene changes in the manner indicated only about once in a million years. Many genes are known to be even more stable than this, at least on a "per generation" basis. On the other hand, some so-called mutable genes are known in which mutation occurs hundreds of times in a single generation. All intermediate conditions seem to occur.

In 1926 H. J. Muller made the important discovery that mutation frequencies could be greatly increased by X radiation.

With the maximum dose tolerated by a male vinegar fly this increase may be as much as 100-fold per generation. Since this amount of radiation may be administered in a very few minutes, the increase during the time of the treatment may be by a factor of a million or more.

It has since been found that other forms of high energy radiation have a similar effect on genes. Thus ultraviolet radiation, high-energy electrons, and neutrons are known to be mutagenic. In an age when large amounts of high-energy radiation are likely to be produced during both peace and war, it is important for man to calculate the risk of destroying himself genetically as well as in less subtle ways.

It has long seemed reasonable to suppose that gene mutations might be produced by chemical means, and many investigations have been turned in this direction since the beginning of the century. It was not until a few years ago that this long search for chemical mutagens was successful. During the war Auerbach and her co-workers [3] found that mustard gas and related compounds are capable of inducing gene mutations in *Drosophila*. This finding has since been confirmed and extended to other organisms.

Unfortunately, it has not yet become clear just what is the nature of gene mutation in terms of the chemical structure of genes. In the case of viruses, mutant types have been distinguished chemically from their parent types and it seems likely that this key biological problem will find its solution from this angle [60].

Directed Gene Mutation

Despite the attempts of geneticists to direct it, gene mutation in higher plants and animals has remained essentially unpredictable. No means has been discovered by which a given gene can be caused to mutate at will in a predetermined manner. The closest approach to this goal has been made in bacteria, where the classical genetic criteria of gene mutation cannot be applied. In the pneumococcal bacterium that causes lobar pneumonia there exist 30 or more distinct immunological types. It has been found possible to bring about permanent transformations of some of these types into others. As an example, type II, which owes its immunological characteristics to its polysaccharide capsule, may mutate spontaneously from a virulent encapsulated strain to an avirulent noncapsulated form which lacks type specificity. These so-called "rough" (R) mutants may then occasionally revert to the virulent encapsulated "smooth" (S) form. When this occurs spontaneously, the S reverted form is invariably of type II. But if the reversion occurs in the presence of a nucleic acid derived from a type III S strain and certain serum components, the reversion, if it occurs, is to type III [4, 44a]. Avery and his co-workers [4, 44a] have presented evidence that the specific transforming principle is a highly polymerized desoxyribonucleic acid. Similar directed transformations have been reported by Boivin and his collaborators [9a] in the common colon bacterium *Escherichia coli.*

In these instances of controlled type transformations it seems likely that the basic phenomenon concerned is gene mutation, though this has not yet been directly demonstrated. They are of particular interest to geneticists, not only because they may well represent artificially directed gene mutation, but also because they appear to indicate a junction of nucleic acids not previously suspected. If it is true that the transforming principle is nucleic acid and not a nucleoprotein impurity, as has been claimed to be at least conceivable [9a], the specificity of at least some genes must reside in their nucleic acid parts. This raises the question of whether all gene specificity might not be attributable to nucleic acids. Until additional evidence is at hand, this most significant question cannot be finally answered.

In the transformation of types in pneumococci and *Escherichia coli,* one wonders whether, instead of directed-gene mutation, actual replacement of missing gene material might not be involved. This possibility, discussed by Wright [68], Muller [52], and others, seems more plausible than it otherwise might in view of the evidence for sex-like phenomena in bacteria and bacterial viruses. According to this hypothesis the transformation of R pneumococcus strains derived from type II S to type III S would involve the actual entrance into the bacterial cell of type III nucleic acid and its direct incorporation in the gene system.

The Linear Order of Genes

In higher plants and in all animals genes are incorporated in chromosomes. These threadlike bodies make possible the orderly and equal distribution of genes from one cell generation to another and from parent organism to offspring. The number of chromosomes per cell is usually constant for a given species but may vary widely from one organism to another. In man there are 24 pairs of these bodies in the nucleus of the fertilized egg, one set of 24 contributed by the mother and one set by the father. At every cell division each chromosome divides longitudinally. The descendent chromosomes are distributed to the daughter cells by the mitotic mechanism in such a way that all cells of the body carry one descendent chromosome for each one present in the fertilized egg. In the vinegar fly *Drosophila melanogaster* there are only four pairs of chromosomes. The mechanisms by which they are multiplied and transmitted are, however, exactly the same in principle as those that operate in man. The bread mold *Neurospora crassa* is characterized by seven pairs of chromosomes in the stage of development just after the fertilization process. In this form, the meiotic divisions, by which the double number of chromosomes is reduced to the single number per nucleus, occur immediately after fertilization, while in man they are delayed until the organism has become multicellular and mature. In addition, in man they are confined to those cells in the germ line which are the progenitors of the gametes.

Barring occasional gene mutation, or slips in the chromosome mechanism, all the cells of a multicellular organism are alike genetically. This is not true for the gametes produced following meiosis. Thus a woman who is a carrier of albinism carries one normal and one defective form of the albino gene in each of her body cells. But the eggs she produces carry only one representative of this gene; on the average, half carry the normal form and half the defective form.

An organism hybrid for two genes produces gametes carrying the four possible combinations of gene forms. If the two genes were located in different chromosome pairs, the four recombinations would be equal in frequency. Thus a woman hybrid for both alcaptonuria and albinism would produce the following four types of eggs:

Alc Alb—Normal forms of both genes
Alc alb—Normal form of *alc* gene, defective form of *alb* gene
alc Alb—Defective form of *alc* gene, normal form of *Alb* gene
alc alb—Defective forms of both genes

in the ratio 1 : 1 : 1 : 1.

If the two genes were carried in one chromosome pair rather than two, the same four types of eggs would be produced, but not in equal numbers. If both defective genes were contributed by one of the parents of the woman concerned, her genetic constitution would be indicated by the formula

$$\frac{Alc \qquad Alb}{alc \qquad alb}$$

where lines symbolize chromosomes. If this were the situation, the four types of eggs would not be equal. Instead those carrying the combinations *Alc Alb* and *alc alb* would be more frequent than those of the combinations *Alc alb* and *alc Alb*. The latter combinations are produced by crossing over, that is, exchange of corresponding segments of the two chromosomes of the pair with the breaks falling between the two genes.

The frequency of such crossing over between two genes in the same chromosome pair is dependent on the distance apart of the genes concerned. Hence, if the frequency of the recombination classes is known from experimental data, the distance apart of the genes can be inferred.

If the woman concerned had received one defective gene from her mother and the other from her father instead of both from one parent, her constitution would be indicated by the formula

$$\frac{Alc \qquad alb}{alc \qquad Alb}$$

In this case the frequent types of gametes would be *Alc alb* and *alc Alb*, but the ratio of new combinations to old would be the same as that for the first possibility considered.

In the case of the genes for albinism and alcaptonuria it is not known whether they are carried in the one chromosome pair or in two. The abnormal forms of both these genes are so infrequent in the population that the chance of an individual being hybrid for both of them is exceedingly small, and obviously such individuals are necessary if one is to determine the relative frequencies of parental and recombination type gametes. In an experimental animal such double hybrids could of course be produced at will by making controlled matings.

The crossover value for any two genes in a chromosome pair tends to be constant: if they are close together, it is low; if far apart, it is high. By experimentally measuring distances between genes in organisms like *Drosophila* that are favorable for genetic study, it is found that genes are arranged in a linear order and at distances apart that tend strongly to remain fixed. In the vinegar fly, in Indian corn, and in a number of other organisms, many genes have been located by such purely genetic methods.

Various kinds of chromosome rearrangements occur spontaneously with a low frequency. Pieces of nonhomologous chromosomes may be exchanged, a segment of one chromosome may become inverted, or pieces may be lost entirely. The frequency with which these aberrations occur is greatly increased by treatment with high-energy radiation or with certain chemicals, notably mustard gas and related compounds. In favorable material such as the giant salivary chromosomes of *Drosophila* or the meiotic prophase chromosomes of Indian corn, such changes in chromosomes can be observed directly by the cytologist. They are accompanied by the genetic changes that would be expected. If a segment of a chromosome is found by cytological examination to be inverted, a corresponding segment of the genetic chromosome map is found by genetic methods to be inverted. Losses of visible segments can often be correlated with genetically detected losses of specific genes. The detailed correspondence between cytologically observed changes and those inferred from genetic data provides complete proof that genes are carried by chromosomes in a fixed and relatively permanent linear order.

Gene Number and Size

In the present state of our knowledge, the existence of a given gene is known only if it exists in two forms and if the difference in the organism resulting from the substitution of one form for the other produces a change that is detected. As an example, there is in man a gene that controls ability to taste the bitter chemical phenylthiourea. This gene exists in two forms in about equal numbers in the population, so that on the average approximately 25 persons out of every 100 carry only the recessive form and do not taste the compound. Until 1931 it was not suspected that such a gene exists, merely because no one had made systematic tests for ability to taste phenylthiourea. It is evident that in any given species many genes will remain unknown to geneticists, either because only one form of them is frequent enough to be known or because the difference between individuals carrying the two forms has not yet been recognized. Because there is no simple way of determining what proportion of the total number of genes remains to be discovered, it is obvious that no simple answer can be given to the question, "How many kinds of genes are there in man or in a vinegar fly?"

Drosophila melanogaster has been studied more carefully by geneticists than any other organism. Over a period of about 40 years, approximately 500 genes have been studied and located in its four chromosomes. During this time at least a thousand man-years have been spent finding, locating, and otherwise investigating genes of this small fly.

If all genes were equally mutable, if the effects of their mutation were equally likely to be detected, and if complete and objective records were kept of mutation frequencies, it would be relatively simple to calculate the total number of genes from recurrence frequencies. Unfortunately, it is known that none of these three conditions is fulfilled. Nevertheless, Muller [51], Gowen and Gay [24], and others have attempted such calculations.

Depending on the assumptions and the data used, these give values of the order of 1,000 to 10,000.

Another estimate can be made on the assumption that the dark bands of the salivary gland chromosomes of *Drosophila* carry one gene each. The number of bands is about 5,000. This is probably a minimum figure for gene number because of the possibility that more than one gene may reside in a single band. It does not seem likely that there would exist an error in the other direction, because natural selection would tend to result in the loss of geneless bands.

These estimates suggest that from one tenth to one twentieth of all the genes in *Drosophila* have been discovered.

The problem of the estimation of gene number is not unrelated to that of determining gene size. If the number were known, the maximum average volume could be found by dividing the total volume of the chromosomes at the time of greatest condensation by the number. Such attempts as have been made to do this suggest that genes may be of the same order of size as medium large viruses—about 50 millimicrons in diameter. Particles of this size are well below the limits of resolving power of the light microscope.

If certain assumptions are made, it is relatively simple to measure gene size experimentally by determining the amount of ionizing radiation necessary to produce mutations in them. The following simplified summary of how this is done is based on D. E. Lea's recent book on the effects of radiations on living cells [39]. When the effects of such radiation on mutation are studied quantitatively, it is found that within the usual range of wave length of X rays, mutation frequency shows a linear relation to dosage, where dosage is measured in terms of the ionization of air under defined conditions. Mutation production is independent of intensity or manner of fractionation. Thus radiation delivered at the rate of 100 r units per hour, one hour per day, for ten days gives the same number of mutations as does 1,000 r units delivered in a single treatment of one minute duration. Since, with short X rays passing through tissues, primary ionizations are spaced at intervals of about one micron, a single gene, which is certainly much smaller in diameter than this, is not likely to have more than one primary ionization produced in it. This consideration plus the observation that effects of X rays are directly proportional to ionizations, regardless of their distribution in time, leads to the conclusion that mutations result from single ionizations or at least small groups of ionizations, each produced by a single primary ionization.

It is possible to determine experimentally the amount of ionizing radiation necessary to produce an average of one mutation per gene. For several genes in *Drosophila* this value turns out to be 10^{-7} or 10^{-8} r units of X radiation. On the single hit hypothesis this means that these dosages produce one ion per gene on the average. Since the concentration of ions per unit volume of tissue can be estimated, it is a simple matter in principle (but not in practice when all complicating factors, such as nonrandom distribution of ionizations, are taken into account) to determine the volume that will on the average contain a single ion pair. If an ion pair inside a gene has a high probability of producing a detectable mutation, while one outside it is unlikely to do so, this volume—the so-called "sensitive volume" or "target size" —will be a reasonable approximation to the true size of the gene. The method can be independently checked by determining if it gives target sizes for enzymes and viruses which agree with their sizes as determined by electron microscopy and by other methods. Lea and his collaborators have in fact found that target sizes calculated from X-ray inactivation data for a number of viruses and the enzyme ribonuclease do agree within a factor of five or less with those based on independent methods. Applied to specific genes, Lea's target-size method gives diameter values of 2 to 6 millimicrons. These correspond to molecular weights of 10^4 to 10^5, values of the same orders of magnitude as those for a number of enzymes.

A different method, which makes use of the amounts of various types of radiation required to produce a given frequency of lethal mutations in the X chromosome of *Drosophila*, gave Lea values of 4 to 9 millimicrons for gene diameter.

Lea has calculated the total number of genes in the X chromosome, using the experimentally measured X-ray dose required to give one lethal mutation per X chromosome and that required to give one mutation per single gene. The ratio of the two dosages, 840, is the answer obtained. This is in good agreement with the number of salivary chromosome bands in this chromosome. Multiplying 840 by 4.2, the ratio of the map length of all chromosomes of *Drosophila* to that of the X chromosome, we obtain 3,500 as the total number of genes in the fly.

While these various estimates of gene size leave a great deal to be desired, it is interesting that they indicate a lower limit about equal to small enzymes and an upper limit of the same order of magnitude as large viruses. It seems probable from target-size measurements that they fall within the range of enzymes, that is, in the molecular weight range 10,000 to 500,000.

A question that often arises, especially in connection with the gene-enzyme hypothesis, is, "Are there enough genes to direct all the enzymatically catalyzed reactions that make up an organism?" Since both the number of enzymes and the number of reactions are unknown, there is not much that can be done at present toward answering this question. There appears to be no simple way to determine whether 4,000 or 5,000 enzymes and a similar number of gene-directed reactions are sufficient to account for the development and functioning of a vinegar fly or a man. It is interesting to note that the number of different kinds of genes known to geneticists is of the same order of magnitude as the number of enzymes known to biochemists. It apparently does not often occur to biochemists to doubt that there are a sufficient number of kinds of enzymes to enable living systems to develop and operate. There is no better reason for doubting that the genes an organism inherits are correspondingly numerous in kind.

Universality of Genes

In the half century which has elapsed since Mendel's findings were first appreciated, it has become generally accepted that gene inheritance is the rule in higher plants and in all animals.

In lower plants, particularly blue-green algae and bacteria, in which organized nuclei and sexual reproduction are not evident, there has been room for reasonable doubt. Classical genetics defines the gene as a unit of inheritance and provides no means of detecting and studying it in the absence of sexual reproduction. But with increases in our knowledge of the nature and function of these units of inheritance, their occurrence in all living systems, cellular and subcellular, has become an inescapable inference.

Bacterial genes. Bacterial protoplasms are chemically remarkably like those of multicellular plants and animals. Their proteins are built up of the same 20 amino acids as are ours. They possess many enzymes in which the same vitamins occur, as prosthetic groups, as those found in higher forms. The mechanisms by which they synthesize vitamins, amino acids, and other essential components of protoplasm are often the same as those employed in other organisms. Many of the metabolic reactions of bacteria are known to be gene-controlled in *Neurospora.* Furthermore, it has recently been shown by Tatum and others [61] that high-energy radiations and mustard gas produce changes in bacteria analogous to those produced in *Neurospora* by these same agents. In *Neurospora* these changes in many instances have been referred to changes in specific genes.

In addition to the evidence from chemical genetics pointing to the occurrence of genes in bacteria, refinements in the cytological methods used in bacteriology have shown that at least many bacteria possess chromosome-like structures that are capable of providing a mechanism by which genes are transmitted from generation to generation in a manner fully as precise as that available to organisms higher in the scale of evolution [57]. If the recent remarkable finding of Lederberg and Tatum [40], that sexual reproduction occasionally occurs in a certain strain of *Escherichia coli,* applies to other groups of bacteria as well, it is evident that our entire concept of genetic mechanisms in these simple organisms will have to be revised [42].

Genes of bacterial viruses. Moving down the evolutionary scale a step below bacteria to bacterial viruses, we find that they, too, contain gene-like units capable of multiplication, mutation, and recombination. Of the viruses that infect bacteria (bacteriophages), those that attack *Escherichia coli*, strain B, are in many respects best known [17]. The several strains of these that have been worked with most extensively vary in body diameter from 45 to 100 millimicrons. Some strains possess tails two to three times the length of the body. Others appear under the electron microscope to be tailless.

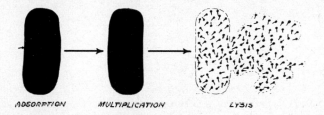

ADSORPTION   MULTIPLICATION   LYSIS

FIG. 47. Diagram of the life cycle of a bacteriophage. The time between adsorption and lysis may vary from 15 to 30 minutes. The number of daughter phages released from a single bacterium is approximately 100 to 300.

The life cycle of an *Escherichia coli* phage may be briefly summarized as follows [17]: In a suitable medium in which both phage and susceptible bacteria are present, phage particles are adsorbed by the bacteria. A given bacterial cell may adsorb one or a large number of phages, but for simplicity in this account, one phage per cell will be assumed unless otherwise stated. After entrance of the phage into the bacterium by an incompletely understood process, there follows a period of multiplication during which from 100 to 300 replicates of the original infecting phage are produced. This occurs in a period of 15 minutes to half an hour. Immediately following this latent period the bacterial cell is lysed, and the phage brood liberated (Fig. 47). Daughter phages are immediately ready to infect additional bacteria.

Like the hosts in which they multiply, bacteriophages are mutable. From a phage strain capable of infecting specific bacterial strains, mutant forms with an altered host range may arise. Mutant types of phage also occur in which the plaques or clear areas produced in a layer of bacterial cells growing on a solid medium are modified in appearance. The frequencies with which such mutations occur spontaneously vary in much the same way as do those of mutation frequencies for the genes of higher organisms. A given mutation may occur once per thousand phage multiplications, another may appear with a frequency of only one per hundred million multiplications.

If two phage particles are of the same or closely related strains, they may simultaneously multiply within a single bacterial cell;

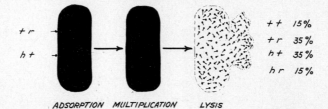

ADSORPTION   MULTIPLICATION   LYSIS

FIG. 48. Diagram of recombination in bacteriophages. The parent phages are + r ("rapid lysis" mutant which produces a characteristic plaque type on a Petri plate culture) and h + (host range mutant which differs from normal in its host strain specificity). In addition to these parental types the two recombination types, + + and h r, are produced in the indicated frequencies. (Based on work of Hershey and Rotman [30].)

otherwise, one gains the upper hand and excludes its competitor. Recently Delbrück and Bailey [18] made the remarkable discovery that recombination of characters occurs if related phages multiply within a single bacterium. Hershey [29] has corroborated and extended this finding. If, for example, two mutant types of a single phage strain, say mutant *a* and mutant *b*, multiply simultaneously in a single bacterial cell, there appear not only offspring like the parent infecting phages but two new types, one showing the characteristics of both mutant strains, the other like the normal strain from which mutants *a* and *b* were originally derived (Fig. 48). It appears that bacterial viruses are multigenic systems that lead some type of sex life, recombining their component hereditary units in a manner not unlike that of higher cellular forms. There is even evidence that phage genes are organized in linkage groups of some kind [30].

Essentially similar conclusions are arrived at by Luria from phage experiments of a different and even more spectacular nature [43]. If a suspension of phage particles is treated with ultra-violet radiation of wave length 2,537 A., which is strongly absorbed by nucleic acid, a certain proportion of the individual phages are inactivated. The quantitative relations are such as to suggest that a single quantum is sufficient to incapacitate one phage particle. If the treatment is arranged so that most phage particles absorb relatively few quanta each, the phage suspension diluted and mixed with bacteria in a concentration that will give one phage per cell on the average, very few bacteria will be infected with phage particles capable of multiplying and destroying the cells. But if the mixture is made in such a way that for each bacterium there are two or more phages, then a high percentage of the bacteria are lysed and yield viable phages. The results can be interpreted qualitatively and quantitatively on the assumption that a phage can be inactivated in any one of 30 or 40 ways, and that if a bacterium is infected with two phage particles incapacitated in different ways, a completely viable and normal phage is reconstituted. (Fig. 49). Presumably each phage is made up of 30 or 40 self-duplicating units which are capable of being exchanged during a certain stage of phage reproduction. Whether these units are capable of reversible mutation and are identical with those studied by Delbrück and Bailey and by Hershey remains to be determined. Also, an understanding of the mechanism by which the elementary phage units are reshuffled requires further information.

Extranuclear Genes—Plasmagenes

During the half century in which our knowledge of the nature of genes and the mechanisms by which they are transmitted has gradually increased, it has become clearer and clearer that these nuclear units are the primary bearers of heredity. No convincing evidence has been brought forward that would indicate the existence of extranuclear elements having a degree of autonomy comparable to that of genes. This remains true despite systematic searches in a great variety of organisms by many competent investigators for cytoplasmic hereditary units. Indeed, unless present knowledge deceives, the existence of such units would not be expected on theoretical grounds. In those forms of life with organized nuclei there exists a beautifully precise mechanism for distributing genes equally to daughter cells. No cellular machinery capable of anything like this degree of precision is known for the cytoplasm. The centrosome is a possible exception to this statement, but it is absent in higher plants and, in those animals in which it is regularly found, its function seems to be a mechanical one in assisting nuclear division rather than one of directing heredity in any gene-like manner.

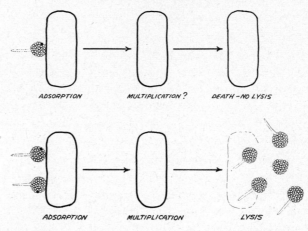

FIG. 49. Production of viable bacteriophages by recombination of parts of inviable phages. *Above.* Fate of phage inactivated by mild treatment ultraviolet radiation. Presumably because of a "single hit," phage has been mutated so that it is unable to reproduce lysis-producing offspring. *Below.* Two phages, each inactivated by ultraviolet single hits, infect a single bacterial cell and during the multiplication phase recombine to produce normal viable offspring. Presumably they have been hit in different vital subunits. To indicate postulated gene-like subunits, phages are shown much enlarged relative to bacterial cells. Burst size here, as in Figures 47 and 48, is 100 to 300. (Based on work of Luria [43].)

Enucleated egg cells of the sea urchin are capable of undergoing division and of carrying on certain metabolic activities for a limited period of time [27]. So far as I know, however, there is no evidence that in the absence of a nucleus such a cell can carry on any significant amount of synthesis of new protoplasm. Apparently in the absence of nuclear genes the cytoplasmic chemical machinery runs down after at most a few cell divisions, presumably because there is no further synthesis of the specific proteins necessary for renewal of enzymes and other protein-containing structures.

It is important to emphasize that what has just been said in no way denies the importance of the cytoplasm and the organized structures within it. Every living thing that has evolved to the cellular level of organization includes cytoplasm as an indispensable component. It is without question the site of many of the vital metabolic processes that go on in cells. It is almost certainly systematic cytoplasmic modifications that make possible the process of differentiation which is so important in the development of complex multicellular systems like ourselves. The nuclear gene system and the cytoplasm are complementary parts of a living cell. Each has its specific duties in the over-all economy of the organism, and both are indispensable.

Plastid inheritance. In the study of the mechanism of inheritance of the many thousands of traits that have been investigated by geneticists, there have been found a few which are dependent on cytoplasmic units capable of at least a limited degree of autonomy. A number of these known in plants belong in a single category characterized by the involvement of chloroplasts.

Chloroplasts are discrete chlorophyll-bearing cytoplasmic bodies found in certain cells of green plants. They vary greatly in size and in shape, but in common flowering plants they are often biscuit-shaped and of the order of 10 microns in diameter. It should be noted that this is an entirely different order of size from that of genes—1,000 times as great in diameter or roughly a billion times as large in volume and easily within range of an ordinary light microscope. Plastids clearly arise from plastid primordia which in size at least are like mitochondria.

The chlorophyll content of chloroplasts may vary for a number of reasons. In the absence of light, none is formed; and if a plant is deprived of iron, it becomes chlorotic because iron is an essential part of the chlorophyll molecule. These deficiencies are readily reversible by supplying light or iron. There are other analogous situations in which plastids are reversibly defective. On the other hand, there are instances known in which plastids become defective because of some factor inherent in themselves or in the cytoplasm of the cells in which they occur, and these defects are virtually irreversible. A classical case of this latter type occurs in the four-o'clock, *Mirabilis jalapa,* and was first studied by the German geneticist Correns. There are strains of *Mirabilis* which are variegated in color; some leaves are green, some are white, while others are variegated with green and white areas. Leaf tissue derived from pure white cells is always white, but that from green cells may be either green or variegated. When flowers from an all-white branch are fertilized with pollen from an all-green normal plant, all the progeny are albinos and die because they cannot carry on photosynthesis. If the reciprocal cross is made, female flower from a normal green plant fertilized with pollen from a flower borne on an all-white branch of a variegated plant, all progeny are normal green plants which thereafter give only normal green offspring. Progeny from the flowers of variegated branches fertilized with flowers from any type of plant give all-green, variegated, or all-white progeny. In summary, the defective plastid type in this instance is inherited through the egg only. Defective plastids are transmitted only in those cases in which the egg came from cells in which defective plastid primordia could have been and presumably were present.

Two explanations have been offered for this situation. The first says that in this type of variegation certain plastid primordia are irreversibly defective, and that if both types of primordia occur together in a cell, the descendants of that cell may by chance inherit all normal, all defective, or a mixture of the two types of plastids. Variegated plants arise from eggs carrying plastid primordia of both kinds, white plants come from eggs with only defective primordia, while normal plants arise if the egg cell carries no defective plastid progenitors. It is supposed that the sperm nucleus does not carry along young plastids. The second explanation proposed differs from that just given in assuming that whether plastids are defective or not is determined by cytoplasmic units other than plastids. The two possibilities could be distinguished if it could be determined through cytological observation whether or not cells occur in which there are two types of plastids.

For the purposes of the present discussion these two interpretations do not differ fundamentally. Both assume the existence of units transmitted through the cytoplasm which are entirely independent in transmission from nuclear units. Similar situations have been found in other plants, for example, in Indian corn, and there is no good reason to question the inference drawn from them that cytoplasmic units with a limited degree of autonomy do exist.

While it seems quite clear that plastids, or other cytoplasmic units which control them, are capable of mutational changes analogous to those which occur in genes, it by no means follows that plastids have the same degree of autonomy as do genes. For one thing dozens of different genes are known, in maize and in other plants, which control plastid development or chlorophyll synthesis. If the normal allele of any one of these is replaced by a mutant allele, all plastids of the cells or plants in which such replacement occurs become defective.

The genetic stability of plastids is likewise known to be genetically controlled. Rhoades [56] has investigated the so-called iojap character in maize which is characterized by chlorophyll variegation. It appears that in plants homozygous for the mutant form of a specific gene, plastids or their primordia become highly mutable. Such plants have many white sectors derived from cells in which all plastids were of the defective mutant type. The mutant plastids seldom if ever revert to normal. Defective plastids are transmitted through the egg in essentially the same way as in the *Mirabilis* case previously discussed. Even though the defective nuclear gene originally responsible for the plastid mutation is replaced by its normal allele, by twice outcrossing variegated plants to normal green male plants, the mutant plastids remain defective.

From the point of view of a geneticist, the situation with regard to plant chloroplasts may be summarized as follows: (1) Chloroplasts are relatively large organized cytoplasmic structures normally containing chlorophyll. (2) They appear to enjoy continuity from one cell generation to another and from one plant generation to the next. They arise from preëxisting primordia; there is no evidence that they or their primordia ever arise *de novo*. (3) They are transmitted readily through the egg cell but, with occasional exceptions, not through the pollen. (4) Their growth from primordia is gene directed, as is the synthesis of the chlorophyll they contain. (5) As compared with nuclear genes, they are larger and probably much more complex units. Like genes they possess the property of self-duplication and are mutable. They possess a limited degree of autonomy but cannot be said to be primary units of heredity.

Cytoplasmic inheritance in Paramecium. In the ciliate protozoan, *Paramecium aurelia*, there are strains capable of producing an extracellular substance, known as *paramecin*, which will kill other strains. The strains that produce paramecin are known as killers; those that are killed are called sensitives. These strains have been studied in great detail by Sonneborn and his associates [59], and it has been found that the production of paramecin is under the dual control of nuclear and cytoplasmic units.

In order to understand the details of the experiments by which this has been shown, it is necessary to know that this protozoan species consists of single-celled individuals which are capable of asexual reproduction by simple fission. Under these conditions all individuals of a single line of descent remain genetically identical except for mutations that occur occasionally. Each individual possesses one macronucleus, probably derived by compounding of the material in the micronucleus from which it is originally derived, and two micronuclei, each diploid. Two types of sexual reproduction occur, one uniparental, the other biparental. In the first type, known as autogamy, the micronuclei undergo meiosis, seven of the eight resulting haploid nuclei degenerate, and the remaining one divides mitotically. These sister nuclei, necessarily of identical genetic constitutions, then fuse to restore the original diploid chromosome number. The diploid nucleus then undergoes two successive mitotic divisions. Of the resulting four nuclei, two become micronuclei. At the next fission the two macronuclei are distributed one to each daughter. During this same fission the two micronuclei divide mitotically, and each daughter cell receives two daughter micronuclei. During the process the old macronucleus degenerates. The essential features of autogamy from a genetic point of view are that all nuclear genes become homozygous during the process and the macronucleus is replaced. Autogamy is illustrated in Figure 50.

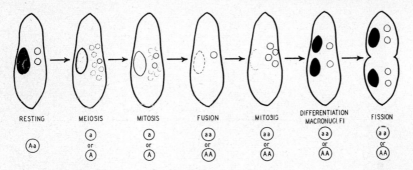

RESTING   MEIOSIS   MITOSIS   FUSION   MITOSIS   DIFFERENTIATION MACRONUCLEI   FISSION

FIG. 50. Diagram of life cycle of *Paramecium aurelia*—autogamy in an individual heterozygous for one gene pair. Large ellipsoid bodies are macronuclei. Micronuclei indicated by open circles. During the process of autogamy the macronucleus degenerates, while micronuclei undergo reduction, division, fusion, division, and differentiation of macronuclei. Following reduction division seven of the eight meiotic products undergo degeneration. Genetic constitutions of micronuclei shown in circles below. Where there is more than one functional micronucleus, all of them are genetically identical. (Based on information given by Sonneborn [59].)

In biparental sexual reproduction, meiotic divisions and degeneration of macronuclei occur as in autogamy. But instead of self-fertilization occurring, two individuals of opposite mating type conjugate and exchange gametic nuclei. The gamete nuclei then fuse to restore the diploid state. Recovery of the normal vegetative state with one macronucleus and two micronuclei follows the same course as in autogamy. It is to be noted that in biparental sexual reproduction, the two exconjugants must be identical with respect to their nuclear genes (Fig. 51).

In the case of the killer character every individual that is to give all killer progeny by asexual reproduction must carry the dominant allele of the gene *K* plus cytoplasmic self-duplicating units known as kappa. The gene *K* is studied by conventional genetic methods. Kappa is shown, by a series of experiments to be described below, to be inherited only through the cytoplasm. Several of these experiments depend on the fact that killer and sensitive strains may be mated without the sensitives being killed. The studies themselves show that ordinarily there is little or no exchange of cytoplasm during conjugation.

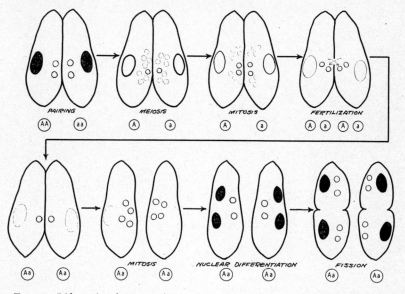

Fig. 51. Life cycle of *Paramecium aurelia*—conjugation of individuals differing by one gene. Individuals of appropriate mating types pair. They then undergo macronuclear degeneration and micronuclear reduction divisions as in autogamy. Reciprocal fertilization occurs, followed by division of micronuclei and formation of new macronuclei from micronuclei. Genetic constitutions of micronuclei indicated in circles below. Unless two genetic types of micronuclei are indicated in a single individual, the two or more functional micronuclei of a single individual are identical. (Based on information given by Sonneborn [59].)

Gene *K* and its allele *k* are transmitted in a straightforward fashion. For example, if a killer line heterozygous for this gene —*Kk*—and carrying kappa in the cytoplasm gives rise to *kk* animals by autogamy (Fig. 52), all descendants of these are sensitives. They cannot be made into killers even though the dominant allele *K* is reintroduced through mating with a killer

(Fig. 53). It is therefore evident that three genetic types of sensitive strains are possible, viz., *KK, Kk,* and *kk.*

A sensitive animal carrying the *K* allele can become a killer by having kappa introduced into its cytoplasm by an aberrant type of conjugation, during which a cytoplasmic bridge is formed between the conjugating animals and persists for a half hour or

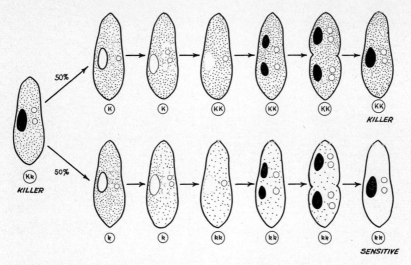

FIG. 52. Production of sensitive strain of *Paramecium aurelia* from a killer strain following autogamy. Kappa elements in cytoplasm indicated by stippling. Micronuclear genetic constitution indicated in circles below. Loss of *K* allele is followed by loss of kappa. Rate of loss of kappa is exaggerated for purposes of diagram. (Based on work of Sonneborn and collaborators [58, 59].)

more (Fig. 54). Except for this abnormal cytoplasmic transfer accompanying bridge formation, kappa is not transferred from one animal to another. Its typical cytoplasmic inheritance is illustrated in Figure 53.

It has been shown both by Preer [55] and by Sonneborn [59] that kappa does not necessarily multiply at the same rate at which a Paramecium line undergoes fission. Kappa multiplication may be differentially affected by both temperature and the food level of the animals carrying it. By controlling the environment in such a way that kappa is slowed down in multiplication, relative to the organism as a whole, killers can be made to run out of kappa and become permanent sensitives. Or they can become sensitives capable of reverting to killers if kappa is reduced in amount but not entirely exhausted. Through the use of ingenious methods which for lack of space cannot be described here, Preer and Sonneborn have shown that killers grown under normal conditions contain about 250 kappa units per animal. Preer has shown that an animal carrying only a single kappa particle is capable of reverting to a killer if conditions are made more favorable for kappa reproduction than for cell division.

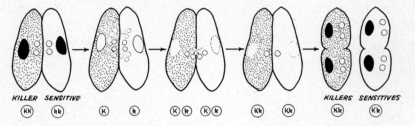

FIG. 53. Cytoplasmic inheritance of kappa. If cytoplasmic connection between exconjugants persists for less than three minutes, kappa is confined to animal that was originally a killer. Exconjugant that was originally sensitive, remains sensitive even though it acquires the K allele during the process of conjugation. (Based on work of Sonneborn and collaborators [58, 59].)

In kappa we have a clear case of a self-duplicating cytoplasmic unit that is regularly transmitted only through the cytoplasm. Like plastids its autonomy is limited, for it cannot go on duplicating itself in the absence of the dominant allele of gene K, the only function of which appears to be in the supervision of kappa multiplication. One of the questions that naturally occurs in considering kappa is, "How general are cytoplasmic elements like it, and how important are they in the hereditary machinery of the organism?" It appears from Sonneborn's studies that in certain strains of Paramecium several heritable traits involve kappa-like cytoplasmic factors. In other strains of the same species they appear not to be present. It may well be, as Sonneborn has pointed out, that kappa-like cytoplasmic units, or plasmagenes as they have been called, are a part of a specialized type of inheritance that has evolved in organisms like Paramecium in which there is a peculiar division of labor between the macro-nucleus, which appears to control immediate phenotype, and the micronuclei, which seem to specialize in the transmission of nuclear genes. The results of detailed investigations of the cytoplasmic factors in Paramecium having to do with mating types, presence of specific antigens, and other traits, may well provide clear answers to many of the questions about plasmagenes that now stand unanswered.

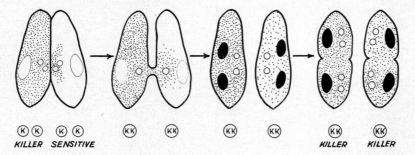

FIG. 54. Transfers of kappa particles during conjugation in which cytoplasmic bridge persists for 30 minutes or more. Rate of multiplication of kappa particles in exconjugant originally lacking these elements is exaggerated. All animals involved are homozygous for K allele. (Based on work of Sonneborn and collaborators [58, 59].)

Carbon-dioxide-sensitivity in Drosophila. Several years ago L'Heretier [28] observed that an ebony stock of *Drosophila melanogaster* he had was abnormally sensitive to carbon dioxide. Normal stocks are anesthetized by short exposure to CO_2 gas, but flies of the ebony stock were killed by similar treatment. This peculiarity of the ebony stock persisted for many generations. Investigation of the inheritance of this CO_2-sensitivity soon showed it to be entirely nonchromosomal and largely maternal. A series of experiments carried on by L'Heretier and his associates have shown conclusively that CO_2-sensitivity results from a cytoplasmic factor that is readily transmitted through the cytoplasm of the egg. It also may be carried through sperm, although much less effectively, as might well be expected from the small amount of cytoplasm carried by a sperm.

If a sensitive strain of flies is grown at a temperature of 30°, it becomes spontaneously "cured" of CO_2-sensitivity, presumably because under these conditions the cytoplasmic factor cannot keep pace in its multiplication with the fly. Resistant flies do not acquire CO_2-sensitivity by intimate contact with sensitives, but it can be transferred to them through hemolymph transfusion or by transplanting tissues from sensitive lines to them. It is occasionally possible to "infect" an egg from a resistant line by a supernumerary sperm that does not function in fertilization. This is possible because, through double matings, a female may carry a mixture of sperm, and several sperms usually enter a single egg though only one regularly combines with the egg pronucleus.

The CO_2-sensitive cytoplasmic unit, while not infectious as are ordinary viruses, nevertheless appears to be able to pass freely from one cell to another, a property not possessed by kappa in Paramecium. Here again it is clear that a self-duplicating cytoplasmic factor is involved in the inheritance of a specific and well-defined trait. Whether this factor is "normal" or represents some unusual accident in the past history of the strain that carries it is not known. No specific directing gene is known in the case of the CO_2-sensitive factor; apparently it will flourish in any strain to which it is transferred, including the related species *Drosophila simulans*.

Self-duplicating enzymes. Several years ago Lindegren and Spiegelmann reported studies on yeast which they interpreted as indicating the existence of a sugar-splitting enzyme melibiase, capable, when stabilized by its substrate, of indefinite self-duplication in the cytoplasm even in the absence of the specific gene responsible for its initiation. The implications of this finding were far-reaching indeed. It now turns out, however, that certain of the basic experimental observations from which this conclusion was drawn were incorrect [41].

Conclusions about extranuclear inheritance. The examples cited above leave no doubt whatever about the existence of cytoplasmic units capable of self-duplication and having a limited degree of autonomy. In most of these cases the cytoplasmic factors concerned seem clearly to be directed in a specific way by nuclear genes. There is no convincing evidence in any single instance of the function of an essential gene being entirely taken over by a so-called plasmagene. On the contrary, the great bulk of the available evidence bearing on the question clearly indicates that the primary control of protein specificity resides in nuclear genes. In view of the elaborate mechanisms of mitosis and meiosis, which have evolved and persisted throughout almost the whole of the plant and animal kingdoms and which evidently have a great selective advantage, it would be most remarkable if the cytoplasm could compete as a carrier and transmitter of hereditary units in any except a few very special circumstances.

THE END POINT OF PARASITIC SPECIALIZATION

The process of evolution is never unidirectional. Rather it is made up of a complex series of forward thrusts and retreats, as ever-shifting gene combinations are tested in various environments. Positive evolution—the acquisition of new abilities by living systems—is probably never completely separated in time from retrogressive changes—loss of structure and loss of function. But under certain circumstances organisms find themselves under conditions where the dominant trend is toward simplification. The habit of parasitism is one that is known to favor such a trend. The end point of this process of simplification should tell us what is the irreducible minimum consistent with reproduction and adaptation; it should automatically sort out and select from more complex systems the basic units of self-duplication and mutation.

Loss of Structure and Function

Morphologists and systematists have long been aware of the strong trend toward simplification in the evolutionary specialization of parasites. The correlated tendency toward progressive loss of synthetic abilities has been clearly recognized only within recent years, largely through the work of Knight [36] and Lwoff [44].

The genetic basis of this specialization through simplification is not difficult to understand. It rests squarely on the phenomena of gene mutation and natural selection. It is implicit in the theory of organic evolution through genetic change, that all genes are mutable. In the relatively few instances in which quantitative studies have been made, the experimental evidence suggests that those mutations that change a gene in such a way that it does its work less effectively are more frequent than the reverse change. And when it is taken into account that all mutational changes leading to inability of a gene to reproduce will automatically lead to irreversible loss of the gene, it becomes evident that any gene whose activity does not give a selective advantage to the individuals that possess it will in time disappear. An alternative to complete loss of an unneeded gene is its acquirement through mutation of a new function that does confer a selective advantage. In terms of genes which control chemical reactions through directing the specificities of the catalyzing enzymes, it follows that if the product of a given reaction is no longer useful, gene mutation will tend to do away with the reaction that gives rise to it.

The time required for a gene that has become neutral to be lost, or to acquire a new function with a selective advantage, may be very long in terms of years or generations but is likely to be short on an evolutionary time scale. Thus, as has already been pointed out, single lines of descent of the normal allele of the hemophilia gene in man are expected to mutate to the recessive or inactive form of the gene on the average about once every million years. If hemophiliacs were exactly equal to normal persons in fecundity, and the mutation completely irreversible, it would take a long time for the normal form of the gene to mutate itself out of the human species. But eventually this would happen if the conditions were as stated. There is of course always a possibility that under certain conditions a gene formerly useful to an organism will become detrimental. If natural selection works positively toward its elimination, the process will be greatly accelerated.

Just as species that have permanently adopted a parasitic mode of life become simpler and simpler morphologically, they likewise undergo progressive loss of synthetic ability. The work on

Neurospora provides abundant evidence as to how this can happen genetically. To illustrate with a hypothetical example, suppose a saprophytic bacterial species like *Escherichia coli,* which is capable of growing on a simple medium containing inorganic salts and some source of energy and carbon such as sugar, were to become parasitic. At present it is capable of synthesizing all the amino acids, vitamins, purines, pyrimidines, and other essential compounds with which it constructs its protoplasm. But, as a parasite, the bacterium would have available these protoplasmic building blocks ready made, and it might therefore no longer be an advantage to be able to synthesize them. Mutations leading to the inactivation of the genes controlling the various steps in the synthesis of these compounds, now freely available from the host, would begin to accumulate. In fact, if the materials in question were always readily available, there might be an actual selective advantage in not making them. A model case of this sort has been reported by Monod in the bacterium *Aerobacter,* where a mutant strain unable to synthesize the amino acid methionine has a higher growth rate in a methionine-containing medium than the type from which it arose [48].

How far can parasitic specialization through progressive simplification go? Apparently to that stage represented by the simplest existing viruses—or, in the words of Burnet [14], until "there are neither organs nor enzymes, nothing but a shadowy, self-replicating residuum of genetic mechanism."

Is there good reason to believe that existing viruses have arisen through retrogressive evolution from more complex forms? In the nature of the case, the evidence is circumstantial. It has been ably presented by Burnet in his stimulating book, *Virus as Organism* [14]. There are three hypotheses as to the origin of viruses, viz., the one just outlined, a second which assumes that they are free genes derived originally from the host in which they reproduce, and a third that they have descended directly as parasites from primitive precellular living systems. There are, among existing organisms, forms with almost every conceivable degree of complexity, from complete autotrophs like algae, down through saprophytes, cellular parasites capable of being grown on nonliving culture media; rickettsia, which are bacterial-like but which have not yet been successfully grown outside a living cell; noncellular complex viruses, like those causing psitticosis, which have organized structure and contain enzyme systems; to the smallest viruses, which appear to do nothing but replicate themselves at the expense of the raw materials of the living host cell. On the view that viruses are nothing more than host genes out of context, it is difficult to see how the larger, more complex viruses arose. Until recently it might have been reasonable to postulate that bacterial viruses arose as free host genes made pathogenic by mutation. But in the light of our present knowledge that these viruses are complex systems, each containing perhaps 50 gene-like substructures, this hypothesis is clearly no longer tenable. Darlington [15] has argued that noninfectious virus-like units, such as that which the King Edward potato carries without harm to itself and which can be transmitted only by grafting to other varieties in which it is disease producing, must have originated by mutation from normal host cell components. This is clearly not a necessary conclusion, for an infectious parasite might well lose its infectivity just as it loses other abilities. Its continued existence is not dependent on infectivity if it can be transmitted cytoplasmically from one generation to the next. The *manner* of survival of a parasitic form—whether by being infective or by being transmitted cytoplasmically—is of little importance. It is rather the *fact* of survival that is biologically indispensable to it.

There appears to be no convincing evidence either for or against the view that present-day viruses are direct descendants of precellular primitive forms that were once free living. Evolutionary survival of such types as parasites of more highly developed creatures is logically possible but seems very much less probable than their secondary origin through backward evolution.

Logically, the three hypotheses as to the origin of viruses are not mutually exclusive: it is conceivable that all may be correct.

Even though one may prefer not to accept the hypothesis that viruses are end points in parasitic specialization, it is difficult to avoid the conclusion that the simplest ones must represent the minimum of structural complexity compatible with mutability and the ability to reproduce in a favorable environment containing the requisite building blocks and energy-supplying mechanisms. Looked at in this light they are, except in name, genes. Like genes they are built of nucleoproteins, like genes they direct the formation of replicas of themselves and, finally, like genes, they are mutable.

Parasitism and Plasmagenes

The interesting suggestion that plasmagenes, such as those found in Paramecium and in the CO_2-sensitive strain of *Drosophila*, are genetic remnants of parasites or symbionts has been made by Altenburg [2]. There is much to be said for this hypothesis, even though it may be untenable in Paramecium or any other particular case. There are many known instances of symbiotic relations between two living systems. In the arthropods, for example, there are found in the fat bodies rickettsia-like structures, known as bacterioids. These have rarely, if ever, been grown outside the living host. It is possible to eliminate them in certain cockroaches by treatment with penicillin, and in this way to show that bacterioid-free roaches invariably die [12]. There can be little doubt that these symbionts, which are regularly transmitted through the eggs of the roach, are in some way necessary for the survival of the insect. Since similar symbionts occur throughout an entire order of insects, it is highly probable that the symbiotic relation is long standing in terms of the time scale of evolution. Presumably the genes of each of the symbiotic partners have taken over functions formerly performed by those of the other, and the two organisms have therefore become mutually dependent. Once a relation of symbiosis becomes established between two systems, this is exactly what is expected on genetic grounds, for, in general, it will be of no selective advantage to the two-organism unit for the same genetic work to be done twice. Rather, each partner will tend to specialize both metabolically and morphologically in complementary directions.

If the bacterioids of the arthropods were to become still further reduced genetically so that they were no longer identifiable as degenerate bacteria, they would certainly be classified as plasmagenes if indeed they were detected at all. Even in their present state they have lost infectivity and have become an integral and indispensable part of the life cycle. We know about them only because they can be seen under the microscope.

As Altenburg points out [2], there are species of Paramecium in which green alga-like symbionts occur in approximately the same numbers per animal as do kappa particles in Paramecia. It is, therefore, an obvious possibility that kappa might be derived from the symbiont. Assuming a sufficiently long period of mutual evolution of the symbiotic system, almost anything could happen genetically, and it is therefore exceedingly difficult to devise a means of testing the Altenburg hypothesis as applied specifically to the killer character. Sonneborn [58] presents a number of arguments against it. Individually they are clearly inconclusive; collectively they carry considerable weight but can hardly be said to answer the question in a final way.

Logically, it seems likely that evolution has often merged diverse lines of descent through establishing symbiotic, parasitic, or other intimate relations between them. While this process has undoubtedly been an important factor in many specific instances, its over-all effect is probably not great, for the simple reason that there seems to be no way in which nuclear gene lines of descent can be brought together once they have diverged so far as to preclude true sexual union.

EVOLUTIONARY CONSIDERATIONS

The Origin of Living Systems

While we can never hope to know in detail how living systems first arose on earth, as our knowledge increases of how they are constructed, how they function, and, more important, how those existing today evolved, our conception of what in principle must have happened becomes increasingly clear. And while the gaps that remain to be bridged are still great enough to stagger the imagination, it is encouraging that the air of mystery surrounding the subject seems gradually to become less dense. This is because of two main trends in our thinking. The first leads us to appreciate that there was almost certainly no one great step by which inorganic compounds came together to create a complex living organism capable of building more of its kind from the inorganic molecules out of which it arose. The second follows from the discovery that systems capable of self-duplication and mutation may be far less complex than a single-celled alga or an amoeba. Both emphasize that exactly where one draws a line between living and nonliving systems is determined by purely arbitrary considerations. Whether tobacco mosaic virus, for example, is living or nonliving is to a large extent a question of polemics. In degree of organization, structurally and functionally, there exists an almost continuous series from simple inorganic molecules to man.

Pre-Life Evolution

The view that a long and complicated process of inorganic evolution took place on earth prior to the advent of organisms as we know them is ably summarized by Oparin [53] and others. With the great variations in temperature, humidity, light, and pressure that must have occurred as the earth cooled and settled down, there must at one time or another have been opportunity for every possible chemical reaction to occur among the inorganic molecules. By chance alone many of these reactions must have produced carbon compounds like simple hydrocarbons. In subsequent reactions, more complex carbon-containing molecules must surely have been built up. As Oparin points out, all of the reactions that go on in present-day living systems are capable of going on in the absence of the enzymes that catalyze them, if the right physical conditions obtain. It is true that the rates of many of these reactions occurring spontaneously would be intolerably low by our standards of measurement. But the scale of time in the pre-life world was very different from ours; there was no hurry then, and there were no living systems to degrade the energy-rich molecules that were slowly formed in this way.

We can, then, assume that there gradually accumulated on

the earth's surface, in its seas and lakes and ponds, a vast variety of carbon-containing molecules of all sorts—aldehydes, alcohols, ketones, amino acids, fatty acids, aromatic compounds, etc. No doubt the quantities of these existing at any one time were exceedingly small. But through local accumulation, interaction by condensation, polymerization, oxidation, reduction, and the cleavage of carbon-to-carbon linkages, even smaller numbers of still larger molecules must have arisen. As the complexity of these derived molecules increased, both the chance of their formation in the first place and the probability of their accidental destruction after formation would have increased, so that there no doubt existed a kind of hierarchy in which simplicity and stability were correlated with large numbers, and complexity and lability with low frequence.

The Protogene

Somehow out of this age-long trial-and-error process there presumably arose molecules with the property of duplicating themselves, that is, capable of catalyzing the process by which they were formed. If such molecules were at the same time sufficiently large and appropriately built to permit chemical modification without loss of the power to multiply their kind systematically, they could become the ancestors of further lines of evolution, now definitely organic.

These first self-duplicating molecules must have been like genes and viruses, at least with respect to the properties of self-multiplication and mutation. Like genes and viruses, they could form more of their kind only in the presence of preformed component parts. The mechanism by which this autosynthesis occurred might well have been essentially like that employed by present-day genes and viruses, an assumption that does not help us much, since we know very little about how these units build more of their kind.

The step by which the first self-duplicating mutable molecule originated is clearly the most difficult one to imagine in the whole evolutionary process. Once this is assumed, it is simple in principle to visualize the mechanisms by which multigenic organisms arose. Protogenes may, of course, have arisen more than once, but it is unnecessary logically to assume that existing organisms trace back to more than one such origin. Purely as a matter of probability, it is likely that this primary step in the origin of life was successfully made only once.

Recognizing that one's thinking about the origin of living systems is unavoidably and strongly influenced by preconceptions that themselves have a long evolutionary history, it is nevertheless interesting and possibly significant that one is almost forced to assume a basic self-duplicating unit with at least many of the characteristics of genes as they are known in living forms that have survived to the present [1].

Heterocatalysis

Protogenes with the property of catalyzing formation of more of their kind in the proper chemical environment could have given rise to present-day systems only if through mutation they acquired heterocatalytic properties. Otherwise the multiplying

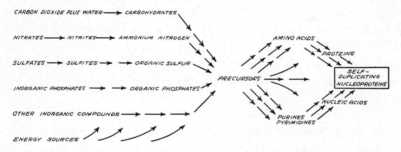

FIG. 55. Schematic representation of synthesis of component parts of self-duplicating nucleoproteins. Autotrophic organisms carry out all syntheses starting from inorganic materials. Energy may be derived from light or from chemical reactions such as oxidation of sulfur or iron compounds. In the original protogene, it is assumed that synthesis of component parts occurred spontaneously.

protogenes would have exhausted the available supply of chance-formed component parts with a cessation of evolutionary progress. Since at least one line of advance did make progress, it is evident that primitive life units must have acquired heterocatalytic properties. In this way multiunit systems were presumably built up which were capable of directing the chemical synthesis of their parts rather than depending on their chance formation. Through evolution in this direction there could ultimately have arisen completely autonomous multigenic organisms capable of obtaining all essential parts from inorganic compounds. Such an organism is represented in a very schematic way in Figure 55. The assumed protogene found its immediate precursors—amino acids, purines, pyrimidines, etc.—ready made. A completely autonomous system, such as a green alga, makes them from the inorganic materials indicated at the left in the diagram. How was the transition between these two extremes in synthetic ability made?

In attempting to formulate an answer to this question in terms of gene mutation and selection, a serious difficulty arises, namely, that chains of synthetic steps, such as are illustrated in Figure 55, would appear to be useful only if they were completely developed. For example, it is not evident how an organism requiring the sulfur-containing amino acid methionine could benefit by being able to reduce sulfate sulfur to sulfite sulfur unless at the same time it could carry out a long sequence of reactions by which sulfur finally ends up in the methionine molecule. Or, to state the problem in more general terms, how can a sequence of chemical reactions evolve if only the end product is useful to the organism? A plausible answer has been given by Horowitz [31].

The Horowitz Hypothesis

If one grants that the protogene ancestral to present organisms arose in an Oparin environment, in which all of its component parts were performed, it is simple to visualize subsequent evolution as consisting of a process by which chains of reactions were built up stepwise in the reverse order of their synthesis from inorganic compounds [31]. To illustrate, suppose the original protogene had included as a component part the substance CP-1, which it took from its environment already formed. Suppose, further, CP-1 capable of being formed from inorganic materials by a series of reactions. Then the entire sequence by which CP-1 could arise and be incorporated in the multiplying protogene could be represented as follows:

$$A \longrightarrow B \longrightarrow C \longrightarrow D \longrightarrow CP\text{-}1 \longrightarrow Protogene.$$

If CP-1 were to become limiting through multiplication of the protogene, and its immediate precursor D were present, then a mutant form of the protogene capable of catalyzing the reaction D $\longrightarrow$ CP-1 would have a definite selective advantage and would tend to replace its ancestral form. The mutant form, possessing both the capacity for self-synthesis and heterocatalysis, would be a true gene. As D in turn became limiting, an original protogene or a representative of true gene-1 could mutate to gene-2 capable of catalyzing the step C $\longrightarrow$ D. This, too, would be a step with selective value, for now gene-1 and gene-2 could, by establishing a symbiotic relationship, multiply in the presence of CP-1 or D or C. Such a union of gene-1 and gene-2 would constitute a simple two-gene organism capable of reproducing in the presence of component parts other than CP-1 plus either CP-1 or one of its two precursors C and D. It would be a living system capable of self-duplication and of directing two reactions. In the same way successive additional steps could be added until a four-gene state were reached capable of carrying out the entire sequence:

$$A \longrightarrow B \longrightarrow C \longrightarrow D \longrightarrow CP\text{-}1$$

Gene-4   Gene-3   Gene-2   Gene-1

In this way it would be possible to build up long chains of synthesis in a way in which each evolutionary step would confer a selective advantage. It should be emphasized that this hypothesis in no way requires that successive evolutionary steps add steps to a single chain of reactions until its completion. On the contrary, it seems much more probable that evolutionary progress toward autonomy, as illustrated in Figure 55, would have tended to add successive steps to the various reaction sequences at random.

A strong argument in favor of the Horowitz hypothesis is that it permits the building up of reaction sequences of unlimited length in such a way that each step is selectively advantageous regardless of whether intermediate products are directly useful to the system. The hypothesis does not exclude the evolutionary building up of sequences in other ways. In the case in which intermediates in the reaction chain are useful to the organism other than by serving as precursors of end products, steps could be added to the sequence in the same order in which synthesis occurs. Also, as Wright has pointed out [67], it is likely in sexually reproducing forms that combinations of mutant genes having a selective advantage may be formed by chance coming together of mutant genes, individually nonadaptive, that have been carried along passively in separate lines of descent. Thus, in the reaction sequence

$$A \longrightarrow B \longrightarrow C \longrightarrow EP$$

in which the end product EP would be advantageous to an organism having access to A but not to B or C, and in which none of the three reaction steps occurs, there might occur in each of three separate organisms gene mutations permitting one organism to carry out the reaction $A \longrightarrow B$, the second to make the conversion $B \longrightarrow C$, and the third to catalyze the transformation $C \longrightarrow EP$. The mutant genes G_1, G_2, and G_3, which separately have no selective advantage over their nonmutant forms, might survive passively in descendent strains until through interbreeding there occurred an organism carrying all three mutant genes. If this combination of mutant genes conferred sufficient selective advantage, it could well be preserved in the species. In this way it is possible that short chains of reactions, the individual steps nonadaptive, could evolve in sexual forms.

New Genes from Old

On the view that any gene not useful in directing a specific protein component of an enzyme or other system will tend to be lost through mutation, it is expected that in general each gene will perform a function useful to the organism. How, then, can a new function be acquired without losing an old one? Or to take a simple hypothetical example, how could a five-gene self-duplicating system, able to carry out five reactions, become a six-gene-system able to carry out one additional transformation? This could occur as a result of one of the original five genes becoming duplicated to give the system G_1 G_1 G_2 G_3 G_4 G_5, and the extra G_1 then becoming G_6 by mutation. In higher organisms, such gene duplications are known to occur. In the vinegar fly *Drosophila*, for example, small segments of chromosomes may occasionally become repeated [45].

A possible genetic model by which an unneeded gene can take over a new function is provided in the work of Houlahan and Mitchell [33] on pyrimidine synthesis in *Neurospora*. If a specific gene necessary for the biosynthesis of this component of nucleic acid becomes inactive through mutation, pyrimidine must be supplied in the medium if normal growth is to occur. In one instance the ability to synthesize pyrimidine was found to be restored as a result of mutation in a genetically independent gene. This is interpreted to mean that the function of gene 1 was taken over by gene 2, which previously existed as an extra gene without an essential role. In a complex organism with 10,000 genes, more or less, it seems likely that at any given time there would be present several such extra genes available for adding new synthetic abilities to those already possessed by the system.

Origin of Sexual Reproduction

Because sexual reproduction has been known until recently only in higher cellular organisms, in which mitotic and meiotic mechanisms are well developed, it is generally assumed that this method of reproduction arose relatively late in the course of evolution [9]. In view of the recently discovered evidence that gene-recombining mechanisms occur in both viruses and bacteria, one wonders whether some sort of sex process might not have evolved in primitive precellular forms. One can imagine systems as simple as two-gene organisms coming together and somehow producing new combinations. This possibility has an important bearing on our thinking about the mechanism of evolution in early forms. For one thing, a recombination mechanism would certainly have greatly shortened the time necessary for living systems to evolve from the protogene to the multigenic stage of nutritional autonomy.

GENES AND THE PROBLEM OF DIFFERENTIATION

In multicellular plants and animals and even in some unicellular organisms, the phenomenon of differentiation becomes of great importance. In a higher plant, for example, there occurs early in embryogeny a differentiation between root and stem. Once this distinction has been established, it tends to remain permanently fixed, although it is possible under special circumstances to have roots develop from stems or stems from roots. In higher animals, too, differentiation is often irreversible.

The basis of this differentiation is a long-standing biological problem on which discouragingly little progress has been made. It is limited to those living systems relatively high in the evolutionary scale, and therefore is not of the same general biological significance as the phenomenon of self-duplication. But because such a high proportion of the organisms in which we have important biological, economic, and medical interests are multicellular, it must nonetheless be regarded as a problem of the greatest importance.

The question of the relation of genes to the process of differentiation is a curious one, in that in one sense they have almost everything to do with it, but in another relatively little. It is clear that the detailed course of development is determined by genetic constitution. That one fertilized egg develops into a human being whereas another, which does not appear to differ greatly in appearance, gives rise to a rabbit, is with little doubt the result of differences in the gene complex in the two cells. On the other hand, the basis of the difference between different parts of a single organism often results from seemingly trivial differentials imposed on the system from the outside. Or, to state the situation somewhat differently: environmental factors alone appear to initiate the differences between one end of a rabbit and the other, but it is primarily heredity which differentiates between the two systems of development characteristic of man and the rabbit.

The problem of differentiation as posed in classical embryology concerns itself primarily with the question of why different parts of one living system have different developmental fates: why do some cells form skin, whereas other cells become organized into nervous tissue? By extension, it includes also the problem of abnormal development as found, for example, in cancer.

The evidence of cytology suggests that with few exceptions all of the cells of a multicellular organism are identical in genetic constitution. This is inferred from the observation that during somatic cell divisions all chromosomes multiply longitudinally in such a way that daughter cells appear to receive identical chromosome and gene sets. It is true that there are special circumstances in which this genetic equality is violated. There are sometimes systematic losses of certain chromosomes, and certain tissues, such as the salivary glands of Diptera, may show multiplication of chromosomes without cell division. It has often been suggested that such deviations in gene content of different cells of a single individual may be related to both normal and abnormal differentiation [34], but the most widely accepted view is that they are not causal.

Gene mutations occurring according to a systematic and predetermined pattern have also been suggested as an explanation of diversification among developing parts, but there is no convincing evidence in favor of the view—in fact, there is much that runs counter to it. In protozoa there is often elaborate differentiation within the confines of a single cell. Obviously, gene mutation cannot be concerned in this. In animal eggs, cytoplasmic localization foreshadowing cellular differentiation is often evident before the first cleavage division or, indeed, even before fertilization. This strongly suggests that nongenic factors are concerned here, just as in protozoa. In the egg of the brown alga, *Fucus*, the differentiation in rhizoid and thallus is clearly influenced by environmental factors before the first nuclear division occurs [65]. Thus, gradients of visible light, ultraviolet radiation, metabolic products, hydrogen ions, and temperature are capable of determining polarity of an egg originally with apparent spherical symmetry. Even mechanical elongation of the egg determines its polarity. Here then, it seems clear that the significant differential in determining what a given part of the egg is going to become is often if not always environmental in origin.

If the gene complements are identical in the different cells of a multicellular organism, what is it that maintains the cells in their characteristic states, even when they are explanted and grown for long periods in tissue culture? Since in so many instances the differentials are first expressed in the cytoplasm of the undivided egg cell, it seems probable that self-duplicating cytoplasmic entities with a certain degree of autonomy provide the basis of the differentiation process [58, 68]. If this view is correct, it is obvious that there must exist some mechanism by which an array of such cytoplasmic elements are systematically assorted during cell division or, alternatively, there must be a means by which the cytoplasmic determinants undergo directed mutations [68]. The loss of kappa particles that regularly occurs in Paramecium in response to experimentally controllable environmental conditions suggests that the former is at least possible [58]. While the phenomenon of plastid mutation in plants indicates how cells of identical genetic constitutions may become differentiated, there is no instance known in which mutation of this kind occurs in the systematic manner required by the plasmagene mutation hypothesis.

It is evident that almost the whole of the differentiation problem remains for the future to solve. We can, however, be sure of one thing—that in the developing organism the gene complement and the cytoplasm and the environment are all part of the system. Genes alone cannot make a cellular organism and neither can genes plus cytoplasm without environment. Cytoplasm is in some respects semiautonomous, but it cannot long continue its activities in the absence of gene direction. If discrete plasmagenes are of general significance in development and function they, like kappa in Paramecium, are almost certainly gene dependent and gene directed.

Since we know so little about the mechanism by which differentiation occurs in normal development, it is not strange that our knowledge about the ways in which the process can go wrong, as in cancer, is even more rudimentary. It is the hope of biology

that the future will rapidly improve our position in both respects. It seems likely that this will be accomplished through
improving our knowledge of the cytoplasm and its self-duplicating elements.

For References see p. 313.

THE EVOLUTION AND FUNCTION OF GENES

By A. H. Sturtevant

California Institute of Technology

Every individual organism is the resultant of the activity of the ultimate hereditary units, or genes, that it carries and of the environmental conditions under which it has developed. The geneticist is likely to lay particular emphasis on the gene as the hereditary component in this dual control, but it must never be forgotten that the environment is also essential. The differences between individuals may be due to differences in either genes or environment. There is one group of characters where caution in interpretation is especially necessary, namely, those having to do with human faculties.

There can, I think, be no doubt that there are differences between people in their inherent, inherited, mental, and psychological potentialities; there can also be little doubt, by analogy with other characters, that there are at least statistical differences between races. But precisely these characters are obviously peculiarly sensitive to environmental effects—to tradition and to social and economic conditions. It seems clear, therefore, that one cannot conclude that there is a very high correlation between the inherited mental potentialities of an individual and the properties that he actually possesses, and this caution is doubly necessary when one compares different races.

GENETIC SIMILARITY OF RELATED SPECIES

An individual belonging to any of the higher plant or animal groups carries numerous different genes. The exact number cannot be specified, for, while there are several methods of arriving at estimates of the number, none of the methods is very satisfactory. It seems safe to suppose that the number is at least in the thousands, but it may well be in the tens of thousands. Perhaps the next question that a physicist or a chemist might ask about the genes, after their number, would be about their size. It is clear that they are small, but again an exact answer is not possible. They are evidently so small as to be beyond the resolving power of an ordinary microscope; they are probably within the size range of large complex organic molecules, but it is not possible to be more specific.

In spite of these uncertainties with respect to such basic matters as their number and their size, genes are important units, for they are responsible for all the characters present in living things, and it is, therefore, desirable to find out all we can about them. One of the many methods that has been used in the study of genes is the comparative one. As a result we now have reasonably satisfactory accounts of the genetic behavior in a wide variety of organisms. Several kinds of vertebrates and of insects are well understood, there is some information on a few other invertebrate animals, extensive data are available on many higher plants, and in recent years we have come to know a good deal about the genetics of some of the lower plants. Perhaps the most important general conclusion to be drawn from a comparison of heredity in these forms is that, by and large, the same principles apply to all of them. There are differences, but these are not sufficient to obscure the essential similarity.

For some comparative purposes, however, it is desirable to consider a series of rather closely related forms. The best understood group of related species occurs in *Drosophila*—a genus of small flies, two to six mm. in length, many of which are convenient laboratory objects. The best known is *Drosophila melanogaster*. This is a small yellowish fly with bright red eyes, commonly found about fermenting fruit in most parts of the world. Owing to its short life cycle of about ten days and to the fact that large numbers of the flies can be reared with little space and expense, *D. melanogaster* has long been a favorite subject for genetical research. More is known about heredity in this species than in any other organism, and much of the modern theory of genetics is based on studies of it.

There are about 500 known species of *Drosophila;* of these, about eight have been reasonably well studied genetically, as many more are less well understood, and there are scattered data on still others [8]. The species so far studied do not constitute a random sample of the genus, since several of the more distinct groups of species do not breed easily under usual laboratory conditions; nevertheless, the available species do represent considerable diversities of type.

There are a few species hybrids recognized in *Drosophila,* and the study of these has yielded much information; in all cases, however, interfertile species are so closely similar as to be of little interest for present purposes. For the other forms here under consideration, the method of study has been to investigate each species separately, and then to compare the information on the gene composition of a particular species with that available for the other species. This usually means a comparison with *melanogaster,* since more genes are known in it than in all the other species combined.

The methods used may be illustrated by a few examples. *D. melanogaster,* as stated, is commonly found in most parts of the world. Although there are minor differences between strains in this species, there is, nevertheless, essentially a single "wild-type" form to be found everywhere, and it is not possible to judge the geographical origin of a specimen or of a strain by an examination of its characteristics. This "wild-type" form is the standard of reference for comparison of gene composition. Occasionally one finds, either in laboratory cultures or in wild populations, individuals with definitely distinct characteristics, and such a new feature can often be shown to be due to a change that has occurred in a single gene. Since the resulting new genes are relatively stable, it is possible to establish strains carrying them and to produce any desired number of individuals showing the distinct new characters.

One such new, or "mutant," gene results in flies possessing shortened kinky bristles. Specimens with this character agree with the "wild type" in all but one of the thousands of genes they carry; the kinky bristles are the consequence of a single gene substitution. It happens, however, that there are two different genes in the "wild type," a change or mutation in either of which will produce kinky bristles; the two resulting mutant characters are not distinguishable by superficial examination of the flies. Each of these genes in the "wild type" undergoes mutation relatively frequently; it is, therefore, possible to obtain a considerable series of separately arisen strains with such bristles. Crosses between flies from these strains show at once that they fall into two, and only two, types. If flies from two *forked* strains are crossed, the offspring are all forked; if flies from two *singed* strains are crossed, the offspring are singed, but if a forked strain is crossed with a singed one the offspring are "wild type." When flies from a series of such types are obtained and examined, a difference does appear; the females are sterile and lay abnormally shaped eggs in many of the singed types, but never in the forked ones.

Similar observations have been made on other species. There are now seven species of *Drosophila* in which two such types are known, and in no species have more than two been found. Furthermore, in several forms one type—evidently singed—has been found to be sometimes associated with female sterility. There can, then, be no serious doubt that in these species the same two "wild-type" genes are present and have similar effects on the development of bristles—even though the test of crossing to known *D. melanogaster* types is here impossible.

A frequently occurring mutant change in *D. melanogaster* is that which results in a completely white eye. There are many genes involved in the production of the red eye of the "wild type," but only one is known to cause, when it mutates, a wholly colorless eye. There are other ways of producing white eyes, but these require changes in more than one gene. The same gene of the "wild type" that may mutate to give a wholly white eye is also subject to other changes that give intermediate eye colors: eosin, cherry, buff, apricot, etc. Here again, in no species is there more than one gene known that is capable of changing in such a way as to produce white eyes, and this one is known in 12 species. Furthermore, in several of the other species intermediate stages are also known that are due to changes in this same gene. Therefore it seems safe to conclude, even without the crucial test of crossing to a known *D. melanogaster* white, that we are dealing with changes in the same "wild-type" gene.

The principal bristles of the head and thorax are constant in their number, position, relative lengths, and in the directions in which they point, in the "wild types" of the various species studied; they are in fact recognizable in a large proportion of all the higher Diptera, including, for example, the common housefly. There are, however, a number of genes in the "wild type" whose mutations affect this bristle pattern. One of the most frequent types of change involves a loss of particular bristles, and there are several different "wild-type" genes giving such changes. In general, however, the new patterns resulting from such changes are sufficiently characteristic in *D. melanogaster* so that, with practice, it is usually possible to determine by simple inspection of a mutant specimen which one is concerned. Crosses to known types have consistently confirmed such identifications. The two most frequently occurring such types in *D. melanogaster* are known as *scute* and *hairless*; types closely resembling both of them are known in other species (scute in 10, hairless in 4). Here the high degree of specificity of the patterns is the chief assurance of the identity of the genes.

The examples just given show some of the ways in which homologies may be established between the genes of different species. By such means, and by others similar in nature, rather detailed comparisons have now been made possible among several forms.

Within each species, study of the linkage, or association in heredity, between genes makes it possible to correlate the genes with particular chromosomes, and even to determine in which part of a chromosome each gene lies. It so happens that the chromosome configurations of the various species are not all alike, but they can all be interpreted in terms of six elements, lettered from A to F, which are variously attached to each other (Fig. 56). When the genes of each species are located, the striking result is that those that are associated in any one element in one

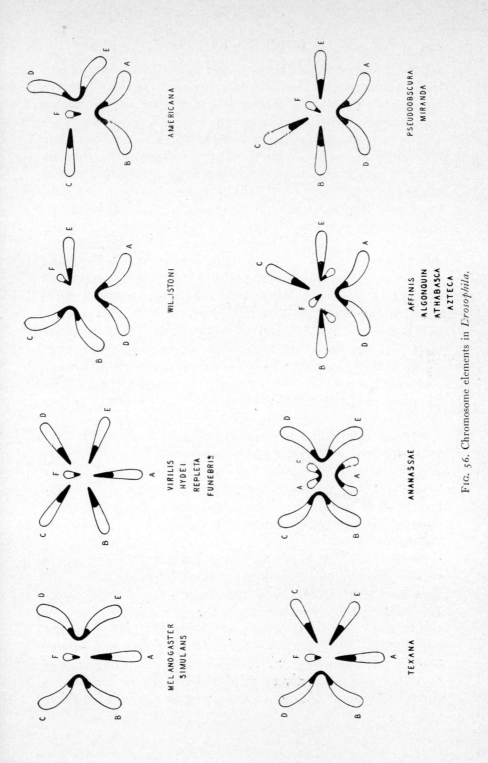

FIG. 56. Chromosome elements in *Drosophila*.

species lie also in the same element in every other species where they can be identified. There is one exception to this rule shown in the diagram—in *D. ananassae* a part of element A is associated with element F—a relation that is known both from direct microscopic examination of the chromosomes and from a comparison of the homologous genes, so that the exception does not in principle upset the parallelism. There are also one or two other probable exceptions concerning species that are as yet little studied and therefore are not well understood.

This rule of the integrity of the elements serves as a strong confirmation of the identification of the genes; for, if one were making many mistakes in identifying them, no such consistent result would be possible. In this connection it should be pointed out that there are many genes that cannot be utilized in such comparisons because the characters associated with them are not sufficiently specific. There are, for example, several different pinkish eye colors in most species; these are not distinguishable (with methods now available) within a species without the test of crossing, and they are therefore of little use in interspecific comparisons. Their presence is not contrary to the scheme, but they cannot be used to support it.

Comparisons of this same nature may be made between related species in several other groups, notably among the rodents and in several groups of seed plants. In no case can the comparisons be pushed so far as in the genus *Drosophila*, since there is in these groups no thoroughly understood standard of comparison equivalent to *D. melanogaster*. The data, however, are in agreement with those from *Drosophila* as far as they go; I think there can be no doubt that, in general, related species have essentially the same complements of genes.

It must be recognized, however, that even in the best-known pair of species the total number of common genes indicated by this method lies only between 50 and 60, which is the number common to *D. melanogaster* and *D. pseudoobscura*—the uncertainty arising from the existence of more or less questionable comparisons. This is only a small fraction of the number of different genes present in each species. It can be concluded, I think, that many more are in fact alike. If one considers the bristle patterns of the "wild type" it is clear that the two species are closely similar, and also that there are identical gene substitutions which result in new patterns that are equally similar. This evidently means that the original patterns were alike because their development was determined in the same way in each species. That is, not only are the genes that give similar mutant types the same, but essentially the whole set of genes controlling bristle development is the same. This argument, when applied consistently to the various characters for which corresponding mutant genes are known, leads to the conclusion that the whole animals are controlled by nearly identical systems of genes.

Such a conclusion may seem to be merely a platitude. After all, these are very similar animals belonging to a single genus, and are much alike in most of their properties. It may be asked —was it worth while to spend so much effort in establishing their essential genetic similarity? Did anyone ever doubt it? The answer is that precisely this point has been seriously doubted, and so it has seemed desirable to examine the situation carefully.

STABILITY OF GENE FUNCTION

The basis for this doubt may perhaps be stated best by first going back a little in the history of genetics. The orthodox view has been that at each particular point, or locus, in each chromosome there is a "wild-type" gene that is consistently present in every such chromosome of every normal, "wild-type" individual. This locus may at times be occupied by a distinctly different mutant gene, and these constitute the working material of the geneticist, but the resulting individuals are somewhat aberrant and are rather rare. The usual typical individual always carries the "wild-type" genes. This is perhaps an oversimplified formulation, but it does, I think, represent something closely approximating the point of view of many geneticists.

This view has now been questioned. It is clear that, at least for some loci, there exist several or many nearly equivalent genes, any one of which may be present without any marked effect on the organism [7]. The earlier interpretation of a single "wild-type" gene at each locus was due to lack of refinement of the methods of the geneticists. It is not yet clear how widespread this phenomenon is; it may be the rule that at each locus there are numerous nearly equivalent genes in the "wild-type" individuals, rather than only one typical one.

Some geneticists, impressed by this evidence, have been inclined to go a step further and to postulate rather frequent changes from one such gene to another. They feel that perhaps the older view of the great stability of genes was also only a first approximation to the true state of affairs; that perhaps the whole system is in a state of flux, and in the course of time the individual genes may undergo extensive changes of function, even to the extent of exchanging their roles in the determination of the properties of the organism.

Perhaps the most extreme statement of this view is that of Harland [4], who writes:

The genes, as a manifestation of which the character develops, must be continually changing [and] . . . we are able to see how organs such as the eye, which are common to all vertebrate animals, preserve their essential similarity in structure or function, though the genes responsible for the organ must have become wholly altered during the evolutionary process, since there is now no reason to suppose that homologous organs have anything genetically in common.

This is a point of view very different from that to which I have been led by the study of the species of *Drosophila*. It is, however, the opinion of an experienced geneticist, and is based on a large body of experimental data derived from species comparisons within the genus *Gossypium*, to which the cotton plant belongs. This evidence may now be examined.

The wild species of cotton usually have a dark purplish or maroon spot at the base of each petal. Some of the cultivated races lack this spot, but its presence is the rule in the wild forms. In this group, as in many others, species comparisons may be made by crossing distinct forms and studying the genetic behavior of their fertile hybrids. When this is done, it is found that the petal spot has a different genetic basis in some species. The genes responsible for its development in one species may be absent in another one, but the spot is still present and is now determined by different genes. Since it is probable that the ancestors of these two species, back to their ultimate common ancestor, all had the petal spot, it is evident why the conclusion has been drawn that some genes have exchanged functions. The argument becomes even stronger when it is shown, as has been done, that certain other characters of cotton plants likewise show differences between the species in their genetic determination. The facts are, I think, not open to doubt, but there is a special reason why the conclusion seems questionable.

The New World cultivated cottons, from which most of the evidence is derived, have 26 pairs of chromosomes, which may therefore be conveniently represented by the letters of the alphabet (Fig. 57). It is clear from several kinds of evidence that these plants are ultimately of hybrid origin, the two parents belonging, respectively, to the group of Old World cultivated types (the only forms known in the Old World before the discovery of America), and the New World wild forms (of no economic importance).* Each of the two parental forms has 13 pairs of chromosomes; in the artificially produced hybrid the maternal and paternal chromosomes fail to pair, and the plant is sterile. Accidental doubling of this complement of 26 chromosomes has given rise to the fertile New World cultivated types.

The two parental types may be supposed to be related in the same way as are the different species of *Drosophila;* in any case, each of them has the full set of genes necessary to produce a cotton plant. When first produced, therefore, the form with 26 pairs of chromosomes had these genes present twice. In general, in such a hybrid one of the duplicating pairs of genes is enough to produce a given character, and the other is likely to be lost by accident. What has happened, then, appears to be that one set of genes necessary for the petal spot has been lost in some of the New World cultivated types, whereas in others this set has been

---

* It is not clear where or when these forms crossed to produce the New World cultivated types. These questions are of great interest, but cannot be discussed adequately here.

retained, but the corresponding set from the other original parent has been lost. On this basis, then, it may be supposed that the differences in genetic determination are only apparent: the

FIG. 57. Chromosome constitution in the cotton plant.

genes concerned are really the same, and are descended from identical genes in the common ancestor of the two 13-chromosome types.*

* This account is somewhat simplified. In particular, some of the evidence is derived from comparisons between different 13-chromosome types. There is, however, a possibility that these are themselves derived from doubling of the chromosomes of still earlier hybrids between forms with lower numbers. As long as this possibility exists these species cannot furnish conclusive evidence for a change in function of genes.

GENE SPECIFICITY AND THE PROBLEM
OF DIFFERENTIATION

There may seem to be a contradiction in what has been stated. I have argued that related species have essentially the same sets of genes, and yet I have admitted that within one species there may be a series of different but similar genes at any one locus in different members of a population. If the characters conditioned by the various genes at any one locus are studied, they turn out to be related. The impression is that all the genes at any one locus are developmentally alike; apparently they are carrying on the same function, but with varying degrees of efficiency, often with different efficiencies (not necessarily parallel) in different parts of the organism. If the genes are thought of as being catalysts, or, as is perhaps more probable, as conditioning the presence of specific catalysts, then one may make a rough analogy to a lock-and-key system in which the different genes at any one locus are keys to the same lock but do not all fit it equally well. It is in this sense that one may conclude that related species have like genes—perhaps not identical, but certainly very similar, and carrying out the same functions. They are keys that fit the same lock.

The chemical composition of the genes is not accurately known, but evidence is accumulating that seems to make it most probable that they are largely or entirely nucleoprotein in nature. The indication of a protein component is of considerable interest, for it suggests that the problem of gene specificity—that is, how it happens that each gene has properties different from those of its fellows—is an aspect of the problem of protein specificity. This in turn means that the geneticist may expect help from the techniques and results of other biologists who are concerned with protein specificities—such groups as enzyme chemists and immunologists.

There is a current tendency to look upon protein specificities as being due to the way in which the molecules are folded—to their shapes rather than to their gross chemical composition [6]. On this basis, the primary specificity may be supposed to be that of the genes, the other proteins having their specific properties impressed upon them by the genes [3]. This is suggested by two circumstances: it is clear that genes can in some way impress their specificities on new material, for this is what must happen each time a gene reproduces itself at cell division; and it is also clear that antibody proteins somehow have their specificities impressed on them by the corresponding antigens in cases of acquired immunity [5]. It thus seems probable that the lock-and-key analogy suggested above is a valid one, though one must think of the keys as reproducing themselves without the intervention of a locksmith.

Every cell of an organism has, in general, the same set of genes as the other cells in the same individual. The problem that arises at once is: how is differentiation possible? If the characters of an organism are dependent on its genes, it follows that the different properties of the various parts of one organism are under gene control, yet the same genes are present in all these parts. This may mean, in terms of the lock-and-key interpretation, that in any given part of the organism all the keys are present but only some of the locks; in other words, that the outcome is determined by which substrates are present rather than which gene-controlled enzymes. This is, however, probably an incomplete picture, since it may also be possible that both substrate and enzyme are present, but some other condition (for example, the hydrogen ion concentration) prevents their interaction.

The relation between different forms of the same gene may be interpreted along similar lines. The effects of these different forms are often not parallel in different parts of the same individual. There is, for example, a gene in the "wild-type" *Drosophila* that mutates to produce a type called *yellow*. There are several different mutant forms of this gene: yellow-1 results in yellow bristles and yellow wings; yellow-2 causes yellow wings, with little effect on the bristles; yellow-3 produces yellow bristles and dark wings. In such cases as this—and they are very frequent —it may be supposed that there are related but slightly different substrates in different parts of the body, and, therefore, the efficiencies of the slightly differently shaped enzymes are not necessarily parallel.

If one accepts the view that there are fairly numerous slightly different genes at many loci, it is probable that those which are concerned in particular reaction systems need to be adjusted to each other. If one gene is working at a high level of efficiency, it is probable that the other genes that influence related reactions should also be working at high levels in order to produce a harmonious and properly adjusted system, though it might be possible to have an equally successful organism if all the genes concerned were working at a lower level. There is some evidence that precisely such differences do occur between related species. It may be suggested that gene systems gradually drift apart in their levels of activity during the differentiation of species; in that case much of the sterility and inviability often found in species hybrids and their offspring may be due to bringing together genes that differ in their levels of activity rather than in their specific effects on development.

The view that related forms of organisms owe their resemblances to the possession of common genes leads to an interpretation of homology. This is a biological concept that lends itself rather easily to somewhat mystical speculations. Accordingly, it has not often been seriously discussed in connection with the results of modern experimental work. There is, nevertheless, something real in the relations covered by the term, whether one considers serial homology within an individual or the homologies between organs in different groups of organisms. The point of view here developed leads to the interpretation that two organs are homologous to the extent that their development is conditioned by the same genes. One consequence of such a formulation is that homology becomes a relative, rather than an all-or-none, phenomenon. This result seems to me an advantage, since it suggests the possibility of a quantitative mathematical approach.

DEVELOPMENT OF NEW FUNCTIONS

If genes do not change their functions, but only change in the relative efficiency with which they carry on their predestined ones, it follows that organisms also cannot develop new functions—which is obviously contrary to fact, for there can be no doubt that new functions do develop in the course of time. It may be taken as probable that most of the genes present in an organism are performing functions that are advantageous to the organism, for otherwise they will not long persist. This is not a teleological view, but one that follows from the observation that most changes in genes are in the direction of loss of activity. Evidently the only stable condition of the gene composition of a particular locus is the absence of the gene in question, and unless there is selection for some particular function resulting from the activity of the genes at that locus, there will come to be no gene there. Most of the genes, then, are needed by the organism, and cannot well be spared for the production of new functions, even when they happen to change in such a way as to initiate new reactions. It seems likely that the most favorable condition for the production of such new functions is one in which some of the usual genes are present in duplicate. Cases of hybrids with doubled chromosome numbers, such as the cottons discussed above, furnish such an opportunity, for in these cases there is a whole extra set of genes, whereas a single set is all that is needed to carry on the functions normal to such an organism. There is evidence, particularly in the case of the tobacco plant [2], that such hybrids gradually lose one set of genes—or rather, parts of the set derived from one original parent, and other parts of the set derived from the other parent. Nevertheless, a considerable period exists in which duplicate genes are present and are available for the initiation of new experiments without the loss of any of the established and useful reactions.

This cannot be the only answer to the problem, for hybrids of this kind, while rather frequent in the higher plants, are very rare in animals, and animals also develop new functions in the course of evolution. It may be suggested that here also there is a source of new genes. It happens that in certain of the Diptera, including *Drosophila*, the chromosomes in the salivary gland cells are unusually large, and permit a study of the details of their structure to a degree of refinement nowhere else attainable. One result of such a study is the discovery of "repeats"—small sections present in duplicate [1]. It is not known how widespread the "repeats" are, for they cannot be detected in most material. Little is known as yet about the gene content of such "repeats." However, it seems probable that they occur in most chromosomes, and that they do in fact represent duplications of genes. These "repeats" may, therefore, be a source of extra genes not needed for the maintenance of existing functions, and which may therefore be used by the organism in trying out new kinds of reactions.

One thing that is definitely known about genes is that they reproduce themselves. At least once per cell division, on the average, each gene somehow conditions the formation of a copy of itself. On the view that gene specificity is due to shape rather than to gross chemical composition, the simplest assumption is that the new gene is molded about the old one. This process may be pictured most easily if each gene is thought of as being only one layer thick, so that determination of the shape of one face automatically fixes the shape of the opposite one also.

There are in *Drosophila* some dozens of successive cell divisions between the egg of one generation and that of the next. It is not known how many generations of individuals separate the members of one species from those of another species, but hundreds of thousands are clearly a conservative estimate. Multiplying these two numbers together, we find that like genes in distinct species must have resulted from some millions of successive copyings during the long period since they had a common model. Whatever be the process of gene reproduction, it is evidently an extraordinarily precise one.

For References see p. 317.

MODERN SOIL SCIENCE

By Charles E. Kellogg

United States Department of Agriculture

Most people probably think of soil as the loose surface material plowed in the field or spaded in the garden. At some time we have taken up a handful and let it run through our fingers, or squeezed it into a soft ball. We have seen sand grains, roots, and worms in it. Sometimes soil is hard, almost like rock; sometimes it is coarse and loose, like cinders and ashes; where most productive, soil is soft and mellow.

We cannot see or feel the chemical composition of the soil, but obviously it must contain a wide variety of elements and compounds. On every kind of soil some plants grow; and we know that even the simplest plants require several nutrient materials besides the carbon, hydrogen, and oxygen that they get from the air and water.

Starting with this simple concept, the making of chemical analyses of soils to increase our knowledge is a natural step, and indeed even the early chemists did this. By analyzing the soils and the plants growing on them it seemed logical to work out a balance sheet of plant nutrients. If the nutrients in a soil and the amounts required by plants are known, it seems reasonable to predict how many crops could be grown before the soil would be exhausted, what crops would be best, and what fertilizers would be necessary.

However, there were many operation difficulties with this simple concept of a balance sheet. Despite support from the great Justus von Liebig, with his towering reputation, this theory failed rather badly on the practical side, and even worse on the scientific side. The fertilizer industry that grew up under the shadow of Liebig did develop useful fertilizers, and these increased yields, but the fertilizers were often inefficient and always uncertain.

It really is unfortunate that the balance sheet theory was so inadequate, since it was refreshingly simple. But the soil is anything but simple. First of all, actual soil in the woods or garden is partly alive. It is quite unlike the dead samples of soil stored in the glass jars of chemical laboratories. A soil consists of thousands of compounds, organic and inorganic. Some of these compounds are highly active even when present in tiny amounts, whereas others, like quartz, are relatively inactive even though their bulk is large. The total chemical analysis conceals these important variations. One must turn to the X ray, the petrographic microscope, the electron microscope, the spectrograph, and similar devices to discover the relevant materials. The soil is much more than the surface film stirred in tillage; it is the group of layers that make up the whole volume of the landscape, extending down as deeply as the living organisms themselves. In fact, soil is the essential link between the lifeless mineral body of the earth and the biological kingdom, including man himself.

If, instead of looking only at the soil in our garden, we look at many gardens, all sorts of differences among these soils are evident. Then if the soils across a continent are examined, a close relationship among vegetation, climate, and soil becomes apparent. Subhumid grasslands and black soils go together; cool, moist climates and evergreen forests go with light-colored soils; tropical rain forests with red soils, and so on.

Soils consist of several distinct sheets, one on top of the other. In an excavation or a cut these sheets appear as layers, or soil horizons. Of course, some layers in the soil are inherited from layers in the original rocks. But regardless of the original rocks, we shall find true soil horizons, resulting from the peculiar environmental conditions of the place. Taken together, from the surface down into the weathered rock beneath, a collection of horizons is called a soil profile. The soil profiles in different kinds of landscapes are strikingly different from one another, yet they are alike in the same kind of landscape wherever that landscape is found.

This recognition, about 1870, of a unique soil profile for each kind of landscape was the greatest single advance ever made in

FIG. 58. Profile of a Podzol soil in Maine under the evergreen forest. A heavy mat of partly decomposed organic matter from the forest lies over a nearly white, strongly leached horizon. Directly beneath this is a dark brown horizon containing colloidal material originating from the horizons above. In this region soil-forming processes do not extend deeply. The parent material—glacial drift—lies at about 20 inches.

fundamental soil science, analogous to the development of anatomy in medicine. One does not need to depend upon inference from the geological nature of the rock, or from climate, or from other environmental factors, considered singly or collectively; the soil scientist can go directly to the soil itself. I hasten to add that rather than making the other sciences useless in soil study, this step in fact made them more valuable. Through soil morphology, soil scientists found a basis on which to classify the results of observations, of experiments, and of practical experience.

THE MATERIAL OF SOIL SCIENCE

The material of soil science covers the land area of the world. Thousands of kinds of soils exist. Because of the complex nature of its materials, soil science is not easily classified as a science in the traditional patterns. Often it is included with the physical sciences, like chemistry and physics. Yet it is also grouped as correctly with the biological sciences, along with plant physiology and bacteriology. Then again, soil science is appropriately grouped with geology and geography as an earth science. Actually soil science uses the principles and methods of all three of these groups; and a soil scientist who uses the principles of only one or two of the groups, to the exclusion of the others, can have only small principles that have little prediction value and soon bog down in contradiction. In addition to those already mentioned, there are important principles and methods peculiar to soil science itself. In application, the principles of soil science must be intimately related to those of the social sciences.

It needs to be emphasized that the experimental method and the method of scientific correlation are essential both in fundamental soil science and in the application of its principles to practical problems in farming, gardening, and forestry.

Soils must be studied in relation to one another and to the whole environment, both natural and cultural, to understand their formation and the influence of the individual factors of climate, vegetation, parent rock, relief, and time. How any one of these factors operates depends upon the others. The significance of any one soil characteristic depends upon the others. Any soil is a combination of characteristics, produced by a combination of factors, each of which influences the functioning of the others.

Experiments are needed, natural and artificial, to learn how individual soils behave and how they respond to treatment. These must be specifically related to individual kinds of soil, however, if the results are to be used in developing principles or as the bases for practical predictions. Thus experimental methods and the methods of scientific coördination are intimately interwoven in productive research in soil science.

SOIL AND LANDSCAPE

Let us look briefly at the implications of this concept of soils. Soils are natural bodies, each with its own unique morphology; they are dynamic bodies, developing with the natural landscape itself; they accurately reflect, at any moment, the combined or synthetic influence of the living matter and climate, acting upon the parent rock through processes conditioned by relief, over a period of time; they are distributed over the earth according to orderly discoverable and definable geographic principles.

The geological processes of mountain building, rock formation, and landscape evolution from which the parent materials of soils originate, are still going on along with soil formation. The natural erosion of the uplands gradually removes a little of the surface bit by bit, while the soil film settles down, and fresh minerals are added to the soil from beneath. With the warping of the landscape these processes are accelerated or retarded.

At several of the Soil Conservation Experiment Stations of the U. S. Department of Agriculture, rates of erosion were determined under permanent vegetation [13]. Under the natural forest cover of the Cecil soil of the Piedmont, erosion proceeds at a rate of about 1 foot in 10,000 years. This value was determined on a 10 per cent slope. Yet on a 14 per cent slope of the Muskingum silt loam of Ohio, considerably over 200,000 years would be required to remove one foot by erosion under the forest cover.

FIG. 59. *A*. Profile of a dark-colored soil developed under tall grasses in Iowa (Webster clay loam—a Wiesenboden). During its development drainage was poor, which has intensified the effects of the grasses in producing abundant supplies of humus and kept leaching at a low point. When drained this is one of the most productive soils in the world for the crop plants of temperate regions. (Photo by Dr. R. W. Simonson.) *B*. Profile of a light-colored, leached soil developed under forest in the humid Atlantic Coast Plain (Ruston sandy loam—a Red Podzolic soil). In this environment little humus accumulates in the soil and leaching is active. The thick black layer so prominent in the Webster soil is essentially absent. Colloidal material has left the surface horizon, and part of it has been moved to the layer beneath. The peculiar mottling of the soil in the lower part is characteristic of those developing in warm humid climates. Although not naturally productive for crop plants, this soil can be made so through proper fertilization to supplement the plant nutrients already in the soil, crop rotations that emphasize the deeply rooted legumes, and water control systems that prevent accelerated run-off and erosion. (Photo by Dr. R. W. Simonson.)

Under a well-established grass cover, normal erosion proceeds slowly on the dark-colored soils developed under tall prairie grasses. On the Marshall silt loam near the Nebraska-Iowa line, with 9 per cent slope, nearly 14,000 years would be required to remove 1 foot under blue grass. On a black soil of East Texas, Austin clay with a slope of 4 per cent, the figure is nearly 900,-000 years.

These values probably do not represent the real extremes, but rather relate to normal erosion. Some soils erode much more rapidly under clean cultivation, with bad effects upon soil productivity. Through proper cropping systems and soil management practices, erosion of soil under use should be kept somewhere near the normal rate.

Percolating water gradually dissolves the minerals in the soil and the rock beneath. Clarke has said that this process alone reduces the surface of the United States on an average of about a foot in 30,000 years [6]. From a study of streams, Dale and Stabler [7] estimated several years ago that the average rate of denudation for the United States as a whole was about one foot in 8,760 years, with suspended matter accounting for about 65 per cent and dissolved matter 35 per cent. Solution progresses much more rapidly than this in areas of soft limestone and high rainfall, and, of course, the process is almost infinitely slow on the hard rocks of steep slopes.

Other landscapes receive part of the erosion products and part of the solution products from the upland. It is probable that a third of the population of the world gets its major food supply from alluvial soils recently rejuvenated by additions of fresh rock minerals to their surface. The Nile is a famous example. In flood stage the water of the Nile contains over 1,000 parts per million of suspended matter relatively rich in phosphorus, potassium, nitrogen, and other plant nutrients. Part of this covers the soil in the flood plain, and part of it moves out into the sea. Barrell [1] estimated that the Nile Delta alone contains the equivalent of nearly 12,000 cubic miles of rock, to say nothing of the soluble material contributed to the sea water. According to Barrell's figures the rock material in the delta of the Niger

River is equivalent to a wedge-shaped mountain range some 18 miles wide at the base, 3 miles high at the top, and 1,000 miles long.

This gives some idea of the enormous movement of surface soil material as a natural process. In addition, in the tropics especially, volcanoes often shower the landscape with fresh rock or ash. A layer of ash only an inch thick amounts to 200 to 300 tons per acre of fresh fine rock material. Usually such ash contains significant amounts of calcium, potassium, magnesium, phosphorus, and other elements essential to plant and animal growth. Even nitrogen is sometimes present in important amounts. An acre-inch of the ash from Paricutin, the new volcano in Mexico, contains the equivalent of over 20 tons of ground limestone. Sometimes productive soils are covered with a rather sterile ash, but more often old leached soils are rejuvenated. In the humid tropics productive soils are generally those that are young, recently developed from volcanic lava, or soils that are kept rejuvenated by the relatively rapid addition of fresh minerals from beneath as the surface erodes away, or by additions of alluvium or volcanic ash to the surface.

The most nearly dead soils are those on flat landscapes of high rainfall that are not rejuvenated by erosion, by new minerals entering the soil from beneath following natural erosion, or by sediments from above. These dead areas must await a new cycle of uplift and erosion before they become productive naturally.

THE MINERAL-ORGANIC CYCLE

We are interested in soil chiefly because it supports green plants, and from green plants all other plants and animals, including man himself, get their food supply, either directly or from other plants and animals that live on the green plants. Of equal importance to this basic fact is the fact that plants, and all the other living matter associated with plants, are chiefly responsible for the kind of soil developed. It can be stated that there is no life without soil, and no soil without life. Life and soil seem to have evolved together in a mineral-organic cycle, or rather in many cycles, because there are many kinds of plant associations, many kinds of landscapes, and many kinds of soils.

After the earth cooled into a solid surface, and before vegetation covered the land, it probably looked something like an extreme desert region looks today, with jagged hills, sharp angles, and deep, irregular stream courses. With the coming of vegetation, soils began to form. Landscapes became more stable; jagged peaks softened into round hills with gentle slopes. Vegetation not only changes the rock material, but holds it in place, allowing it to slip away only gradually and harmlessly.

The plants select the essential elements from the mass of rock material into which they extend their roots. The great bulk of most soils consists of various combinations of silicon, aluminum, and oxygen along with significant, but often tiny, amounts of the other 92 elements. Plants take in phosphorus, calcium, potassium, manganese, copper, and other elements which they require, and build them into characteristic fruits and leaves, bark and wood. As the leaves and fruits and other parts fall, and as plants die, this organic matter becomes in turn the food of bacteria and other decay organisms. With their help, the chemical decomposition releases the nutrients to the soil for other plants.

Estimates have been made of the annual production of organic matter in the natural landscape [10]. Unfortunately, few data exist for the roots. For tall grass prairie, the figures for annual production are from around one ton to over two tons per acre. In temperate forests, values of around three tons per acre have been reported, with about one half wood and one half needles or leaves. Figures for tropical vegetation are much harder to determine, but estimates run up to 90 tons per acre per year. Of course, one year is but a moment in the life of a soil. But in 1,000 years a truly enormous influence is exerted on the soil by this root-sorting and the biological and chemical reactions associated with the production and decomposition of such vast quantities of plant material—quantities ranging from perhaps a low of 100 tons per acre, through a medium of 3,000 tons, to nearly 90,-000 tons, depending upon the kind of landscape.

To have some notion of the magnitude of this organic-mineral cycle in terms of a few specific elements, we might look at data

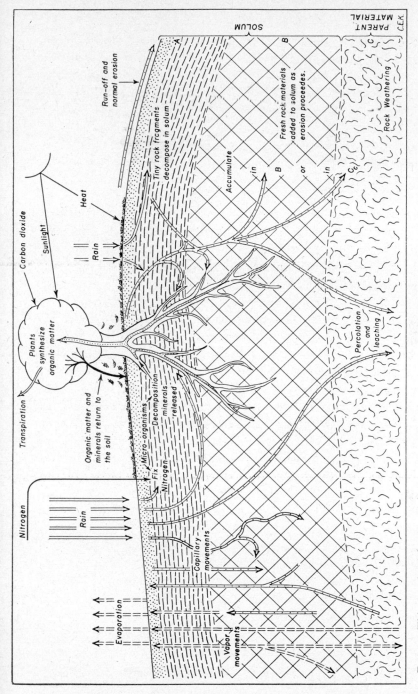

Fig. 61. This oversimplified sketch indicates many of the main processes going on in an ordinary soil. Plant roots remove water and nutrients from the whole soil, combine these with the carbon from the air to manufacture plant foods that are built into fruits, leaves, stems, and so on. These ultimately return to the soil to be decomposed, and the nutrients return again to plants. The macro- and micro-organisms of the soil are vital to this nutrient cycle and also in maintaining the structure of the soil.

for the annual leaf fall in ordinary hardwood and evergreen
forests in northern United States (Table I) [4, 5].

TABLE I

Element	Pounds per acre Hardwood	Evergreen
Calcium	65.6	26.5
Nitrogen	16.6	23.6
Potassium	13.5	6.5
Magnesium	9.2	4.5
Phosphorus	3.3	1.8

These figures are broad averages and conceal significant differences among the specific organic-mineral cycles of individual soil
types. Then too, the cycle varies in speed. In tropical areas it is
very rapid: a small amount of a plant nutrient goes a long way,
since it is used over and over again in its rapid cycle from the
soil to a plant, to the soil, and back to another plant again.

Thus it is clear that there is a continuous cycle of nutrients out
of the soil into the plants and back into the soil again. We are
concerned both with the amounts involved and with the conditions that affect them. In fact, the amounts considered alone can
be misleading. For example, in the arid to subhumid regions, the
rainfall is insufficient to remove the calcium, which accumulates
in a special horizon called the "lime zone" in the lower part of
the soil profile. Calcium would not need to be added to this type
of soil even after thousands of harvested crops. Yet in humid
forested regions the leaching of calcium completely out of the
soil is so great, in relationship to that brought up by the plants,
that it must be returned to the soil in agricultural practice, either
through the addition of organic matter or through mineral
amendments. In the famous Kentucky Blue Grass Region the
underlying rock is very rich in phosphorus. The soil contains supplies for thousands of crops. Yet in most parts of the world this
critical element must be added by the farmer to supplement the
natural mineral-organic cycle.

The kind of vegetation in the natural landscape has much to
do with these vitally important cycles of elements. On the whole,
trees do not require large amounts of phosphorus, and they do

not preserve it in the soil to the extent that the grasses do. Thus, when the vegetation is removed and replaced by the crop plants, the soil is often found to be deficient in one or more of the plant nutrients. What man is doing is establishing a new landscape— an unnatural one, if you please. He must discover the appropriate mineral-organic cycle through trial and research, and then introduce practices to compensate for the change. This gets at the heart of the fundamental problem to which soil science addresses itself in its practical application to agriculture.

Soil fertilization, for example, is not simply a matter of replacing the nutrients removed by harvested crops. Some soils may be able to supply all or certain nutrients indefinitely; others may need heavy fertilization, far beyond what the plants take out, for long initial periods. Nor are we concerned simply with the effects on just one crop or of the crops that can be grown on the soil anyway. Rather, we must think of the various combinations of crops and practices, and their immediate and long-time influence upon the soil and upon one another, to the end that a combination will be developed which will maximize the ratio of production to labor and materials on a permanent basis.

LITTLE PLACES AND BIG PLACES

It is obvious that some sort of soil classification is essential, since the world has a great many thousands of kinds of landscapes, soil profiles, and mineral-organic cycles. Of course, one cannot deal with all of these soils at one time, nor do they present equal contrasts. Actually, there are few sharp lines between soil types; rather, the soil of the world is a continuum that may be divided into reasonably homogeneous units, according to the state of our knowledge and the demands for accuracy and scientific prediction. The soil is a natural product, and no two soil profiles are identical any more than two oak trees or two college professors are identical. Soil types are man-made creations. In one soil type are included all the soils that appear to have the same kind of profile, even though they are not alike in every single respect.

This is not the place to go into the age-old problem of classification. All the natural sciences have the same problem. A

classification is good to the extent that it serves as an aid to re-
membering characteristics, seeing relationships, and developing
principles. A classification is bad to the extent that scientists become slaves to it, and twist their data and ideas to fit the classification. It improves as our knowledge grows. Some wonder when
soil classification will "settle down"—when names and defini-
tions will no longer be changed. This will happen when soil
science has ceased to discover anything new, in other words, when
it dies.

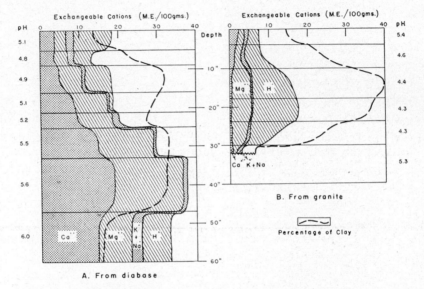

FIG. 62. A comparison of the clay content and exchangeable bases from two soils
developed in similar environments, except for the difference in parent rock. The
fundamentally important differences are obvious between the soils and among
horizons within each soil [9].

Let us now consider the significance of the lower groups, or
local soil types, in contrast to the great soil groups, or continental
soil types. The differences that are apparent between our garden
and our neighbor's, or between one plot of crops or trees and the
adjoining one, are differences related to the local conditions of
rocks, relief, and age. The soil of one garden is derived from
sandstone and another from granite; one garden is hilly and
one is flat; one is on an old slope and one is on a young stream

terrace. Associated with these differences are characteristics of great practical and scientific interest. Soils too sandy for gardens are often found mixed in an intricate pattern with soils that are too heavy in clay; soils too steep for cultivation, with soils that are flat and wet. If these soils are studied carefully, one can determine how they differ from one another and what direct relationships exist between the soil characteristics and the factors of the environment. Nevertheless, because of failure to see the common characteristics of unlike soils found in the same ecological region, serious errors may be made as to the causes of soil characteristics.

In a broader study one might reach altogether different conclusions. Suppose, for example, that one studies in detail the upland soils on smooth slopes from limestone and sandstone in West Virginia, in contrast to those on smooth slopes from limestone and sandstone in western North Dakota and in southern Arizona. Here again, striking differences are apparent, but the most important of these relate to differences in climate and vegetation; geology would seem relatively unimportant.

Thus by grouping the local soil types into higher categories, the broad soil groups that dominate the landscapes of great regions are compiled. When one considers individual practices in the garden, on the farm, or in the forest, it is the local landscape and the local soil types that are important. When one considers the great movements of population, the potentialities of nations, and the historical trends of peoples, the significant factors are the great soil groups. Thus the gardener sees soil characteristics with an emphasis different from that of the geographer, but soil science has much to contribute to both.

PRIMITIVE SOCIETIES ON THE SOIL

The soil supports plants, animals, and man himself. Primitive man must have been as much the helpless product of his environment as were the wild animals. He lived close to the soil and was a food gatherer. He took the plants and animals, including fish, that were available in his own landscape. Most of these were eaten with little change by cooking, storage, or refining. No doubt it was a risky business. Families might fail to get food because of drought, deep snows, wars, or other calamities, and starve. However, when things went well, although they might live on a few foods for a time, during the year there was usually a variety.

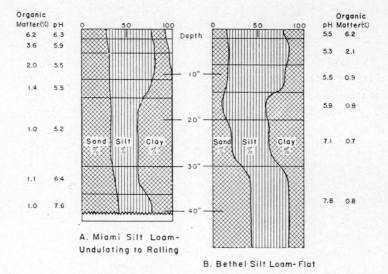

FIG. 63. A comparison of the mechanical composition of two soils developed from similar parent materials and in similar environments, except for relief. On soils of undulating to gently rolling relief there is continually a small amount of erosion in the natural landscape. As the surface is thus slowly eroded, each soil horizon works down into the one beneath. Over a period of several thousand years the whole soil profile, while remaining at the same length, may sink into the landscape a foot or more. Thus the soil is kept constantly renewed with new minerals. This is illustrated by the Miami silt loam at the left. The soil at the right is developed from similar material on flat upland where there is little or no erosion in the natural landscape. The leached material accumulates at the surface, and clay formation and the accumulation of clay are accentuated in the middle portion of the profile, with the development of a claypan. Whereas the Miami silt loam is a well-drained soil, pervious to roots and water, the Bethel is an imperfectly drained soil. During wet periods excess water is held up by the claypan which is also impenetrable to most roots. Kinds of crops and soil management practices for optimum production are quite different indeed, even though the soils lie side by side on the same farm [2].

Then too, primitive man ate vigorously. He ate whole foods—skins, hulls, seeds, and other parts that are now thrown away. It is only recently that modern man has attempted to create a balanced diet. Early man received or failed to receive his proteins, minerals, and vitamins unconsciously. Of course, no scientist was

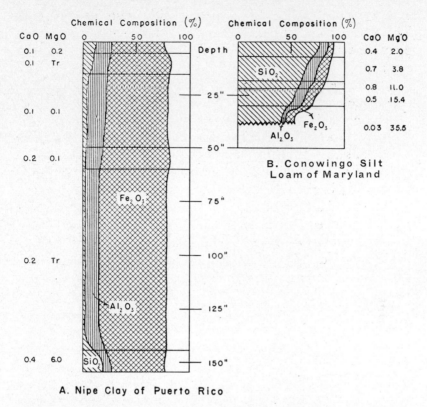

A. Nipe Clay of Puerto Rico

FIG. 64. A comparison of some of the chemical properties of two soils developed from similar serpentine rocks, one in tropical Puerto Rico, and one in temperate Maryland. Under temperate conditions the silica has been preserved, whereas it has nearly all been removed under tropical conditions. Further, under tropical conditions there has been an enormous increase in the amount of iron, and the tropical soil has been affected by weathering and soil-forming processes to a much greater depth. Of course, along with these obvious chemical changes are a great many other changes reflected in the mineralogical composition and physical properties of the two soils. Both of them are relatively unproductive naturally and require quite different methods for their improvement [14, 15].

available to study our savage ancestors at the time, but many studies have been made of relatively primitive peoples and of the physical degeneration caused by the substitution for native whole foods, like cereal grains, milk, cheese, fruits, and meat, of refined sugar, white flour, and similar products of more "advanced" societies [12]. Thus native peoples may become degenerate, or even extinct, after contact with western Europeans. There are reasons to suggest that over a long period people, like plants and animals, come to an adjustment with their food supply [11].

Marett held that people having food deficient in some essential element, say calcium, phosphorus, or iodine, gradually develop the ability to conserve this element. That is, in the evolutionary process the ability to get along satisfactorily with only a little of some element would have survival value. Such people would be most likely to have children able to thrive and grow strong. But in the process, size, skin color, and other features, even the psychological characteristics and social traits, are altered. Marett believed that differences in food composition, most of which were closely related to the local environment before the modern period, had a great deal to do with the origin of races, with the physical and social differences among the different peoples of the earth.

Marett argued, for example, that in regions with acid soils, deficient in calcium, people of small size would be favored. The physiological strain of lactation upon females would be much greater in humid regions where soils are generally leached and acid, and the foods deficient in calcium and phosphorus, than in arid regions where soils usually contain abundant lime (calcium). Thus on acid soils, where food is deficient in calcium, the bodily strain would lead to adjustments for economizing lime through decreased size, especially of bones. He suggested that the operation of these forces may have been important in the development of fine bones among modern people as contrasted to our more coarse-boned ancestors. Such changes are very gradual, and are not marked until after long living in a particular landscape.

MAN AS A CULTIVATOR

As civilization developed, man became a cultivator. He began to direct the course of nature toward his own ends and ceased to be simply a food gatherer, dependent only upon the natural bounty of the landscape. He ceased to be primarily a thief, and became a grower, a homemaker, a planner, and a conservationist in the only sense the term has any social meaning. As he gained in experience he learned to satisfy himself more easily; in fact, some people in the society could cease to be food gatherers. Social structures rose with the evolution of trades and professions. As the efficiency of food production increased, more and more people could be released from food gathering to develop the arts and sciences, to make the other things man needed for his health and comfort, and unfortunately, to make war.

From the dawn of history to the rise of modern science the accumulation of learning about agriculture was a very slow process. Experience, which was passed down from father to son over the generations, was the only guide. Only a few departures were made, because there was no substitute for such experience. Further, there was little realization that experience on one soil, in one landscape, could not be relied upon where another soil was involved. For this reason, migrations were often disastrous. Then too, world history records changes in the landscape under the very feet of the farmer, like the slow spread of the Sahara Desert as it gradually expands to its former position, following the moist period of glacial times [8].

Unfortunately, the early scientists of Greece and Rome reached little into the problems of agriculture. With a few conspicuous exceptions, the philosophers of that day accepted farming as the job of slaves, beneath the dignity of trained scholarship.

THE GREAT DISCOVERIES

The tempo of man's struggle with his environment completely changed with two great forces: the rise of modern science and the great discoveries. The most important fact of Western culture was the opening of new land in the world. The forces leading to the pessimism of Malthus were already destroyed before his famous essay on population had been printed. Science began to increase productive efficiency. Western Europeans found new homes in the landscapes of the Americas.

Europe had been bound by an aristocracy based upon land. Although many came to the new world to seek gold and adventure, most people came to find land and to build homes on the only security they knew. Gradually the east coasts of the new world filled up. In the beginning, people were confined to land near the sea and to navigable waters, as they had been in the centuries before. But modern science came to the aid of discovery. The European colonists pushed into the interior, especially in North America. Railroads had made possible the exploitation of interiors of continents, of the great areas of black soils. Except for a few isolated spots, these soils were scarcely used by civilized people at the time of the Treaty of Westphalia, when modern nationalism had its birth. During the nineteenth century the black soils (Chernozem and Prairie soils) and the brown soils (Chestnut and Brown soils) in North America were occupied. The frustrated, the persecuted, the seekers of new opportunity had a place to go, and it was a good place with good soil. For over 200 years a man and woman could carve themselves out a farm home on the colonial frontier, in the Ohio Valley, on the great prairies of Illinois and Iowa, and finally on the Great Plains to the west. Grassland needed only cultivation, once transportation was established.

In addition to the fine soils, there were other free resources, the forests and minerals. There was land in North America, Central America, South America, New Zealand, and Australia. Following the great discoveries Europeans found opportunities throughout the world. This progress is credited by many people to Western civilization, but it would have been a poor civilization indeed that could not have succeeded with these riches. With such abundant resources for its citizens, it is hard to imagine how any American government could possibly have failed.

At the present time, however, people must succeed where they are, or else move into areas where a great deal of careful planning is necessary for successful agriculture or industry. There is no more fertile soil in the world waiting only for the plow. But there is a great deal of unused land in the world that can be made productive through the application of modern science, land that is made up of thousands of unique types of soil.

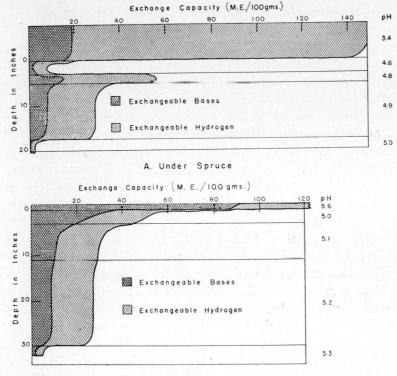

A. Under Spruce

B. Under Hardwood

FIG. 65. These graphs illustrate a comparison of total exchangeable bases and exchangeable nitrogen in two soils developed under similar environmental conditions, except for the vegetation. Because the spruce needles and twigs decompose slowly there is a considerable accumulation before decomposition is equal to the annual drop from the forest. Since the hardwoods drop nearly twice as much calcium and other bases each year, soils developed under hardwoods have a relatively higher amount of exchangeable bases. The upper chart indicates clearly the horizon of extreme leaching lying almost directly under the organic mat of a Podzol [3].

MODERN SCIENCE

The great discoveries themselves owe much to modern science. When the Treaty of Westphalia was signed, an insignificant part of the bread grains of the world were grown on the black Chernozem soils of the subhumid grasslands. Now these same black soils are contributing more than one half the supply of bread grains to the world. Within some 250 years man has occupied these soils. At first he applied the old methods and the old traditions, with poor results. Then from modern science he acquired railroads, proper machinery, and power. Whereas 100 years ago most cities of importance in the world were located on Gray-Brown Podzolic soils, like those of the Ohio Valley and northwestern Europe, now there are great cities on the black soils and on the brown soils like them. In fact, the great modern army that stopped the Germans at Stalingrad was raised on these soils.

Our early application of science toward a better adjustment between man and his environment was uneven. The various sciences have developed unevenly, and they are applied unevenly in different parts of the world. Early attempts to build the Panama Canal showed the failure of engineering without medicine, and there are similar failures of engineering and medicine without improved husbandry. Soil depletion due to erosion in parts of Africa has followed attempts to buy the wares of the peddler before husbandry had improved the efficiency of agriculture. In fact, soil depletion through accelerated erosion, exhaustion of plant nutrients, accumulation of excess salts, and loss of mellow structure follow the decline of the people. The great opportunities for future development depend not on science alone but on a symmetrical science.

Of course, some object to machines and to the planning inevitable to the use of science. They talk about going back to nature. But this would not be possible unless we were willing to do away with a large part of our population and with all of our modern gadgets. Scientists, and agricultural scientists in particular, were blamed by some for the last great depression. It was said that if scientists had not developed all of these new methods, surpluses and low prices would not have existed. This reasoning, of course, appears ridiculous to a scientist, since millions of people are in need of essential food and clothing for health. To the scientist, surpluses are market phenomena within man's control and due to imperfections that are subject to control. The good life requires abundance, and abundance depends upon the efficient use of all our knowledge.

To return to the relationship between man and the soil, or landscape, where he finds himself: the optimal or ideal adjustment can be approached by changing the environment, changing the soil, or by man's adapting himself to the environment. Actually, of course, man does some of both, and science helps both processes. From our understanding of the soil and the environment, we learn how to change it and how to adapt ourselves to it.

The soil is not easily changed, however, for in spite of all we learn to do through husbandry there still remains a closer relationship between the quality of foods and the natural soil type than there is between their quality and modern agricultural practices. Of course, irrigation of the desert or drainage of swamp land, by means of large-scale engineering devices, brings an immediate change. But most changes come slowly and often indirectly. A little change in the soil can set in motion a whole series of fundamental changes.

For example, most of the soils developed in humid forested landscapes are acid. Although they are productive for a time, these soils produce only a few of the plants man needs. By adding some lime, often some phosphate, and sometimes other materials in relatively small amounts, the farmer can widen his choice of crops. He can grow the deep-rooted legumes where he could not before. These crops, in turn, have a pronounced influence upon the soil and upon the crops that follow them. Similarly, by compensating through fertilization for the extra leaching in the humid climate, the farmer in the humid region can develop a soil approaching the notoriously productive Chernozem of the subhumid grasslands. Although fertilizer has not been found to have a dependable influence on the quality of food crops, through fertilization the farmer can so expand his range of crops that he can select those most nutritious for animal feed and human food.

Every natural soil has certain limits to its potentialities. Through modern science these limits can be expanded in terms of kinds of crops and yields. *No very close relationship exists between the natural fertility of soils and their actual productivity in society*. The important factor is their response to management. Some of the most productive soils in the United States are in the southeastern region, soils that are notoriously infertile when first cultivated as compared to the black soils of the Middle West.

Man's adjustment to the natural soil is not merely a matter of doing a few things. It is the process of substituting a new environment, with all its varied effects on living matter and the dynamic processes within the soil, for the old one. With the smooth-lying soils of the Iowa prairies the farmer gets nearly maximum yields from his first cultivation; in fact, there is no practical way now known to maintain the nutrient supply and productivity of these soils as high as they were under continuous grass, and still use them for crops under anything like present economic conditions. However, these soils can be maintained in cultivation at a slightly lower level of productivity under practices that maintain the nutrient supply and organic matter and control the water supply to avoid excess run-off and erosion. This is to be expected, since these soils were developed under grasslike plants, similar to the crops the farmer wants to grow.

The situation is different when the forest is removed from a leached soil in the humid region. The organic matter and nutrients must be built up far above the levels present in the natural soils, and the balance is delicate, both the natural balance and the one created by man. Too much lime added, and other nutrients become unavailable. Too much nitrogen added, and plants are weak, poor in quality, and easy prey to diseases. Water control without proper fertility may be impractical and wasteful. Rarely can the maximum economic production from soils in humid forested regions be realized by the application of just one or two scientific practices.

CONCLUSIONS

In the past, the environment determined man's development and set definite limits on his activities. His music and architecture, his economic and political institutions, in fact, his whole social being was strongly influenced by the potentialities of the soil. As modern soil science develops further, the environment will determine less what man is and more what he does. Scientists will learn more precisely how to carry specific management practices from one soil to another, in order to achieve good productivity.

As science progresses there will be increasing emphasis upon symmetry in science, upon fitting the parts together. Although such an emphasis runs counter to the modern trend of specialization, organizational devices will be created both in research and in education, so that teams of scientists in different specialities work together. Only in this way can even a small part of our agricultural potentialities be realized, or more than a small part of our soil science be put to work.

Even now, there would be enough food if soil science were used to the fullest extent. There are no apparent limits to our potentiality; it is far away—far beyond our present production. Even in this great country there is needless inefficiency in agriculture, needless from the standpoint of proved scientific principles and practices. Some farmers do not know what to do; others have no way of knowing the practices or of following them if they did know. Thus, even on the soil already occupied, the opportunities for more food are enormous. In addition, there are still areas in the interior of continents that are only partly utilized, for lack of industry or transportation. This is especially true of Asia.

Even more important than these wasted opportunities are the great areas of tropical soils. Some say that the resources of the tropics are almost without limit; other say they are nonexistent. The truth is that without modern science their productivity is small; thus it might be said that the tropics are overpopulated now. However, with the application of a symmetrical soil science, the potentialities of the tropics are enormous. Most of the soils are naturally infertile in terms of our present practices in temperate regions, but it is possible to modify the mineral-organic cycle of these soils and get good production of cultivated plants on a secure basis. All of the agricultural sciences will be involved, along with soil science, medicine, engineering, economics, and political science.

This outline of soil science in modern society leaves a million details untold. If peace and abundance in the world are achieved, thousands of soil scientists will have contributed their whole lives toward it, along with other people. The data of soil science show that abundance is possible. Whether it should be achieved, and whether it will be achieved, are not scientific questions. But if the people of the world decide that they want peace and enough food, and if they address themselves to the economic and social problems standing in the way, soil science says it is possible.

For References see p. 318.

REFERENCES

CHAPTER I

From X Rays to Nuclear Fission by H. D. Smyth

1. University of Chicago catalog, 1893–1906.
2. GLASSER, O. Wilhelm Conrad Roentgen and the early history of the Roentgen rays. Chap. I, 1934.
3. *Ibid.*, Chap. II.
4. SITZBER, *d. Wurzburger Phys-Med. Ges.*, December, 1895, and March, 1896.
5. MAGIE. Source book of physics. McGraw-Hill, New York, pp. 600–601, 1935.
6. *Compt. Rend. Acad. des Sci. Paris, 122,* 420, 1896. Also MAGIE. Source book of physics, pp. 610–613.
7. See any edition of THOMSON, J. J. Conduction of electricity through gases and MILLIKAN, The electron.
8. RUTHERFORD and ROYDS. *Phil. Mag., 17,* No. 6, 281, 1909.
9. —— Nobel Lecture in Nobelstiftelsen, 1908.
10. —— *Phil. Mag., 21,* No. 6, 699, 1911.
11. —— Radioactive substances and their radiations. Cambridge, pp. 184, 185, 616–620, 1913.
12. *Ann. der physik, 12,* No. 4, 735, 1903.
13. *Verh. d. Phys. Ges. z. Berlin, 7,* 128, 1896. See also MAGIE. Source book of physics, pp. 384–386.
14. *Ann. der physik, 17,* No. 4, 891, 1905, and *23,* No. 4, 371, 1907.
15. *Ann. der physik, 4,* No. 4, 553, 1901. See also JEANS, SIR JAMES. Report on radiation and the quantum theory or kinetic theory of gases. Chap. XVII.
16. See BALY, E. C. Spectroscopy. 3d ed. Vol. III, Chap. I.
17. See his Theory of spectra and atomic constitution. Cambridge University Press, 1922. Also his papers in *Phil. Mag., 26,* No. 6, v, 476 and 857, 1913.
18. *Deutsche Phys. Gesells. Verhandl., 16,* 457, 1914. HARNWELL. Experimental atomic physics, pp. 314–320.
19. Three papers in *Ann. der physik, 79,* No. 4, 1936, translated in his Collected papers on wave mechanics. Blackie, 1928.
20. *Zeitschr. Physik, 33,* 879, 1925.
    See also his own survey in *Naturwiss., 17,* 490, 1929. And DIRAC. Principles of quantum mechanics. 2d ed. pp. 118–126. Or ROJANSKY. Introductory quantum mechanics. Chap. X.
21. Full survey, with references to original papers, in ASTON. Mass spectra and isotopes. Chap. I.

22. *Proc. Roy. Institution of Gt. Brit., 20,* 591, or his Rays of positive electricity, pp. 212–216.

23. *Phil. Mag., 37,* No. 6, 523, 1919.

24. *Phil. Mag., 37,* No. 6, 581, 1919, described in RUTHERFORD, CHADWICK,
and ELLIS, pp. 283–290.

25. *Zeitschr. physik, 66,* 289, 1930.
Compt. Rend. Acad. des Sci. Paris, 194, 273, 1932.
Proc. Roy. Soc. London, 136, 692, 1932.
This general subject is surveyed in some detail in STRANATHAN, Particles
of modern physics, pp. 386–392.

26. TURNER, *Rev. of Mod. Phys., 12,* 1–29, 1940, with full bibliog.

27. *Naturwiss., 27,* 11, 1939.

28. *Nature, 143,* 239, 1939.

29. At Institute of Physics, Copenhagen, *Nature, 143,* 276, January 16, 1939.
At Curie Laboratory, *Compt. Rend. Acad. des Sci. Paris, 208,* 341, Jan-
uary 30, 1939.
At Univ. of California, *Phys. Rev., 55,* 417, January 31, 1939.
At Johns Hopkins, *Phys. Rev., 55,* 417, *February* 4, 1939.
At Carnegie Institution, *Phys. Rev., 55,* 416, February 4, 1939.
At Vienna, *Naturwiss., 27,* 134, February 14, 1939.
At Columbia, *Phys. Rev., 55,* 511, February 16, 1939.
At Kaiser Wilhelm Institute, *Naturwiss., 27,* 198, March 17, 1939.

30. FERMI, *Science, 105,* 27, 1947. Also SMYTH. Atomic energy for military
purposes. Appendix 4.

CHAPTER II

Elementary Particle Physics by John A. Wheeler

A more extensive bibliography is to appear in the *American Scientist*
in 1949, under the title Guide to Literature of Elementary Particle
Physics.

1. Based on Sigma Xi National Lectures, 1946, and a paper presented before the National Academy and Philosophical Society Symposium on
atomic energy and its implications (November, 1945).
Proc. Am. Phil. Soc. 90, 1, 1946. A first revision appears in *Am. Sci.,*
Spring Issue, 1947, *35,* No. 2, 177.

2. Nuclear chain reactions:
GOODMAN, CLARK, ed. The science and engineering of nuclear power.
Addison-Wesley Press, Inc., Cambridge 42, Mass., 1947.

3. Following recommendations on terminology for the elementary particles
made in October, 1947, by the Cosmic Ray Commission of the Interna-
national Union of Pure and Applied Physics, as published in *Science, 107,*

60, 1948. See also the report on terminology as published by the I.U.P.A.P., Paris, 1948, Document RC48-1.

4. Nucleonic Physics:
ROSENFELD, L. Nuclear forces. Interscience Publishers, Inc., New York, 1948.
Also reference 2.

5. Mass of ordinary meson:
FRETTER, W. B. *Phys. Rev. 70*, 625, 1946.

6. For the discovery of the positon:
ANDERSON, C. D. *Phys. Rev., 41*, 405, 1932; *Phys. Rev., 43*, 491, 1933; *Phys. Rev., 44*, 406, 1933.
For the light meson see the history given by
NEDDERMEYER, S. H., and ANDERSON, C. D. *Rev. Mod. Phys., 11*, 191, 1939.

7. Life of the ordinary meson:
NERESON, N., and ROSSI, B. *Phys. Rev., 64*, 199, 1943.
See also references 49, 113, and 123.

8. Observation and properties of 300-mass meson:
LATTES, C. M. G., MUIRHEAD, H., OCCHIALINI, G. P. S., and POWELL, C. F. *Nature, 159*, 694, 1947.
—— OCCHIALINI, G. P. S., and POWELL, C. F. *Nature, 160*, 453, 1947; *160*, 486, 1947.
Mass determinations:
GARDNER, E., and LATTES, C. M. G. *Science, 107*, 270, 1948.
LATTIMORE, S. *Nature, 161*, 518, 1948.

9. Production of 200- and 300-mass mesons by cyclotron bombardment:
GARDNER, EUGENE and LATTES, C. M. G. *Science, 107*, 270, 1948.
See also reference 101.

9a. Evidence for a new meson which decays into three charged particles:
BROWN, R., CAMERINI, U., FOWLER, P. H., MUIRHEAD, H., POWELL, C. F., and RITSON, D. M. *Nature*, scheduled for publication, January, 1949. (The figure presenting photographic evidence is printed on page 294.)

10. For properties of the specific nuclear forces between nucleons see for example:
ROSENFELD, L. Nuclear forces. Interscience, New York, 1948.

11. See GAMOW, G. *Physics Today, 1*, No. 3, 4, 1948, for a brief history of the evolution of the neutrino concept.
See also references 88, 89, 95, 98, 99.

12. For indications about the possibility that high-energy gamma rays may produce mesons see for example:
MORETTE, CECILE, and PENG, H. W. *Nature, 160*, 61, 1947.

13. For theoretical estimates of meson production probability as function of energy of collision of nucleons see for example:

McMillan, W. G., and Teller, E. *Phys. Rev.*, *72*, 1, 1947.

14. Observed energy dependence of meson production probability:
    Schein, M. Yngve, V. H., and Kraybill, H. L., *Phys. Rev. 73*, 928, 1948.

15. Evidence for multiple production of mesons:
    Schein, M., and Stroud, W., as reported in Montgomery, D. J. X. Cosmic-ray physics. Princeton University Press, Princeton, N. J., December, 1948.

16. For discussion of accelerators see:
    Schiff, L. I. *Rev. Sci. Inst.*, *17*, 6, 1946.

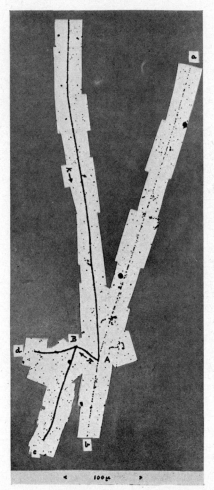

Photographic Evidence of a New Type of Meson

The line marked K is the track made in photographic emulsion by a particle identified as having a mass 1080 ± 160 times the mass of an electron. After being brought to rest it disintegrates into 3 mesons (a and b). Two of them escape from the emulsion. The third is identified as the previously known meson of mass about 286, which is stopped at B, absorbed by a nucleus, and ejects two protons (c and d). This photograph is reproduced with the permission of C. F. Powell, whose paper is scheduled to appear in *Nature*, January, 1949. [9a]

17. Argonne National Laboratory:

DANIELS, F. *Bull. Atomic Scientists* (Chicago), *4*, 177, 1948.

Brookhaven National Laboratory:

Ordnance, *32*, 175, 1947.

18. For a general account of the cosmic radiation see:

AUGER, P. What are cosmic rays? University of Chicago Press, Chicago, 1945.

LEPRINCE-RINGUET, L. Les rayons cosmiques. Michel, Paris, 1948; English trans. to be published by Prentice Hall Co., New York.

JANOSSY, L. Cosmic rays and nuclear physics. The Pilot Press, Ltd., London, 1948.

MILLIKAN, R. A. Electrons ($+$ and $-$), protons, photons, neutrons, mesotrons and cosmic rays. University of Chicago Press, 1947.

For a more detailed account see:

ROSSI, B. *Rev. Mod. Phys.*, *20*, 537, 1948.

MONTGOMERY, D. J. X. Cosmic ray physics. Princeton University Press, Princeton, N. J., December, 1948.

JANOSSY, L., Cosmic rays. Clarendon Press, Oxford, and Oxford University Press, New York, 1948.

HEISENBERG, W., ed. Cosmic radiation. English trans. by JOHNSON, T. H., Dover Publications, New York, 1946.

EULER and HEISENBERG, *Ergebnisse der Exakten Naturwissenschaften*, *17*, 1–70, Berlin, Springer, 1938.

19. Evidence for cosmic-ray events with energies in the range 10^{12} to 10^{18} ev has been presented by:

AUGER, P., and MAZE, R. *Comptes Rendus*, *207*, 228, 1938 (at least $10^{12} - 10^{13}$ ev).

LAPP, R. E. *Phys. Rev.*, *64*, 129, 1943.

ALICHANIAN, A., ASATIANI, T., and ALEXANDRIAN, A. *Jour. Phys.*, *U.S.S.R.*, *9*, 148, 1945; and by many others.

See also reference 106 for penetrating particles in extensive air showers, and reference 56 for large bursts in ionization chambers, some of which are due to extensive air showers, and reference 65 for showers of very large extension.

20. For results obtained by way of V-2 rockets see:

GOLIAN, S. E., KRAUSE, E. H., and PERLOW, G. J. *Phys. Rev.*, *70*, 776, 1946.

TATEL, H. E., and VAN ALLEN, J. A. *Phys. Rev.*, *73*, 245, 1948, and other publications by these authors.

21. For some description of the balloon technique see:

JOHNSON, T. H. *Jour. Frank. Inst.*, *223*, 339, 1937.

National Geographic Society, *Stratosphere Series 2*. Washington, 1936.

Also SPILHAUS, A. F., SCHNEIDER, C. S., and MOORE, C. B. *Jour. Meteorology 5: 130*, 1948.

22. For a recent discussion of balloons of the constant volume type see for example:
BERGER, P. *Arch. Sci. Phys. Nat.* (Geneva), *29*, 151, 1947.
SPILHAUS, A. F., SCHNEIDER, C. S., and MOORE, C. B. *Jour. Meteorology*, *5*, 130, 1948

23. The Mt. Evans Laboratory now operates under the University of Denver with participation by several other universities.

24. For a description of the Italian national high-altitude cosmic-ray laboratory see *Nature, 161*, 254, 1948. A world directory of cosmic-ray laboratories is now being prepared by the Commission on Cosmic Radiation of the International Union of Pure and Applied Physics under the editorship of P. AUGER.

25. For references to work carried out at high altitudes by Air Force planes see citations of 1947 and 1948 publications by SCHEIN, M., BARBER, W. C., BRODE, R., ROSSI, B., SANDS, M., SWANN, W. F. G., YUAN, L., and others.

26. Ionization chamber:
SHERR, R. *Rev. Sci. Inst., 18*, 567, 1947.
Crystal counters:
VAN HEERDEN, P. The crystal counter. Utrecht thesis, 1945; *Electronics, 20*, 144, 1947.
HOFSTADTER, R. *Phys. Rev., 74*, 100, 1948 (and references cited therein).
Photographic plates:
POWELL, C. F., OCCHIALINI, G. P. S., LIVESEY, D. L., and CHILTON, L. V. *Jour. Sci. Inst., 23*, 102, 1946 and *24*, 136, 1947.
DEMERS, P. *Phys. Rev., 70*, 86, 1946; *Canad. Jour. Res., A 25*, 223, 1947.
High speed counters:
KEUFFEL, J. W. *Phys. Rev., 73*, 53, 1948.

27. Heavily ionizing particles in the primary cosmic radiation:
FREIER, P., LOFGREN, E. J., NEY, E. P., OPPENHEIMER, F., BRADT, H. L., and PETERS, B. *Phys. Rev., 74*, 213, 1948. COOR, T., JR. Ionization chamber bursts at high altitudes. Ph.D. thesis. Princeton University, 1948.

28. Abundance of the elements in nature:
GOLDSCHMIDT, V. M. Geochemische Verteilungsgesetze der Elemente. Norske Videnskaps Akademi, Oslo, 1938. Fig. 1, p. 117 and Fig. 2, p. 118.

29. Speculations on the possible existence of reversed matter and negative protons:
ARLEY, N. *Phys. Rev., 70*, 975, 1946, and references therein cited.

30. Excess of western over eastern intensity:
JOHNSON, T. H. *Rev. Mod. Phys., 10*, 193, 1938.

SCHEIN, MARCEL, YNGVE, VICTOR H., and KRAYBILL, HENRY L. *Phys. Rev.*, *73*, 928, 1948.

31. Evidence against more than one electron per 100 incoming cosmic ray particles:
HULSIZER, R. I. *Phys. Rev.*, *73*, 1252, 1948.

32. Electromagnetic disturbances from sunspots:
MENZEL, D. H., and SALISBURY, W. W. *Nature*, *161*, 91, 1948.

33. Acceleration of particles in space by changes in relative orientation of magnetic fields of two neighboring stars:
ALFVEN, H. *Zeitschr. f. Physik*, *107*, 579, 1937.

34. Acceleration by changes in magnetic field of one star:
TERLETZKY J. *Jour. Phys. U.S.S.R.*, *10*, 337, 1946.
BABCOCK, H. W. *Phys. Rev.*, *74*, 489, 1948.
The changes in field observed:
BABCOCK, H. W. *Astrophys. Jour.*, *105*, 105, 1947; *Phys. Rev.*, *72*, 83, 1947; *Publ. Astron. Soc. Pacif.*, *59*, 112, 1947.

35. The sun can impart to a dust particle with dimensions of the order of 10^{-5} cm. a kinetic energy sufficient to carry an elementary positive charge of electricity through a potential rise of the order of 10^{-13} volts. For discussion of interstellar dust as intermediary in the process of condensation of molecules, as inteceptor of radiation, and as carrier of electricity see for example:
WHIPPLE, F. L. *Astrophys. Jour.*, *104*, 1, 1946.
C. S. BEALS. *Popular Astron.*, *52*, 209, 1944.
SPITZER, L., JR. *Astrophys. Jour.*, *107*, 6, 1948.

36. Thunderstorm type of mechanism, suggested by J. Franck in a personal discussion. See also HOYLE, F. *Mon. Notices Roy. Astr. Soc.*, *106*, 384, 1946.

36a. Magneto-hydrodynamical disturbances as cosmic-ray accelerator:
ALFVEN, H., FERMI, E., and TELLER, E., unpublished results.

37. Characteristic energy distribution of cosmic radiation:
MILLIKAN, R. A., NEHER, H. V., PICKERING, W. *Phys. Rev.*, *61*, 406, 1942.

38. Evidence for the constancy of cosmic-ray intensity in time—and therefore in direction:
DUPERIER, A. *Proc. Phys. Soc. London*, *57*, 464, 1945 (small periodic changes in cosmic-ray intensity and their correlation with meteorological changes).
NICOLSON, P., and SARABHAI, V. *Proc. Phys. Soc. London*, *60*, 509, 1948 (diurnal changes).

39. Small fraction of stellar energy required to generate cosmic rays:
ALFVEN, H. *Zeitschr. f. Physik*, *107*, 579, 1937.

40. Considerations on a possible galactic magnetic field:
ALFVEN, H. *Zeitschr. f. Physik*, *107*, 579, 1937.

41. Energy loss of cosmic-ray particles circulating through galaxy via interaction with matter and radiation:
  FEENBERG, E., and PRIMAKOFF, H. *Phys. Rev.*, *73*, 449, 1948.
  FOLLIN, J. Propagation of cosmic rays through interstellar space. Ph.D. thesis. Calif. Inst. Tech., Pasadena, 1947.

42. Effect of sun's magnetic field in excluding from earth cosmic-ray particles of energy less than a critical amount:
  ALFVEN, H. *Phys. Rev.*, *72*, 88, 1947 (absence of diurnal changes associated with solar field).
  JANOSSY, L. *Zeitschr. f. Physik*, *104*, 430, 1937 (original suggestion on effect of sun's field).
  KANE, E. O., SHANLEY, T. J. B., and WHEELER, J. A. *Rev. Mod. Phys.* (in press).

43. Earlier evidence from magnetic splitting of spectral lines for dipole moment of sun corresponding to polar field of roughly 50 gauss:
  HALE, G. E., SEARES, F. H., VAN MAANEN, A., and ELLERMAN, F. *Astrophys. Jour.*, *47*, 206, 1918.
  THIESSEN. *Observatory*, *66*, 230, 1946.

44. Recent indications from magnetic splitting of spectral lines for changes in sun's moment:
  THIESSEN. Personal communication to author, June, 1948.
  VON KLUBER, H. *Zeitschr. f. Astrophys.*, *24*, Nos. 1–2; 1 and 21, 1947.
  BABCOCK, H. W. Oral report at meeting of American Astronomical Society, Pasadena, June 29, 1948.

45. Electromagnetic field of the sun and the stars:
  DAVIS, JR. *Phys. Rev.*, *72*, 632, 1947 (static electric field).
  REBER, G., and GREENSTEIN, L. *Observatory*, *67*, 15, 1947 (review article).
  See also references 32 and 34.

46. For general surveys of cosmic-ray physics see reference 18.

47. For the theory of the equilibrium between electrons and mesons see
  ROSSI, B., and GREISEN, K. *Rev. Mod. Phys.*, *13*, 240, 1941.
  BERNANDINI, G., CACCIAPUOTI, B. N., and QUERZOLI, P. *Phys. Rev.*, *73*, 328, 335, 1947.

48. Penetration of cosmic-ray particles deep underground:
  WILSON, V. C. *Rev. Mod. Phys.*, *11*, 230, 1939.
  MARSHAK, R., and Bethe, H. A. *Phys. Rev.*, *72*, 506, 1947.
  GREISEN, KENNETH I. *Phys. Rev.*, *73*, 521, 1947.

49. Considerations favoring life of order of 10^{-8} sec for 300-mass meson:
  MARSHAK, R., and BETHE, H. A. *Phys. Rev.* 72, 506, 1947.
  GREISEN, K. *Phys. Rev.*, *73*, 521, 1947; see also FORRO, below.

50. Determination of energy of 200-mass meson emitted in decay of 300-mass meson:

LATTES, C. M. G., MUIRHEAD, H., OCCHIALINI, G. P. S., and POWELL, C. F. *Nature, 159*, 694, 1947.

———, OCCHIALINI, G. P. S., and POWELL, C. F. *Nature, 160*, 486, 1947.

51. A preliminary estimate of the mass of the neutral meson:
LATTES et al. reference 50.
In connection with the properties of the neutral meson see also:
MARSHAK, R. E. *Bull. Am. Phys. Soc., 22*, No. 6, 14, 1948; and *Phys. Rev., 73*, 1226, 1948.
K. GREISEN, *Phys. Rev., 73*, 521, 1948

52. Total cosmic-ray flux as a function of altitude:
BIEHL, MONTGOMERY, NEHER, PICKERING and ROESCH. *Rev. Mod. Phys., 20*, 360, 1948.
WINCKLER, J. R., STROUD, W. G., and SCHENCK, J. *Phys. Rev., 74*, 837, 1948.
VAN ALLEN, J. A., and TATEL, H. E. *Phys. Rev., 73*, 245, 1948.

53. For summary of the evidence for the production of electronic radiation in nuclear interactions see:
ROSSI, B. *Rev. Mod. Phys., 20*, sec. 15, 554, 1948.

54. Direct observations of acts of electron production:
FRETTER, W. B. *Phys. Rev., 73*, 41, 1948.
DAUDIN, J. *C. R. Acad. Sci. Paris, 218*, 275, 1944.
BRIDGE, H., HAZEN, W. E., and ROSSI, B. *Phys. Rev., 73*, 179, 1948.
See also reference 53.

55. A theory of multiple meson production:
Lewis, H. W., Oppenheimer, J. R., and Wouthuysen, S. A. *Phys. Rev., 73*, 127, 1948.
See also reference 101.

56. For the experimental evidence on nuclear stars see for example the review by BAGGE, E., in HEISENBERG's Cosmic radiation, cited in reference 18.

57. Rate of increase of neutron intensity with altitude:
AGNEW, H. M., BRIGHT, W. C. and FROMAN, D. *Phys. Rev., 72*, 203, 1947.

58. Evidence for a maximum in the neutron intensity:
YUAN, L. C. *Phys. Rev., 74*, 504, 1948.

59. Theory of variation of neutron intensity with altitude:
BETHE, H. A., KORFF, S. A., and PLACZEK, G. *Phys. Rev., 57*, 573, 1940.

60. Increase of neutron intensity near the ground:
YUAN, L. C., unpublished observations.

61. Effect of near-by clouds on neutron intensity:
AGNEW, H. M., BRIGHT, W. C., and FROMAN, D. *Phys. Rev., 72*, 203, 1947.

62. For survey of the subject of the interaction of electrons and radiation see for example:
HEITLER, W. The quantum theory of radiation. 2d ed. Oxford University Press, 1944.
PAIS, A. Developments in the theory of the electron. Princeton University Press, 1948.

63. Initiation of the theory of extensive electron showers:
AUGER, P., and ROSENBERG, A. *C. R. Acad. Sci. Paris*, *200*, 447, 1935.
BHABHA, H. J., and HEITLER, W. *Proc. Roy. Soc. London*, A *159*, 432, 1937.
CARLSON, J. F., and OPPENHEIMER, J. R. *Phys. Rev.*, *51*, 220, 1937.

64. For experimental evidence on extensive air showers see reference 19.

65. Evidence on air showers of very great extension:
AUGER, MAZE and ROBLEY. *C. R. Acad. Sci., Paris*, *208*, 1641, 1939.

66. Experiments on positon-negaton annihilation:
KLEMPERER, O. *Cambridge Phil. Soc. Proc.*, *30*, 347, 1934.
See also HEITLER, W., reference 62, p. 208, for further references.

67. Observation of polarization of annihilation radiation:
BLEULER, E., and BRADT, H. L. *Phys. Rev.*, *73*, 1398, 1948.

68. Polyelectronic entities:
Wheeler, J. A. *Annals of N. Y. Acad. of Sci.*, *48*, Art. 3, 219, 1946.
ORE, A. *Phys. Rev.*, *73*, 1313, 1948.
—— *Phys. Rev.*, *71*, 93, 1947.
—— and HYLLERAAS, E. A. *Phys. Rev.* *71*, 493, 1947.
HYLLERAAS, E. A. *Phys. Rev.*, *71*, 491, 1947.

69. Scattering of radiation in the field of force of the nucleus:
DELBRUCK, M. *Zeitschr. f. Physik*, *84*, 144, 1933.

70. Neutron-electron interaction:
FERMI, E., and MARSHALL, L. *Phys. Rev.* *72*, 1139, 1947.

71. More on neutron-electron interaction:
HAVENS, W. W., JR., RABI, I. I., and RAINSWATER, L. V. *Phys. Rev.*, *72*, 634, 1947.

72. Anomalous ratio of hyperfine structures of hydrogen and deuterium:
NAGLE, D. E., JULIAN, R. S. and ZACHARIAS, J. R. *Phys. Rev.*, *72*, 971, 1947.
ARNOLD, W. R., and ROBERTS, A. *Phys. Rev.*, *71*, 878, 1947.
NAFE, J. E., NELSON, E. B., and RABI, I. I. *Phys. Rev.* *71*, 914, 1947.
—— and NELSON, E. B. *Phys. Rev.*, *73*, 718, 1948.
BOHR, A. *Phys. Rev.*, *73*, 1109, 1948.

73. Experimental determination of the anomalous electronic magnetic moment:
KUSCH, P., and FOLEY, H. M. *Phys. Rev.*, *72*, 1256, 1947; *73*, 412, 1948, and *74*, 250, 1948.

74. Theory of interaction of electron with surrounding electromagnetic and pair field:

BREIT, G. *Phys. Rev.*, *72*, 984 and 1410, 1947.

SCHWINGER, JULIAN. *Phys. Rev.*, *73*, 415, 1948.

75. Shift in energy of those atomic states in which electron experiences high accelerations.

LAMB, WILLIS E., JR., and RETHERFORD, ROBERT C. *Phys. Rev.*, *72*, 241, 1947 (microwave observations on hydrogen).

76. Increase with altitude of frequency of nuclear stars:

Reference 56.

77. Cloud-chamber evidence on radiation responsible for star production has been obtained by POWELL, W., and DAUDIN, J.

78. Earlier view that photons produce a large number of the stars:

BAGGE, reference 56.

79. Negligible rate of star production underground:

CHOU, CHANG-NING. *Phys. Rev.*, *74*, 1659, 1948.

80. Photodisintegration of nuclei:

BALDWIN, G. C., and KLAIBER, G. S. *Phys. Rev.*, *71*, 3, 1947.

81. Stars produced by particles from Berkeley cyclotron, and measurements on interception of nucleons in matter:

HILDERBRAND, R., and MOYER, B. J. *Phys. Rev.*, *72*, 1258, 1947.

COOK, L. J., McMILLAN, E., PATERSON, J. M., and SEWELL, D. C. *Phys. Rev.*, *72*, 1264, 1947.

82. For continuous extraction methods:

STRAIN, H. H. Chromatographic adsorption analysis. New York, Interscience, 1942.

83. Theory of the penetration of nucleons through matter:

SERBER, R. *Phys. Rev.*, *72*, 1114, 1947.

ROSENFELD, L. Nuclear forces. Interscience, New York, 1948.

84. Tentative theory of dependence of photonuclear cross section on frequency:

WEISSKOPF, V. *Phys. Rev.*, *59*, 318, 1941.

SCHIFF, L. I. *Phys. Rev.*, *73*, 1311, 1948.

FESHBACH, H., and SCHIFF, L. I. *Phys. Rev.*, *72*, 254, 1947.

85. Oral suggestion from E. Teller to the author.

86. Evidence on the neutrino from the beta-decay of atomic nuclei:

See reference 11.

87. For observations on electrons from decay of light mesons see:

SHUTT, R. P., DE BENEDETTI, S., and JOHNSON, T. H. *Phys. Rev.*, *62*, 552, 1942.

POWELL, W. *Phys. Rev.*, *69*, 385, 1946.

FOWLER, E. C., COOL, R. L., and STREET, J. C. *Phys. Rev.*, *74*, 101, 1948.

ZAR, J. L., HERSHKOWITZ, J., and BEREZIN, E. *Phys. Rev.*, *74*, 111, 1948.

ANDERSON, C. D., LLOYD, P. E., RAU, R. R., SAXENA, R. C. *Rev. Mod. Phys.*, *20*, 334, 1948

—— ADAMS, R. V., LLOYD, P. E., and RAU, R. R. *Phys. Rev.*, *72*, 724, 1947.

RETALLACK, J. B. *Phys. Rev.* *73*, 921, 1948.

CONVERSI, M., and PICCIONI, O. *Phys. Rev.*, *70*, 874, 1946.

THOMPSON, R. W. *Phys. Rev.*, *74*, 490, 1948.

STEINBERGER, J. *Phys. Rev.* *74*, 500, 1948.

88. Correlation in direction of electron and neutrino emitted in beta-decay:
JACOBSEN, J. C., and KOFOED-HANSEN, O. *Phys. Rev.* *73*, 675, 1948 and *Kgl. Danske Videns. Sels. Math. fys. Medd.*, *23*, No. 12, 1945.

89. Theory of directional correlation of electron and neutrino:
HAMILTON, D. R. *Phys. Rev.*, *71*, 545, 1947.

90. Radioactive decay of free neutron:
SNELL, A. *Science*, *108*, 167, 1948.

91. Absence of gamma rays in meson decay processes:
HINKS, E. P., and PONTECORVO, B. *Phys. Rev.*, *73*, 257, 1948; *73*, 1122, 1948.
SARD, R. D., and ALTHAUS, E. J. *Bull. Am. Phys. Soc.*, *23*, No. 2, 20, 1948.

92. On the spectrum of electrons from meson decay see reference 87.

93. Evidence that less than half the energy of decaying mesons appears in electronic form:
ROSSI, B. *Rev. Mod. Phys.*, *20*, 573, 1948.

94. For the possibility of setting a lower limit to the life of the 300-mass meson see:
GARDNER, E., and LATTES, C. M. G. *Science*, *107*, 270, 1948, and later unpublished Berkeley results.
See also reference 49.

95. For estimates of the probability of neutrino absorption experiments see reference 11. Also:
CRANE, H. R., *Rev. Mod. Phys.*, *20*, 292, 1948 (a general review).
See especially WOLLAN, E. O. *Phys. Rev.*, *72*, 445, 1947, for a search for neutrino scattering by hydrogen.

96. The author is indebted to B. Pontecorvo, D. R. Hamilton, and A. Wightman for discussions of the rate of neutrino absorption processes which may be induced by available sources.

97. See reference 82.

98. Absorption of neutrinos in the sun:
BETHE, H. A. *Camb. Phil. Soc. Proc.*, *31*, 10, 1935.

99. Preliminary evidence for identity of neutrinos and antineutrinos:
FIREMAN, E. L. *Phys. Rev.* in press.

100. Nuclear absorption of 300-mass mesons:
LATTES, C. M. G., OCCHIALINI, G. P. S., and POWELL, C. F. *Nature*, *160*, 453 and 486, 1947.
GARDNER, EUGENE, and LATTES, C. M. G. *Science*, *107*, 270, 1948.

101. Evidence for increase of meson-producing power of primary with its energy:
SCHEIN, M., YNGVE, V. H., and KRAYBILL, H. L. *Phys. Rev.*, *73*, 928, 1948.
JANOSSY, L., and NICHOLSON, P. *Proc. Roy. Soc. London*, *192*, 99, 1947.

102. Variation of neutron intensity with latitude:
SIMPSON, J. A., JR. *Phys. Rev.*, *73*, 1389, 1948.

103. Many mesons per nucleon or many nucleons per nucleus in multiple meson production?
BETHE, H. A. *Phys. Rev.*, *70*, 787, 1946.

104. Excess of positive mesons over negatives:
CORRELL, M. *Phys. Rev.*, *72*, 1054, 1947.
DUERCIA, I. F., RISPOLI, B., and SCIUTI, S. *Phys. Rev.*, *73*, 516, 1948.

105. Theory of production of mesons by interaction of gamma rays with nuclei:
MORETTE, C., and PENG, H. W. *Nature*, *160*, 59, 1947.
FERETTI, B. *Nuevo Cim.*, *3*, 301, 1946.
FESHBACH, H., and SCHIFF, L. I. *Phys. Rev.*, *72*, 254, 1947.
KOBAYASHI, M., and IMAEDA K. *Prog. Theor. Phys.*, *1*, 101, 1946.

106. Observations of penetrating showers by cloud chambers:
FRETTER, W. B. *Phys. Rev.*, *73*, 41, 1948.
Observations via counters:
TREAT, J. E., and GREISEN, K. I. *Phys. Rev.*, *74*, 414, 1948.
WATAGHIN, G. *Phys. Rev.*, *70*, 787, 1946.
GEORGE, E. P., and JANOSSY, L. *Phys. Rev.*, *70*, 773, 1946 (penetrating bursts).
BROADBENT, D., and JANOSSY, L. *Proc. Roy. Soc. London*, A *192*, 364, 1948 (production of penetrating particles); A *190*, 497, 1947, and A *191*, 519, 1947.

107. Loss of 300-mass mesons by decay in flight: reference 49.

108. Evidence for meson of mass greater than 300:
LEPRINCE-RINGUET, L., and L'HÉRETIER, M. *Jour. de phys. et de rad.*, *7*, 66, 1946.
ROCHESTER, G. D., and BUTLER, C. C. *Nature*, *160*, 856, 1947.
ALICHANIAN, ALICHANOV, and WEISSENBERG. *Jour. Phys. U.S.S.R.*, *2*, 97, 1947.
BRODE, R., oral report, Millikan anniversary conference on cosmic rays, Pasadena, June 22, 1948.
See also reference 9a.

109. Scattering and radiative deceleration of mesons (and their bearing on the spin of the meson):

CHRISTY, R. F., and KUSAKA, S. *Phys. Rev.*, *59*, 414, 1941.

110. Energy levels of the meson in the field of the nucleus:
WHEELER, J. A. *Phys. Rev.* *71*, 320, 1947.
Report of Commission on Cosmic Rays, Cracow, Poland, October, 1947.
International Union of Physics, Paris, 1948, Document RC48-1.
Recently W. Y. Chang has obtained evidence for emission of gamma rays in transitions between these levels. *Rev. Mod. Phys.* (in press).

111. Mechanism of capture of slow negative mesons into Bohr orbits:
FERMI, E., and TELLER, E. *Phys. Rev.*, *72*, 399, 1947.

112. Dependence of meson capture probability on atomic number:
WHEELER, J. A. *Phys. Rev.*, *71*, 320, 1947.
Cracow Cosmic Ray Conference, International Union of Physics, Paris, 1948, Document RC48-1.

113. Observational evidence on dependence of reaction probability on atomic number and on mechanism of reaction:
From dependence of meson lifetime on atomic number:
KISSINGER, C. W., and COOPER, D. *Phys. Rev.*, *74*, 349, 1948 (carbon).
VALLEY, G. E. *Phys. Rev.*, *73*, 1251, 1948 (beryllium).
NERESON, N. *Phys. Rev.*, *74*, 509, 1948 (boron-10 and boron-11).
KRAUSHAAR, W. L. *Phys. Rev.*, *73*, 1408, 1948 (carbon).
VALLEY, G. E. *Phys. Rev.* *72*, 772, 1948 (water, beryllium, iron, carbon).
TICHO, H. K., and SCHEIN, M. *Phys. Rev.*, *73*, 81, 1948 (sodium fluoride).
—— *Phys. Rev.*, *72*, 255, 1947 (aluminum); *74*, 492, 1948 (sulfur).
VALLEY, G. E., and ROSSI, B. *Phys. Rev.*, *73*, 177, 1948 (aluminum).
SIGURGEIRSSON, T., and YAMAKAWA, A. *Phys. Rev.*, *71*, 318, 1947 (beryllium, carbon, sodium fluoride, teflon [$\sim CF_2$], aluminum, magnesium, sulfur).
SARD, R. D., and ALTHAUS, E. J. *Phys. Rev.*, *73*, 1251, 1948 (no energetic gamma rays).
HINKS, E. P., and PONTECORVO, B. *Phys. Rev.*, *73*, 257, 1948 (does not decay into photons).
SARD, R. D., ITTNER, W. B., III, CONFORTO, A. M., and CROUCH, M. F. *Phys. Rev.*, *74*, 97, 1948 (neutrons released)
GROETZINGER, G., and MCCLURE, G. W. *Phys. Rev.*, *74*, 341, 1948 (also find neutrons).

114. For a general account of the relativity theory see W. Pauli's article, Relativitätstheorie. In: Encyclopadie der Mathematischen Wissenschaften, A. Sommerfeld, ed. V (2), issue 4, art. 19. Leipzig, Teubner, September 15, 1921.

115. For a recent survey of the status of the relativity theory see:
EINSTEIN, A. The meaning of relativity. Princeton University Press, 1945.

116. See for example the presentation of electromagnetism by M. ABRAHAM and R. BECKER. The classical theory of electricity and magnetism. London and Glasgow, Blackie & Sons, 1932.

117. For a discussion of the general principles of quantum theory see BOHR, N. Atomic theory and the description of nature, Cambridge University Press, 1934, especially p. 10 where the principle of complementarity is briefly stated.

118. The theory of electron pairs:
For a summary of the literature and critical survey of the field, see PAIS, A. Developments in the theory of the electron. Princeton University Press, 1948.

119. BOHR, N., and ROSENFELD, L. *Kgl. Dansk. Vid. Sels. Math. fys. Medd. 12*, No. 8, 1933 (the measurability of electromagnetic field quantities).

120. Before the existence of the meson was recognized experimentally, the possibility of a similar explanation of the nuclear forces in terms of an electron-neutrino field was first proposed in 1934 lectures by Heisenberg, according to Bethe and Bacher, reference 7. The proposal of particles of intermediate mass was first published and worked out in detail by YUKAWA, H., *Proc. Phys. Math. Soc. Japan, 17*, 48, 1935, and led to recognition of the existence of such particles in the cosmic radiation.

121. Summary of meson theory:
PAULI, W. Meson theory, Interscience, New York, 1946.
WENTZEL, G. *Rev. Mod. Phys., 19*, 1, 1947.

122. Correlation of magnetic moments of proton and neutron:
SCHWINGER, J., unpublished results.

123. Theory of beta-decay of nucleus through intermediate virtual meson state:
YUKAWA, H., SAKATA, S., and TAKETANI, M. *Proc. Phys. Math. Soc. Japan, 20*, 319, 1938.
ROZENTAL, S. *Phys. Rev., 60*, 613, 1941, see also references therein cited.
SCHIFF, L. I. *Phys. Rev.*, in press.
TANIKAWA, Y. *Prog. Theor. Phys., 2*, 31, 1947.

124. Relativistic formulation of quantum theory:
See reference 74, also citations 72, 73, and 75 for references to the relevant experiments.

125. Departures from Coulomb law:
PAULI, W., and ROSE, M. E. *Phys. Rev., 49*, 462, 1936.
UEHLING, E. *Phys. Rev., 48*, 55, 1935.

126. Action at a distance:
WHEELER, J. A., and FEYNMAN, P. P. *Rev. Mod. Phys., 17*, 157, 1945.
PLASS, G. N., and WHEELER, J. A. *Phys. Rev., 70*, 793 A, 1946.
—— Princeton thesis, 1946.
FEYNMAN, P. P. Princeton thesis, 1942.

127. Reaction of gravitational radiation on source:
EINSTEIN, A., INFELD, L., and HOFFMAN, B. *Ann. Math.*, *39*, 65, 1938.
HU, N., *Proc. Roy. Irish Acad.*, *51 A*, 87, 1947.
128. For the two particle problem in general relativity see:
EINSTEIN, A., and MAYER, W. *Preuss. Akad. Wiss Sitzber, Phys. Math. Klass*, *111*, 193. See also:
WEYL, H. *Ann. Physik*, *54*, 117, 1917; and an appendix by Weyl in the paper of
R. BACH, *Math. Zeitschr.*, *13*, 134, 1922. Also:
EINSTEIN, A., and PAULI, W. *Ann. Math.*, *44*, 131, 1943.
For the general question of compatibility of the present gravitational theory as represented by the two mass problem with the basic idea of Ernst Mach that the inertia of a given particle is determined by the distribution of matter in the rest of the universe, see the dialogue of H. WEYL, Massenträgheit und Kosmos in his collection Was ist Materie? Berlin, Springer, 1924, the discussion by Einstein in the new section of his book cited in reference 72, as well as E. Mach himself, The science of mechanics (trans. from German ed.), pp. 229–237 and pp. 511–516, Chicago, Open Court, 1893.

CHAPTER III

High Energy Physics by Ernest O. Lawrence

The undertaking was made possible by the generous support of the Rockefeller Foundation, the Research Corporation, and the John and Mary Markle Foundation. Since the war the project has been supported by the Manhattan District and the Atomic Energy Commission.

1. McMILLAN, E. M. *Phys. Rev.*, *68*, 143–145, 1945.
2. VEKSLER, V. *Jour. of Phys. of U.S.S.R.*, *9*, 153–158, 1945.
3. MOYER, B. J., HILDEBRAND, R., KNABLE, N., PARMLEY, T. J., and YORK, H. *Bull. Am. Phys. Soc.*, *22*, 11, 1947.
4. POWELL, W. *Bull. Am. Phys. Soc.*, *22*, No. 4, July 11, 1947.
5. PERLMAN, I., GOECKERMANN, R. H., TEMPLETON, D. H., and HOWLAND, J. J. *Phys. Rev.*, *72*, 352, 1947.
6. HELMHOLZ, A. C., McMILLAN, E. M., SEWELL, D. *Bull. Am. Phys. Soc.*, *22*, 5, 1947.
7. SERBER, R. *Bull. Am. Phys. Soc.*, *22*, 6, 1947.
8. In process of publication in the *Phys. Rev.*
9. CUNNINGHAM, B. B., HOPKINS, H. H., LINDNER, M., MILLER, D. R., O'CONNOR, P. R., PERLMAN, I., SEABORG, G. T., THOMPSON, R. C. *Bull. Am. Phys. Soc.*, *22*, 5, 1947.
SEABORG, G. T., CUNNINGHAM, B. B., HOPKINS, H. H., LINDNER, M.,

O'CONNOR, P. R., PERLMAN, I., THOMPSON, R. C. *Bull. Am. Phys. Soc.*, *22*, 5, 1947.

10. In process of publication in the *Rev. Sci. Inst.*

CHAPTER IV

The Eight New Synthetic Elements by Glenn T. Seaborg

1. For a discussion of the evidence for the natural occurrence of elements 43, 61, 85, and 87 see, e. g., WEEKS, M. E., Discovery of the elements, Chap. XXVII, published by the *Jour. of Chem. Edu.*, 1945.

2. See, e. g., JENSEN, H. *Naturwiss.*, *26*, 381, 1938.

3. MATTAUCH, J. *Zeitschr. Physik*, *91*, 361, 1934.

4. KOHMAN, T. P. *Phys. Rev.*, *73*, 16, 1948.

5. PERRIER, C., and SEGRÈ, E. *Jour. Chem. Phys.*, *5*, 712, 1937.

6. CACCIAPUOTI, B. N. *Phys. Rev.*, *55*, 110, 1939.
   See also CACCIAPUOTI, B. N., and SEGRÈ, E. *Phys. Rev.*, *52*, 1252, 1937.

7. MOTTA, E. E., BOYD, G. E., and BROSI, A. R. *Phys. Rev.*, *71*, 210, 1947.

8. EDWARDS, J. E., and POOL, M. L. *Phys. Rev.*, *72*, 384, 1947.

9. SULLIVAN, W. H., SLEIGHT, N. R., and GLADROW, E. M. *Phys. Rev.*, *70*, 778, 1946.

10. HELMHOLZ, A. C. *Phys. Rev.*, *60*, 415, 1941.

11. PANETH, F. A. *Nature*, *149*, 565, 1942.

12. PERRIER, C., and SEGRÈ, E. *Nature*, *159*, 24, 1947.

13. SEGRÈ, E., and SEABORG, G. T. *Phys. Rev.*, *54*, 772, 1938.

14. SEABORG, G. T., and SEGRÈ, E. *Phys. Rev.*, *55*, 808, 1939.

15. SEGRÈ, E., and WU, C. S. *Phys. Rev.*, *57*, 552, 1940.

16. Plutonium Project compilation: Nuclei formed in fission, *Jour. Am. Chem. Soc.*, *68*, 2411, 1946; *Rev. Mod. Phys.*, *18*, 513, 1946.

17. MOTTA, E. E., BOYD, G. E., and LARSON, Q. V. *Phys. Rev.*, *73*, 1270, 1947.

18. INGHRAM, M. G., HESS, D. C., JR., and HAYDEN, R. J. *Phys. Rev.*, *73*, 1269, 1947.

19. PEED, W. F., SAUNDERS, B. G., and BURKHART, L. E. *Phys. Rev.*, *73*, 347, 1948.

20. ABELSON, P. H. *Phys. Rev.*, *56*, 753, 1939.

21. PARKER, G. W., REED, J., and RUCH, J. W. Isolation of milligram amounts of element 43 from uranium fission. Atomic Energy Commission Declassified Document, AECD 2043, Jan. 9, 1948.

21a. FRIED, S. *Jour. Am. Chem. Soc.*, *70*, 442, 1948.

22. MOONEY, R. C. L. *Phys. Rev.*, *73*, 1269, 1947.

23. POOL, M. L., and QUILL, L. L. *Phys. Rev.*, *53*, 437, 1938.

24. LAW, H. B., POOL, M. L., KURBATOV, J. D., and QUILL, L. L. *Phys. Rev.*, *59*, 936, 1941.

25. KURBATOV, J. D., McDONALD, D. C., POOL, M. L., and QUILL, L. L. *Phys. Rev.*, *61*, 106, 1942.

26. ——— and POOL, M. L. *Phys. Rev.*, *63*, 463, 1943.

27. WU, C. S., and SEGRÈ, E. *Phys. Rev.*, *61*, 203, 1942.

28. See, e. g., *Chem. Eng. News*, *25*, 2556, 1947.

29. BOTHE, W., *Naturforsch.*, *1*, 179, 1946.

30. MARINSKY, J. A., GLENDENIN, L. E., and CORYELL, C. D. *Jour. Am. Chem. Soc.*, *69*, 2781, 1947.

31. JOHNSON, W. C., QUILL, L. L., and DANIELS, F. *Chem. Eng. News*, *25*, 2494, 1947; see also, *Jour. Am. Chem. Soc.*, *69*, 2769, 2777, 2786, 2792, 2800, 2812, 2818, 2830, 2836, 2849, 2859, 2866, 1947, for publication of papers on ion-exchange separations methods given at American Chemical Society symposium which took place at September, 1947, meeting in New York City.

32. HAYDEN, R. J., and LEWIS, L. G. *Phys. Rev.*, *70*, 111, 1946.

33. INGHRAM, M. G., HESS, D. C., HAYDEN, R. J., and PARKER, G. W. *Phys. Rev.*, *71*, 743, 1947.

33a. PARKER, G. W., and LANTZ, P. M. The separation of milligram quantities of element 61 from fission. Atomic Energy Commission Declassified Document AECD 2160, June 18, 1948.

34. KETELLE, B. H., and BOYD, G. E. Private communication, December 8, 1947.

35. For an excellent discussion of this question see YOST, D. M., RUSSELL, H., JR., and GARNER, C. S. The rare earth elements and their compounds. Chap. IV. John Wiley and Sons, New York, 1947.

36. See, e. g. WELSBACH, A. v. *Chem. Zeit.*, *50*, 990, 1926, and the recent publication by Takvorian describing his thorough work, TAKVORIAN, S. *Ann. chim.*, *20*, No. 11, 113, 1945.

37. See, e. g., *Chem. Eng. News*, *25*, 2889, 1947.

38. CORSON, D. R., MacKENZIE, K. R., and SEGRÈ, E. *Phys. Rev.*, *58*, 672, 1940.

39. ——— *Nature*, *159*, 24, 1947.

40. KARLIK, B., and BERNERT, T., *Naturwiss.*, *32*, 44, 1944.

41. ——— *Naturwiss.*, *31*, 492, 1943.

42. ——— *Naturwiss.*, *31*, 298, 1943.

43. ——— *Naturwiss.*, *33*, 23, 1946.

44. See, e. g., FLÜGGE, S., and KREBS, A. *Naturwiss.*, *32*, 71, 1944.

45. MINDER, W. *Helv. Phys. Acta 13*, 144, 1940.

46. HULUBEI, H., and CAUCHOIS, Y. *Compt. Rend.*, *210*, 696, 1940.

47. LEIGH-SMITH, A., and MINDER, W. *Nature*, *150*, 767, 1942.

48. KARLIK, B., and BERNERT, T. *Naturwiss.*, *30*, 685, 1942. *Sitzber. Akad. Wiss. Wien. Math.-naturw. Klasse, Abt. IIa*, *151*, 255, 1942.

49. HAGEMANN, F., KATZIN, L. I., STUDIER, M. H., GHIORSO, A., and SEA-
    BORG, G. T. *Phys. Rev.*, *72*, 252, 1947.
50. ENGLISH, A. C., CRANSHAW, T. E., DEMERS, P., HARVEY, J. A., HINCKS,
    E. P., JELLEY, J. V., and MAY, A. N. *Phys. Rev.*, *72*, 253, 1947.
51. PEREY, M., *Compt. Rend.*, *208*, 97, 1939; *Jour. Phys. Radium*, *10*, 435,
    1939.
52. MEYER, ST., HESS, V. F., and PANETH, F. A., *Sitzber. Akad. Wiss. Wien.
    Math.-naturw. Klasse*, *Abt. IIa*, *123*, 1459, 1914.
53. PEREY, M., *Jour. chim. phys.*, *43*, 155, 1946.
    See also PANETH, F. A. *Nature*, *159*, 8, 1947, for symbol Fr.
54. —— *Jour. chim. phys.*, *43*, 262, 1946.
55. PETERSON, S., Private communication, 1946.
56. PEREY, M., *Jour. chim. phys.*, *43*, 269, 1946.
57. For summary of some early ideas and researches concerning the trans-
    uranium elements, see, e. g., QUILL, L. L. *Chem. Rev.*, *23*, 87, 1938.
58. HAHN, O., and STRASSMANN, F. *Naturwiss.*, *27*, 11, 89 and 163, 1939.
59. See, e. g., SEABORG, G. T., and SEGRÈ, E. *Nature*, *159*, 863, 1947.
    SEABORG, G. T. *Science*, *104*, 379, 1946, and *Chem. Eng. News*, *23*,
    2190, 1945; *24*, 1192, 1946; *25*, 358, 1947.
60. MCMILLAN, E. M., and ABELSON, P. H. *Phys. Rev.*, *57*, 1185, 1940.
61. SEABORG, G. T., MCMILLAN, E. M., KENNEDY, J. W., and WAHL, A. C.
    Phys. Rev., *69*, 366, 1946; SEABORG, G. T., WAHL, A. C., and KEN-
    NEDY, J. W. *Phys. Rev.*, *69*, 367, 1946.
62. KENNEDY, J. W., SEABORG, G. T., SEGRÈ, E., and WAHL, A. C. *Phys.
    Rev.*, *70*, 555, 1946.

CHAPTER V

Chemical Achievement and Hope for the Future by Linus Pauling

1. PAULING, L. *Jour. Am. Chem. Soc.*, *62*, 2643, 1940.
2. BREINL, F., and HAUROWITZ, F. *Zeitschr. physiol. Chem.*, *192*, 45, 1930.
   MUDD, S. *Jour. Immunol.*, *23*, 423, 1932.

CHAPTER VI

Chromatography and Spectroscopy in Organic Chemistry and Stereochemistry
by L. Zechmeister

During the last decade far more than one thousand papers have been published in which adsorption methods have been successfully applied in the solution of various problems in organic chemistry. As a background to the above lecture, mention of the following monographs will suffice: H. H. Strain, Chromatographic adsorption analysis, 2d printing, Interscience Publ. Inc., New
York, 1945; T. I. Williams, An introduction to chromatography, Blackie &

Son, London, 1946, and Chem. Publ. Co., Brooklyn, 1947; L. Zechmeister and L. Cholnoky, Principles and practice of chromatography, 2d printing, Chapman & Hall, London, and John Wiley & Sons, New York, 1943. A survey by the writer, "*Cis-trans* isomerization and stereochemistry of carotenoids and diphenylpolyenes," appeared in *Chem. Rev.*, *34*, 267–344, 1944. There was a Conference on Chromatography held in New York at the end of 1946, the results of which have been published in the *Ann. New York Acad.*, *49*, 141–326, 1948. Investigations by Deuel et al. on the bio-potency of stereoisomeric carotenoids can be found in the *Arch. Biochem.*, 1944–47.

In the course of recent experimental work which has been carried out in this Laboratory, the writer enjoyed the excellent collaboration of his colleagues, R. B. Escue, F. Haxo, R. M. Lemmon, A. L. LeRosen, W. H. McNeely, J. H. Pinckard, A. Polgár, A. Sandoval, W. A. Schroeder, J. W. Sease, W. T. Stewart, and B. Wille.

CHAPTER VII

Virus Research: Achievement and Promise by W. M. Stanley

1. ANSON, M. L., and STANLEY, W. M. Some effects of iodine and other reagents on the structure and activity of tobacco mosaic virus. *Jour. Gen. Physiol.*, *24*, 679–690, 1941.

2. BEARD, JOSEPH W. The ultracentrifugal, chemical, and electron micrographic characters of purified animal viruses. *Proc. Inst. Med. of Chicago*, *15*, No. 13, 1945.

3. BURNET, F. M. Virus as organism. Harvard University Press, Cambridge, Mass., 1945.

4. CHANDLER, JOSEPH P., GERRARD, MARTHA W., DU VIGNEAUD, VINCENT, and STANLEY, W. M. The utilization for animal growth of tobacco mosaic virus as a sole source of protein in the diet. *Jour. Biol. Chem.*, *171*, 823–828, 1947.

5. COHEN, SEYMOUR S., and STANLEY, W. M. The molecular size and shape of the nucleic acid of tobacco mosaic virus. *Jour. Biol. Chem.*, *144*, 589–598, 1942.

6. KNIGHT, C. A. The nature of some of the chemical differences among strains of tobacco mosaic virus. *Jour. Biol. Chem.*, *171*, 297–308, 1947.

7. LAUFFER, MAX A., and STANLEY, W. M. Stream double refraction of virus proteins. *Jour. Biol. Chem.*, *123*, 507–525, 1938.

8. —— The physical chemistry of tobacco mosaic virus protein. *Chem. Rev.*, *24*, 303–321, 1939.

9. LORING, HUBERT S., and STANLEY, W. M. Isolation of crystalline tobacco mosaic virus protein from tomato plants. *Jour. Biol. Chem.*, *117*, 733–754, 1937.

10. MILLER, GAIL LORENZ, and STANLEY, W. M. Derivatives of tobacco

mosaic virus. I. Acetyl and phenylureido virus. *Jour. Biol. Chem.*, *141*, 905–920, 1941.

11. RIVERS, T. M. Viral and rickettsial infections of man. J. B. Lippincott Company, Philadelphia, Pa., 1948.

12. ROSS, A. FRANK, and STANLEY, W. M. The partial reactivation of formolized tobacco mosaic virus protein. *Jour. Gen. Physiol.*, *22*, 165–191, 1938.

13. STANLEY, W. M. Isolation of a crystalline protein possessing the properties of tobacco mosaic virus. *Science*, *81*, 644–645, 1945.

14. —— Chemical studies on the virus of tobacco mosaic. VI. The isolation from diseased Turkish tobacco plants of a crystalline protein possessing the properties of tobacco mosaic virus. *Phytopath.*, *26*, 305–320, 1936.

15. —— The inactivation of crystalline tobacco mosaic virus protein. *Science*, *83*, 626–627, 1936.

16. —— The reproduction of virus proteins. *Am. Naturalist*, *72*, 110–123, 1938.

17. —— The architecture of viruses. *Physiol. Rev.*, *19*, 524–556, 1939.

18. —— The biochemistry of viruses. *Ann. Rev. Biochem.*, *9*, 545–570, 1940.

19. —— Purification of tomato bushy stunt virus by differential centrifugation. *Jour. Biol. Chem.*, *135*, 437–454, 1940.

20. —— Some chemical, medical, and philosophical aspects of viruses. *Science*, *93*, 145–151, 1941.

21. —— The size of influenza virus. *Jour. Exp. Med.*, *79*, 267–283, 1944.

22. —— Viruses. In: Currents in biochemical research, D. E. Green, ed., pp. 13–23. Interscience Publishers, Inc., New York, N. Y., 1946.

CHAPTER VIII

The Tubercle Bacillus and Tuberculosis by René J. Dubos

1. DAVIS, B. D. Physiological significance of the binding of molecules by plasma proteins. *Am. Scientist*, *34*, 611, 1946.

2. —— The estimation of small amounts of fatty acid in the presence of polyoxyethylene sorbitan partial fatty acid esters ("Tween") and of serum proteins. *Arch. Biochem.*, *15*, 351, 1947.

3. —— The preparations and stability of fatty acid-free polyoxyethylene sorbitan monooleate ("Tween" 80). *Arch. Biochem.*, *15*, 359, 1947.

4. —— and DUBOS, R. J. Interaction of serum albumin, free and esterified oleic acid and lipase in relation to cultivation of the tubercle bacillus. *Arch. Biochem.*, *11*, 201, 1946.

5. —— and DUBOS, R. J. Serum albumin as a protective rather than nutritive growth factor in bacteriological media. *Federation Proc.*, *5*, 246, 1946.

6. —— and DUBOS, R. J. The binding of fatty acids by serum albumin, a

protective growth factor in bacteriological media. *Jour. Exp. Med.*, *86*, 215, 1947.

7. —— and DUBOS, R. J. The inhibitory effect of lipase on bacterial growth in media containing fatty acid esters. *Jour. Bact.*, *55*, 11, 1948.

8. DUBOS, R. J. Rapid and submerged growth of mycobacteria in liquid media. *Proc. Soc. Exp. Biol. and Med.*, *58*, 361–362, 1945.

9. —— The experimental analysis of tuberculous infection. *Experientia*, *3*, 45, 1947.

10. —— The effect of lipids and serum albumin on bacterial growth. *Jour. Exp. Med.*, *85*, 9–22, 1947.

11. —— The effect of sphingomyelin on the growth of tubercle bacilli. *Jour. Exp. Med.*, 1948, in press.

12. —— The effect of wetting agents on the growth and susceptibility of tubercle bacilli. *Jour. Bact.*, 1948, in press.

13. —— Cellular structures and functions involved in parasitism. *Bact. Rev.*, 1948, in press.

14. —— and DAVIS, B. D. Factors affecting the growth of tubercle bacilli in liquid media. *Jour. Exp. Med.*, *83*, 409, 1946.

15. —— DAVIS, B. D., MIDDLEBROOK, G., and PIERCE, C. H. Effect of water soluble lipids on the growth and biological properties of tubercle bacilli. *Am. Rev. Tuberc.*, *54*, 204, 1946.

16. —— and MIDDLEBROOK, G. Media for tubercle bacilli. *Am. Rev. Tuberc.*, *56*, 334, 1947.

17. —— and MIDDLEBROOK, G. The effect of synthetic wetting agents on the growth of tubercle bacilli. *Jour. Exp. Med.*, 1948, in press.

17a. —— and PIERCE, C. H. The effect of diet on experimental tuberculosis of mice. *Am. Rev. Tuberc.*, *57*, 287, 1948.

18. FRIDMODT-MOLLER, J. Dissociation of tubercle bacilli. Investigations on the mammalian types including BCG. H. K. Lewis & Co. Ltd., London, 1939.

19. GOMORI, G. The microtechnical demonstration of sites of lipase activity. *Proc. Soc. Exp. Biol. and Med.*, *58*, 362–364, 1945.

20. LURIE, MAX, B. Heredity, constitution and tuberculosis, an experimental study. *Suppl. to the Am. Rev. Tuberc.*, *44*, 1941.

21. KIRBY, W. M. M., and DUBOS, R. J. Effect of penicillin on the tubercle bacillus *in vitro*. *Proc. Soc. Exp. Biol. and Med.*, *66*, 120–123, 1947.

22. KNIGHT, V., SHULTZ, S., and DUBOIS, R. The relation of the type of growth of *M. Tuberculosis* to the antituberculous activity of subtilin. *Jour. Bact.*, 1948, in press.

22a. LONG, ESMOND R. The decline of tuberculosis mortality with special reference to its generalized form. *Bull. Institute Hist. Med.*, *8*, 819, 1940.

23. MAXIMOV, A. Etude comparative des cultures de tissus inoculées soit avec le bacille tuberculeux du type bovin soit avec le bacille BCG de calmette-guerin. *Ann. Inst. Pasteur*, *42*, 225–245, 1928.

24. METALNIKOV, S., and SECREBOVA, V. Phagocytose et destruction des bacilles tuberculeux. *Ann. Inst. Pasteur, 41,* 301, 1927.

25. MIDDLEBROOK, G. Media for the cultivation of tubercle bacilli and their clinical and experimental applications. *Proc. of the New York State Assn. of Public Health Laboratories, 27,* 28, 1947.

26. —— and DUBOS, R. J. The effect of tubercle bacilli on the antigenicity of a synthetic ester of oleic acid. *Jour. Immunol., 56,* 301, 1947.

27. ——, DUBOS, R. J., and PIERCE, C. H. Virulence and morphological characteristics of mammalian tubercle bacilli. *Jour. Exp. Med., 86,* 175, 1947.

28. PETROFF, S. A. and STEENKEN, W. Biological studies of the tubercle bacillus. I. Instability of the organism-microbic dissociation. *Jour. Exp. Med., 51,* 831, 1930.

29. PIERCE, C. H., DUBOS, R. J., and MIDDLEBROOK, G. Infection of mice with tubercle bacilli grown in Tween-albumin liquid media. *Proc. Soc. Exp. Biol. and Med., 64,* 173–174, 1947.

30. ——, DUBOS, R. J., and MIDDLEBROOK, G. Infection of mice with mammalian tubercle bacilli grown in Tween-albumin liquid medium. *Jour. Exp. Med., 86,* 159, 1947.

31. PINNER, M. Pulmonary tuberculosis in the adult. Chap. XIX. Springfield, Ill., Charles C. Thomas, 1945.

32. PUFFER, RUTH. Familial susceptibility to tuberculosis. Harvard University Press, Cambridge, Mass., No. V, 1944.

33. RICH, A. The pathogenesis of tuberculosis. Chap. XXI. Springfield, Ill., Charles C. Thomas, 1944.

34. SAZ, A. K. The effect of hydrocarbons on the metabolism of the tubercle bacilli. *Jour. Bact.,* 1948, in press.

35. VOLKERT, M., PIERCE, C., HORSFALL, F., and DUBOS, R. J. The enhancing effect of concurrent infection with pneumotropic viruses on pulmonary tuberculosis in mice. *Jour. Exp. Med., 86,* 203, 1947.

36. WRIGHT, S. and LEWIS, P. A. Factors in the resistance of guinea pigs to tuberculosis, with especial regard to inbreeding and heredity. *Am. Naturalist, 55,* 20, 1921.

37. YELTON, S. E. Tuberculosis throughout the world. *Public Health Reports, 61,* 1144–1160, 1946.

38. YOUMANS, G. P. A method for the determination of the culture cycle and the growth rate of virulent human type tubercle bacilli. *Jour. Bact., 51,* 703, 1946.

CHAPTER IX

Genes and Biological Enigmas by G. W. Beadle

1. ALEXANDER, J. Life: its nature and origin. Reinhold Publishing Corporation, New York, 1948. 291 pp.

2. ALTENBURG, E. The "viroid" theory in relation to plasmagenes, viruses, cancer and plastids. *Am. Naturalist, 80,* 559–567, 1946.

3. AUERBACH, C., ROBSON, J. M., and CARR, J. G. The chemical production of mutations. *Science, 105,* 243–247, 1947.

4. AVERY, O. T., McLEOD, C. M., and McCARTY, M. Studies on the chemical nature of the substance inducing transformation of pneumococcal types: Induction of transformation by a desoxyribonucleic acid fraction isolated from Pneumococcus type III. *Jour. Exp. Med., 79,* 137–158, 1944.

5. BEADLE, G. W. Genetics and metabolism in *Neurospora. Physiol. Rev., 25,* 643–663, 1945a.

6. —— Biochemical genetics. *Chem. Rev., 37,* 15–96, 1945b.

7. —— Genes and the chemistry of the organism. *Am. Scientist, 34,* 31–53 (also 76), 1946.

8. —— Genes and the chemistry of the organism. In: Science in progress. Yale University Press, New Haven, 1947. 353 pp.

9. —— and COONRADT, V. Heterocaryosis in *Neurospora crassa. Genetics, 29,* 291–308, 1944.

9a. BOIVIN, A. Directed mutation in colon bacilli, by an inducing principle of desoxyribonucleic nature: its meaning for the general biochemistry of heredity. *Cold Spring Harbor Symp. Quant. Biol., 12,* 6–17, 1947.

10. BONNER, D. The identification of a natural precursor of nicotinic acid. *Proc. Nat. Acad. Sci., 34,* 5–9, 1948.

11. —— and BEADLE, G. W. Mutant strains of *Neurospora* requiring nicotinamide or related compounds for growth. *Arch. Biochem., 11,* 319–328, 1946.

12. BRUES, C. T., and DUNN, RUTH C. The effects of penicillin and certain sulfa drugs on the intracellular bacteroids of the cockroach. *Science, 101,* 336–337, 1945.

13. BULLOCH, WILLIAM and FILDES, PAUL. Haemophilia. Treasury of human inheritance. University Press, Cambridge, England, 1911. Parts V and VI, Section XIVa, pp. 169–354.

14. BURNET, F. M. Virus as organism. Harvard University Press, Cambridge, Mass., 1945. 134 pp.

15. DARLINGTON, C. D. Heredity, development and infection. *Nature, 154,* 164–169, 1944.

16. DELBRÜCK, M. A theory of autocatalytic synthesis of polypeptides and its application to the problem of chromosome reproduction. *Cold Spring Harbor Symp. Quant. Biol., 9,* 122–124, 1941.

17. —— Bacterial viruses or bacteriophages. *Biol. Rev., 21,* 30–40, 1946.

18. —— and BAILEY, W. T., JR. Induced mutations in bacterial viruses. *Cold Spring Harbor Symp. Quant. Biol., 11,* 33–37, 1946.

19. FISHER, R. A. The Rhesus factor. *Am. Scientist, 35,* 95–102 and 113, 1947.

20. FÖLLING, A. Über Ausscheidung von Phenylbrenztraubensäure in den

Harn als Stoffwechselanomalie in Verbindung mit Imbezillität. *Zeitschr. physiol. Chem.*, *227*, 169–176, 1934.

21. —— MOHR, O. L., and RUUD, L. *Oligophrenia phenylpyrouvica*, a recessive syndrome in man. *Skrifter Norske Videnskaps-Academi Oslo. Mat.-Naturv. Klasse.*, No. 13, 1945. 44 pp.

22. GARROD, A. E. Inborn errors of metabolism. 2d ed. Oxford Medical Publications, Oxford University Press, London, 1923. 216 pp.

23. GOLDSCHMIDT, R. Genetic factors and enzyme action. *Science*, *43*, 98–100, 1916.

24. GOWEN, J. W., and GAY, E. H. Gene number, kind, and size in *Drosophila*. *Genetics*, *18*, 1–31, 1933.

25. GROSS, O. Über den Einfluss des Blutserums des Normalen und des Alkaptonurikers auf Homogentisinsäure. *Biochem. Zeitschr.*, *61*, 165–170, 1914.

26. HALDANE, J. B. S. The rate of spontaneous mutation of a human gene. *Jour. Genetics*, *31*, 317–326, 1935.

26a. —— New paths in genetics. Harper & Bros., New York, 1942. 206 pp.

27. HARVEY, ETHYL B. A comparison of the development of nucleate and non-nucleate eggs of Arbacia punctulata. *Biol. Bull.*, *79*, 166–187, 1940.

28. L'HERITIER, Ph., and DESCOEUX, F. H. Transmission par graffe et injection de la sensibilité héréditaire au gaz carbonique chez la drosophile. *Bull. Biol. France and Belgique*, *81*, 70–91, 1947.

29. HERSHEY, A. D. Spontaneous mutations in bacterial viruses. *Cold Spring Harbor Symp. Quant. Biol.*, *11*, 67–76, 1946.

30. —— and ROTMAN, R. Linkage among genes controlling inhibition of lysis in a bacterial virus. *Proc. Nat. Acad. Sci.*, *34*, 89–96, 1948.

31. HOROWITZ, N. H. On the evolution of biochemical syntheses. *Proc. Nat. Acad. Sci.*, *31*, 153–157, 1945.

32. —— Methionine synthesis in *Neurospora*. The isolation of cystathionine. *Jour. Biol. Chem.*, *171*, 255–264, 1947.

33. HOULAHAN, M. B., and MITCHELL, H. K. A suppressor in *Neurospora* and its use as evidence for allelism. *Proc. Nat. Acad. Sci.*, *33*, 223–229, 1947.

34. HUSKINS, C. L. Chromosome multiplication and reduction in somatic tissues. *Nature*, *16*, 80–83, 1948.

35. IRWIN, M. R. Immunogenetics. *Advances in Genetics*, *1*, 133–159, 1947.

36. KNIGHT, B. C. J. G. Bacterial nutrition. Medical Research Council (Brit.) Special Report Series, No. 210, 1936. 182 pp.

37. LAWRENCE, J. S., and CRADDOCK, C. G., JR. Hemophilia: the mechanism of development and action of an anticoagulant found in two cases. *Science*, *106*, 473–474, 1947.

38. LAWRENCE, W. J. C., and PRICE, J. R. The genetics and chemistry of flower colour variation. *Biol. Rev.*, *15*, 35–58, 1940.

39. LEA, D. E. Actions of radiations on living cells. University Press, Cambridge, England, 1947. 402 pp.

40. LEDERBERG, J. Gene recombination and linked gene segregations in *Escherichia coli. Genetics, 32,* 505–525, 1947.

41. LINDEGREN, C. C., and LINDEGREN, G. The cytogene theory. *Cold Spring Harbor Symp. Quant. Biol., 11,* 115–127, 1946.

42. LURIA, S. E. Recent advances in bacterial genetics. *Bacteriol. Rev., 11,* 1–40, 1947.

43. —— Reactivation of irradiated bacteriophage by transfer of self-reproducing units. *Proc. Nat. Acad. Sci., 33,* 253–264, 1947.

44. LWOFF, A. Les facteurs de croissance pour les microorganismes. *Ann. Inst. Pasteur, 61,* 580–617, 1938.

44a. McCARTY, M. Chemical nature and biological specificity of the substance inducing transformation of pneumococcal types. *Bacteriol. Rev., 10,* 63–71, 1946.

45. METZ, C. W. Duplication of chromosome parts as a factor in evolution. *Am. Naturalist, 81,* 81–103, 1947.

46. MIRSKY, A. E., and RIS, HANS. The chemical composition of isolated chromosomes. *Jour. Gen. Physiol., 31,* 7–18, 1947.

47. MITCHELL, H. K., and NYC, J. F. Hydroxyanthranilic acid as a precursor of nicotinic acid in *Neurospora. Proc. Nat. Acad. Sci., 34,* 1–5, 1948.

48. MONOD, J. Sur une mutation affectant le pouvoir de synthèse de la méthionine chez une bactérie coliforme. *Ann. Inst. Pasteur, 72,* 879–890, 1946.

49. MOORE, A. R. A biochemical conception of dominance. *University California Publications in Physiol., 4,* 9–15, 1910.

50. MORGAN, T. H. The theory of the gene. Yale University Press, New Haven, 1926. 343 pp.

51. MULLER, H. J. One the dimensions of chromosomes and genes in Dipteran salivary glands. *Am. Naturalist, 69,* 405–411, 1935.

52. —— Pilgrim Trust Lecture: The gene. *Proc. Roy. Soc. London, B 134,* 1–37, 1947.

53. OPARIN, A. I. The origin of life. Trans. by S. Morgulis. The Macmillan Company, New York, 1938. 270 pp.

54. PENROSE, L. S. Inheritance of phenylpyruvic amentia (Phenylketonuria). *Lancet, 229* (Vol. 2 for 1935), 192–194, 1935.

55. PREER, J. R. Some properties of a genetic cytoplasmic factor in Paramecium. *Proc. Nat. Acad. Sci., 32,* 247–253, 1946.

56. RHOADES, M. M. Plastid mutations. *Cold Spring Harbor Symp. Quant. Biol., 11,* 202–207, 1946.

57. ROBINOW, C. F. Nuclear apparatus and cell structure of rod-shaped bacteria. In Dubos: The bacterial cell. Harvard University Press, Cambridge, Mass., 1945.

58. SONNEBORN, T. M. Experimental control of the concentration of cytoplasmic genetic factors in Paramecium. *Cold Spring Harbor Symp. Quant. Biol.*, *11*, 236–248, 1946.

59. —— Recent advances in the genetics of Paramecium and Euplotes. *Advances in Genetics*, *1*, 264–358, 1947.

60. STANLEY, W. M. In Virus research: achievement and promise. Science in progress, Series VI. Chap. VII. Yale University Press, New Haven, 1949.

61. TATUM, E. L. Induced biochemical mutations in bacteria. *Cold Spring Harbor Symp. Quant. Biol.*, *11*, 278–283, 1946.

62. —— and BONNER, D. Indole and serine in the biosynthesis and breakdown of tryptophane. *Proc. Nat. Acad. Sci.*, *30*, 30–37, 1944.

63. TEAS, H. J., HOROWITZ, N. H., and FLING, M. Homoserine as a precursor of threonine and methionine in *Neurospora. Jour. Biol. Chem.*, *172*, 651–658, 1948.

64. TROLAND, L. T. Biological enigmas and the theory of enzyme action. *Am. Naturalist*, *51*, 321–350, 1917.

65. WHITAKER, D. M. Physical factors of growth. *Growth*, Suppl. to Vol. IV, 75–90, 1940.

66. WRIGHT, S. The physiology of the gene. *Physiol. Rev.*, *21*, 487–527, 1941.

67. —— Statistical genetics and evolution. *Bull. Am. Math. Soc.*, *48*, 223–246, 1942.

68. —— Physiological aspects of genetics. *Ann. Rev. Physiol.*, 7, 75–106, 1945.

CHAPTER X

The Evolution and Function of Genes by A. H. Sturtevant

This list is intended only as a series of suggestions for those who may be interested in following up particular subjects.

1. BRIDGES, C. B. Salivary chromosome maps. *Jour. Hered.*, *26*, 60–64, 1935.
2. CLAUSEN, R. E. Polyploidy in Nicotiana. *Am. Nat.*, *75*, 291–306, 1941.
3. EMERSON, S. Genetics as a tool for studying gene structure. *Ann. Mo. Botan. Gard.*, *32*, 243–249, 1945.
4. HARLAND, S. C. The genetical conception of the species. *Biol. Rev.*, *11*, 83–112, 1936.
5. LANDSTEINER, K. The specificity of serological reactions. Cambridge, Mass., 1945. 310 pp.
6. PAULING, L., CAMPBELL, D. H., and PRESSMAN, D. The nature of the forces between antigen and antibody and of the precipitation reaction. *Physiol. Rev.*, *23*, 203–219, 1943.
7. STERN, C., and SCHAEFFER, E. W. On wild-type iso-alleles in *Drosophila* melanogaster. *Proc. Nat. Acad. Sci.*, *29*, 361–367, 1943.

8. STURTEVANT, A. H., and NOVITSKI, E. The homologies of the chromosome elements in the genus *Drosophila*. *Genetics*, *26*, 517–541, 1941.

CHAPTER XI

Modern Soil Science by Charles E. Kellogg

1. BARRELL, JOSEPH. The strength of the earth's crust. *Jour. of Geol.*, *22*, 28–48, 1914.
2. BROWN, IRVIN C., and THORP, JAMES. Morphology and composition of some soils of the Miami family and the Miami catena. *Tech. Bull.*, *834*, U. S. Dept. Agric., 1942. 55 pp.
3. CHANDLER, ROBERT F. Exchange properties of certain forest soils in the Adirondack section. *Jour. Agric. Res.*, *59*, 491–505, 1939.
4. —— The amount and mineral nutrient content of freshly fallen leaf litter in the hardwood forests of central New York. *Jour. Am. Soc. Agron.*, *33*, 859–871, 1941.
5. —— Amount and mineral nutrient of freshly fallen needle litter of some northeastern conifers. *Proc. Soil Sci. Soc. of Am.*, 8, 409–411, 1943.
6. CLARKE, FRANK WIGGLESWORTH. The data of geochemistry. 5d ed. *U. S. Geol. Survey Bull.*, *770*, p. 841, Washington, 1924.
7. DALE, R. B., and STABLER, H. Denudation in papers on the conservation of water resources. *Water-Supply Paper*, *234*, pp. 78–93, U. S. Geological Survey, 1909.
8. GAUTIER, E. F. Sahara, the great desert. Trans. by Dorothy Ford Mayhew. New York, 1935. 264 pp.
9. HUMBERT, R. P., and MARSHALL, C. E. Mineralogical and chemical studies of soil formation from acid and igneous rocks in Missouri. *Univ. of Mo. Res. Bull.*, 1943. 60 pp.
10. JENNY, HANS. Factors of soil formation. New York, 1941. 281 pp.
11. MARETT, R. DE LA H. Race, sex and environment: a study of mineral deficiency in human evolution. Hutchinson, London, 1936. 343 pp., illus.
12. PRICE, WESTON A. Nutrition and physical degeneration. A comparison of primitive and modern diets and their effects. Hoeber, New York, 1939. 431 pp., illus.
13. Reports of investigations at the soil conservation experiment stations. *U. S. Dept. Agric. Tech. Bull.*, *558, 837, 759, 860, 873, 888, and 916*.
14. ROBERTS, R. C. et al. Soil survey of Puerto Rico. Series 1936, No. 7, U. S. Dept. Agric., 1942. 503 pp., illus., maps.
15. ROBINSON, W. O., EDINGTON, GLEN, and BYERS, H. G. Chemical studies of infertile soils derived from rocks high in magnesium and generally high in chromium and nickel. *Tech. Bull.*, *471*, U. S. Dept. Agric., 1935. 28 pp.

INDEX